FAO Investigates Ferro-Cement Fishing Craft

Laboratory Analysis
Construction Methods
Service Experience

FAO Investigates Ferro-Cement Fishing Craft

Laboratory Analysis
Construction Methods
Service Experience

Edited by JOHN FYSON

Published by
Fishing News (Books) Ltd
23 Rosemount Avenue
West Byfleet
Surrey, England

Editorial assistance by: Ø. Gulbrandsen
M. Lindemann

ISBN: 0 85238 061 5

Made and Printed in Great Britain by
The Whitefriars Press Ltd., London and Tonbridge

Contents

Discussion on the Material Properties of Ferro-Cement

Part II—SCANTLINGS AND REGULATIONS

Ferro-Cement Boat Hulls Analysed by the Finite Element Method
J C Scrivener and A J Carr

Estimation of Design Loads   G L Bowen

Discussion of Scantlings Design and Various Official Regulations

Part III—CONSTRUCTION METHODS AND COSTS

Construction, Maintenance and Repair of a 26-Metre Ferro-Cement Stern Trawler   P A Leonard

Ferro-Cement Vessels on the Pacific Coast of North America
P Noble and W Cleaver

Construction of a 32-Metre Ferro-Cement Barge and Other Applications of Ferro-Cement   D Nontanakorn

Ferro-Cement Boats—Commercial Production Methods in New Zealand
W M Sutherland

Use of a Cavity Mould for Constructing 15-Metre Ferro-Cement Fishing Boats
R W Behnke and E C Doleman

The Use of Kit-Sets for Amateur Construction   G Carkeek

Ferro-Cement Boats—Service Experience in New Zealand

W M Sutherland

Discussion on Aspects of Service Experience

List of Contributors and Participants

Introduction

This book is derived from the papers and discussions of the first FAO Seminar on the Design and Construction of Ferro-Cement Fishing Vessels held in Wellington, New Zealand, from 9 to 13 October 1972.

When FAO began investigating the possibilities of ferro-cement as a boatbuilding material in 1967, the relatively high component of unskilled labour plus the widespread availability of most of the necessary construction materials suggested that this might be of considerable value in promoting the construction of simple, comparatively inexpensive fishing boats in the developing world. The opinions expressed and the reports quoted in the discussions in Part IV of this book confirm this assumption and suggest that the use of ferro-cement in construction may also be extended into many other fields of interest to developing nations.

The building of small fishing vessels has traditionally been a field in which very little engineering data have been available concerning the forces acting on hulls. In contrast to the detailed studies of the stresses to which large ship hulls are subjected, there was little information for small vessels. Design of small boats relied heavily on past experience and tables of scantlings for traditional construction materials were evolved through trial and error. This situation has changed in recent years. By 1972 engineering studies of material properties had provided more detailed information for the designer, new construction techniques had been evolved for different labour situations, and sufficient numbers of boats had been built, and data collected on them, for a pattern of service experience to emerge providing a further fund of information for designers and builders.

One of the most important factors contributing to the development and application of any new material is the rapid and wide dissemination of information about current work being done, both in the experimental determination of engineering properties and in the field of practical applications. FAO, therefore, considered it timely to arrange for an exchange of information between people working world-wide in this field. The Seminar, on which this book is based, was the result and it is hoped that the information from the Seminar, as presented here, will assist in the promotion of this most interesting material, especially in its application in the developing world.

Thanks are due to the authors of papers and to the speakers who contributed to the discussions. Special reference should be made to the work of the late Mr W Morley Sutherland, a pioneer in ferro-cement boat construction, who contributed two papers to the Seminar. Failing health prevented him from attending the Seminar, to the regret of all participants, and his untimely death is a loss to the field of ferro-cement.

We at FAO express our gratitude to the Government of New Zealand, not only for their invitation to act as hosts for the Seminar but also for their highly efficient organizational support, which contributed so much to the success of the Seminar. It was particularly appropriate for the meeting to be held in New Zealand because that country is in the forefront of development in the use of ferro-cement and participants were able to see, on the spot, the varied range of construction now being undertaken by New Zealand boatbuilders, both amateur and commercial.

F E Popper

Assistant Director-General (Fisheries)
Food and Agriculture Organization of the
United Nations
Rome
September 1973

Symbols and Abbreviations

Geometry of ship

B = beam or breadth moulded of ship;
C_B = block coefficient;
D = depth moulded of ship;
Loa = length overall of ship;
Lwe = length of waterline in general;
Ta = draught at aft perpendicular;
Tf = draught at forward perpendicular;
Ti = draught loaded;
To = draught light;
Δ = displacement weight;

Concrete technology

A_m = area of matrix;
A_f = area of fibres;
A_s = area of skeletal steel per unit width;
C = total compressive force per unit width;
D = flexural rigidity of plate;
E = modulus of elasticity of composite;
E_c = effective modulus of elasticity of composite;
E_f = modulus of elasticity of fibres;
E_i = modulus of elasticity of fibre i;
E_m = modulus of elasticity of matrix;
E_p = modulus of elasticity of particle;
E_t = effective modulus of elasticity in tension of composite in cracked range;
F_c' = ultimate strength of mortar;
F = fibre efficiency;
F_i = efficiency of fibre i;
h = thickness of the slab;
h_c = depth of compression zone;
h_c' = depth of compression zone at yield range;

h_s = depth of skeletal steel from extreme compression face;
h_t = depth of tension zone;
h_t' = depth of tension zone at yield range;
K = specific surface coefficient;
M = bending moment per unit width;
$M_0, M\mu$ = maximum ultimate moment;
q = transverse load per unit area;
T' = total tensile force per unit width;
T_f = tensile force due to fibres per unit width;
$T\mu$ = tensile force of reinforcement;
T_s = tensile force due to skeletal steel per unit width;
V_f = volume fraction of fibres;
V_i = volume fraction of fibre i;
V_m = volume fraction of matrix;
V_p = volume fraction of particle;
w = deflection;
λ_1, λ_2 = length fractions of fibres;
v = Poisson's ratio;
σ = average stress in composite section;
σ_c = ultimate strength of the composite in compression;
σ_c^* = compressive stress in bending;
σ_t = stress in the fibres;
σ_{ft} = ultimate strength of the fibres;
σ_{fy}, σ_{mu} = yield strength of the fibres;
σ_i = stress of fibre i;
σ_m, σ_{mu} = stress in the matrix;
σ_{sy} = yield strength of skeletal steel;
σ_t^* = tensile stress in bending;
σ_t = ultimate strength of the composite in tension;
$\varepsilon_c, \varepsilon_t$ = unit elongations in compression and tension.

Gauge Numbers and Millimetre Equivalents

Gauge No.	American or Brown and Sharpe's		Birmingham or Stubs'	
	Inches	Millimetres	Inches	Millimetres
1	0.2893	7.348	0.300	7.620
2	0.2576	6.543	0.284	7.214
3	0.2294	5.827	0.259	6.579
4	0.2043	5.189	0.238	6.045
5	0.1819	4.620	0.220	5.588
6	0.1620	4.115	0.203	5.156
7	0.1443	3.665	0.180	4.572
8	0.1285	3.264	0.165	4.191
9	0.1144	2.906	0.148	3.759
10	0.1019	2.588	0.134	3.404
11	0.09074	2.305	0.120	3.048
12	0.08081	2.053	0.109	2.769
13	0.07196	1.828	0.095	2.413
14	0.06408	1.628	0.083	2.108
15	0.05707	1.450	0.072	1.829
16	0.05082	1.291	0.065	1.651
17	0.04526	1.150	0.058	1.473
18	0.04030	1.024	0.049	1.245
19	0.03589	0.912	0.042	1.067
20	0.03196	0.812	0.035	0.889
21	0.02846	0.723	0.032	0.813
22	0.02535	0.644	0.028	0.711
23	0.02257	0.573	0.025	0.635
24	0.02010	0.511	0.022	0.559
25	0.01790	0.455	0.020	0.508
26	0.01594	0.405	0.018	0.457
27	0.01420	0.361	0.016	0.406
28	0.01264	0.321	0.014	0.356
29	0.01126	0.286	0.013	0.330
30	0.01003	0.255	0.012	0.305

Conversion Factors

SI and Imperial units

Physical quantity	Symbol	Name of SI unit	Symbol of SI unit	Name of Imperial unit	Symbol of Imperial unit	Conversion factors SI unit to Imperial unit	Conversion factors Imperial unit to SI unit
length	l	kilometre	km	nautical mile	n mile	1 km = 0.54 n mile	1 n mile = 1.853 km
		metre	m	mile	mile	1 m = 3.28 ft	1 mile = 1.609 km
		centimetre	cm	foot	ft	1 cm = 0.393 in	1 ft = 0.305 m
		millimetre	mm	inch	in	1 mm = 0.0393 in	1 in = 25.40 mm
area	A, S	square kilometre	km²	square mile	sq mile	1 km² = 0.386 sq mile	1 sq mile = 2.590 km²
		square metre	m²	square foot	sq ft	1 m² = 10.76 sq ft	1 sq ft = 0.093 m²
		square centimetre	cm²	square inch	sq in	1 cm² = 0.155 sq in	1 sq in = 6.45 cm²
		square millimetre	mm²			1 mm² = 0.0155 sq in	1 sq in = 64.5 mm²
volume	V	cubic metre	m³	cubic foot	cu ft	1 m³ = 35.314 ft³	1 cu ft = 0.028 m³
		cubic decimetre (litre)	dm³ (l)	UK gallon	UK gal	1 dm³ = 0.22 UK gal	1 UK gal = 4.546 dm³ (l)
		cubic centimetre	cm³	cubic inch	cu in	1 cm³ = 0.061 cu in	1 cu in = 16.387 cm³
velocity	v	kilometre per hour	km/h	knot	knot	1 km/h = 0.539 knots	1 knot = 1.853 km/h
		metre per second	m/s	mile per hour	mph	1 km/h = 0.621 mph	1 knot = 0.515 m/s
				foot per second	ft/s	1 m/s = 3.280 ft/s	1 mph = 1.609 km/h
						1 m/s = 1.945 knots	1 ft/s = 0.304 m/s
mass	m	tonne	tonne	UK ton	UK ton	1 tonne = 0.984 UK ton	1 UK ton = 1.016 tonne
		kilogramme	kg	pound	lb	1 kg = 2.204 lb	1 lb = 0.453 kg
density	δ	kilogramme per cubic metre	kg/m³	pound per cubic foot	lb/cu ft	1 kg/m³ = 0.062 lb/cu ft	1 lb/cu ft = 16.018 kg/m³
force	F	Newton	N	pound force	lbf	1 N = 0.224 lbf	1 lbf = 4.448 N
		kiloNewton	kN	UK tonne force	UK ton f	1 kN = 0.102 ton f	1 ton f = 9.964 N
pressure or stress	p, P	Newton per square metre	N/m²	pound force per square foot	lbf/sq ft	1 N/m² = 0.021 lbf/sq ft	1 lbf/sq ft = 47.9 N/m²
		kiloNewton per square metre	kN/m²	pound force per square inch	lbf/sq in	1 kN/m² = 0.145 lbf/sq in	1 lbf/sq in = 6.9 N/m²
		mega Newton per square metre	MN/m²			1 MN/m² = 145 lbf/sq in	

Part I—MATERIAL PROPERTIES

The Intensity and Distribution of Cracking in Ferro-Cement Panels Subject to Flexure   T E Buchner

Ferro-cement was introduced and developed in the 1940s by Professor Pier Luigi Nervi as a material suitable for the construction of boats of small tonnage. Following this introductory work, the material was adapted for architectural and structural applications, both as a roofing membrane and also as a wall cladding.

Published articles give little information regarding the formation and distribution of cracks at various levels of stress and strain through the material. Since this factor is of prime importance when considering the suitability of the material to waterproof an environment, this investigation was undertaken to determine some of the factors affecting crack propagation in a ferro-cement element subject to flexural action.

Since recommended design technique is to consider ferro-cement as a homogeneous material, the strain intensity at the surface of the material at crack-free and limited-crack conditions was investigated. In addition, the control of cracking as affected by various percentages and distribution of reinforcement was also considered.

In the original application of ferro-cement the material consisted of layers of mesh laid continuously through the section with nominal cover provided at each face. The continuous layers of mesh were subsequently modified by replacing the central reinforcement with spacer rods of approximately 6 mm diameter. It was felt that effectiveness of this central reinforcement was doubtful and in the investigation the central spacer rod was omitted. The total quantity of mesh was reduced to levels below those mentioned in Professor Nervi's articles in an attempt to ascertain the limit at which effective control of cracking would commence.

LIMITS OF INVESTIGATION

Test specimens and recording

Due to the large number of variables possible both when considering the composition of the material, and also the methods of testing, the following limitations were applied:

(a) the mesh was limited to a maximum of three sizes;
(b) use of a single method of steel placement (i.e. no central core) for all test specimens;
(c) fix the cover over the mesh at a single value;
(d) maintain the mortar mix (both sand gradings and water : cement ratio) at a fixed value;
(e) limit the size of the test specimen to 1.37 m × 300 mm × 22 mm deep (approx.) and the number of test specimens to 7;
(f) limit the method of observation and measurement of crack distribution to the use of a travelling microscope and a linear scale;

(g) the minimum amount of reinforcement which would still allow behaviour as a homogeneous material and effectively limit and control cracking required definition and hence the maximum weight of reinforcing mesh provided was limited to approximately 2 kg/m^2/cm thickness;
(h) limit the test by recording only the distribution of cracking along the panel at various levels of strain and omitting the recording of width of individual cracks.

TEST SPECIMEN AND APPARATUS

Test specimens

Seven test specimens were moulded using different reinforcing mesh arrangements and percentages of steel. The reinforcement used consisted of ductile mild steel wires of:

(i) 18 SWG in a 25 mm × 25 mm mesh;
(ii) 21 SWG in a 12 mm × 12 mm mesh;
(iii) 11 SWG in a 50 mm × 76 mm mesh.

In order to investigate the effectiveness of reduced percentages of steel mesh, the test panels were lightly reinforced in terms of recommended values for ferro-cement, the maximum weight of mesh used being equivalent to 2.02 kg/m^2/cm thickness.

The layers of reinforcing mesh were laid both regularly and staggered through the section and the use of spacer rod was omitted.

The ferro-cement panels were tested in flexure in a four-point loading configuration producing zero shear and constant flexure along the mid-panel section. The load was applied in the form of weights on a hanger.

Cover

Due to the problem of maintaining accurate cover on both faces of the ferro-cement specimens it was decided to fix the cover on the tension face (since measurement of strain and cracking intensity was recorded at this face), allowing any variations that might occur to be carried to the compression face.

The cover over the tension face was fixed by suspending the mesh from cross-spacers as shown in Fig. 1. The

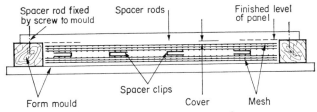

Fig. 1 Detail of maintaining cover over mesh

mesh was tied to these spacers by light gauge wires which were left in position until the mortar had attained a plastic set. They were then cut, the spacer rods removed and mortar trowelled into the voids until a homogeneous smooth surface finish was obtained.

Mortar

Mortar consisted of clean sand and ordinary Portland cement mixed in the following proportions—13.6 kg sand : 9.0 kg cement : 3.6 kg water. Weighing was by ordinary pan scale and the above quantities constituted a single batch.

The sand was oven dried and a sieve analysis carried out, giving the grading curve shown in Fig. 2.

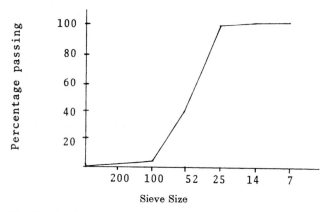

Fig. 2 Grading curve British Standard sieve numbers

PLACEMENT OF MESH

The reinforcing mesh was laid parallel through the test panel, in some instances being staggered to give a smaller grid on the horizontal projection.

Moulding test panel

The mortar was hand trowelled into position using a wood float. During moulding, compaction was achieved by hand vibrating (striking blows with a small hammer). The vibration continued at intervals until air bubbles ceased to rise to the surface. Between each cycle of vibration the surface was trowelled by means of a wood float, considerable pressure being exerted to assist in compaction.

After a period of 4 to 6 h (depending on the ambient temperature) the mortar attained a plastic set. The cover spacer rods were then removed, the voids filled and the surface received a hard trowelling. A screed board was then used to ensure the surface was true to level and a steel trowel finish was applied.

Beam mould sample

Concurrent with moulding the test panel a beam mould was filled and compacted, the dimensions being fixed at 46 mm × 73 mm × 760 mm long. This specimen was tested in a four-point loading jig in a compression testing machine to give values of ultimate strain for the mortar. Cubes were then cut to ascertain the ultimate value of compressive stress.

During moulding provision was made for holes to accommodate the hangers which were to be used in the application of loading during the test cycle. Ordinary

corks were used, being fixed in position by a single nail driven through the cork and into the plywood base of the mould.

All specimens (test panel and beam mould) were moist cured for a period of seven days. Curing was by means of wet hessian sacks.

TEST FRAME

The test frame was fabricated from mild steel angle sections. Loading of the specimen was by weights applied to hangers fixed to the panel as shown in Fig. 3.

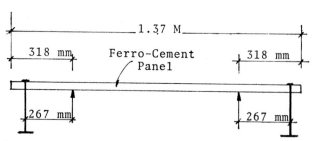

Fig. 3 Test frame panel in position with ferro-cement self weight of hanger and fittings = 0·86 Kg.

The loading for the ferro-cement panels was arranged so as to produce zero bending moment at mid span of the panel under self-weight conditions.

A portable battery operated strain bridge, together with strain gauges (333 Ω, ga = 2.50 cm), in a woven nylon carrier was used. In addition dial guages reading to 0.0025 mm were used to check mid-span deflection of the ferro-cement panels.

TEST PROCEDURE AND RESULTS

Properties of Mortar

Tension Test. One beam specimen was moulded with each batch of mortar mixed, and a strain gauge fixed at the centre of the specimen. A gauge attached to a similar test specimen was used as a dummy. The strain bridge was balanced in a half bridge circuit.

The specimen was tested in a four-point loading configuration in a compression testing machine.

Loading was applied to the specimens at the rate of 180 kg/min and simultaneous readings of strain and load were recorded.

The computed values refer to "theoretical" modulus of rupture on triangular stress block distribution through the beam and overestimate the true value.

Compression Test. Following on the modulus of rupture test, two prisms 50 mm × 50 mm × 48 mm were cut from each beam specimen by means of a concrete saw. The prism was capped and then tested in a compression machine.

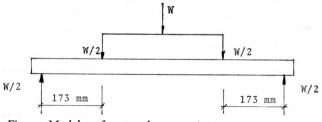

Fig. Modulus of rupture beam specimen

TABLE 1. MODULUS OF RUPTURE

Test sample from panel batch	Strain bridge reading (Microstrain)	Load at failure kg	Computed value of stress kgf/mm²
A	240	200	.422
B	—	—	
C	250	204	.429
	220	182	.382
D	320	264	.555
	270	227	.478
E	210	172	.365
	170	141	.295
F	302	245	.258
	270	218	.458
G	250	204	.429
	280	231	.488

TABLE 2. MODULUS OF ELASTICITY

Test sample from panel batch all 50×50mm	Load failure kg	Compressive stress at failure kgf/mm²	Value of adjusted F'c kgf/mm²	Modulus of elasticity kgf/mm²
A	8000	3.1	2.11	1.772×10^6
	6740	2.60		
B	7820	3.02	2.46	1.94×10^6
	9260	3.59		
C	8900	3.44	2.59	2.0×10^6
	8900	3.44		
D	5270	2.11	1.80	1.6×10^6
	6900	2.67		
E	7820	3.02	2.40	1.9×10^6
	8710	3.27		
F	6900	2.67	2.35	1.87×10^6
	9260	3.59		
G	8200	3.16	2.53	1.97×10^6
	9260	3.59		

The compressive stress at failure on the cube specimen has been related to an equivalent F'c value. The factor of 0.75 relating cube to cylinder strength has been obtained from Fig. 1 of SAA No. A104 1957 (Australian standard method of test for compressive strength of concrete specimens).

The modulus of elasticity has been calculated from the formula:

$$E_c = (1,000,000 + 500F'c) \quad \text{lbf/in}^2$$

This value being given in AS CA2 1963, SAA Code for Concrete in Buildings.

Testing of panels

The panel was marked to record the position of its centre line, position of supports and cantilever overhang and then was accurately positioned on the frame, the hangers bolted in position and all dimensions noted. A strain gauge (250 mm, 350 Ω, in a woven nylon carrier) was attached along the axis of the specimen. A strain gauge was also fixed to a beam specimen which was used as a dummy.

NOTE: In the early experiments a second gauge was attached to the test specimen approximately 150 mm off the centre line position and connected to a second strain bridge, to enable continuity of experiment in the event of the first gauge slipping or being in open circuit. Dual readings were also taken to compare for possible variations in strain along the specimen. The variations in strain, as recorded by the two bridges, were small and hence, in other tests, were not recorded.

The active and dummy gauges were connected in full bridge circuit to a battery-operated strain bridge direct reading to 5U (with interpolation to 1U) and balanced. A dial gauge was clamped to the frame, centred and set on the centre line of the tests specimen. A stereo microscope was positioned to facilitate crack detection and a quartz crystal flood lamp was focused on the panel.

The loading was applied to the specimen in increments of approximately 2.5 to 5.0 kg in the form of weights suspended on hangers. For each loading, the reading on the dial gauge and strain bridge was recorded.

Loading was continued until excessive deflexion resulted or the specimen was on the point of collapse.

The surface was examined both visually and also under the microscope to determine the incidence and development of cracks.

TABLE 3. DETAILS OF TEST SPECIMENS

Mesh	Area of steel each face cm²	Area of tensile steel cm²	Perimeter of tensile steel mm
A 3 layers 18 SWG 25 mm × 25 mm mesh. Each face overlaid to give 25 mm × 25 mm square grid on horizontal projection.	0.84	0.42	138.68
B 3 layers 18 SWG 25 mm × 25 mm mesh. Each face overlaid to give 8 mm × 8 mm square grid on horizontal projection.	0.84	0.42	138.68
C 2 layers 18 SWG 25 mm × 25 mm mesh. Each face overlaid to give 12 mm × 12 mm square grid on horizontal projection.	.580	.290	91.95
D 1 layer 18 SWG 25 mm × 25 mm mesh each face.	.285	.143	45.97
E 2 layers 21 SWG 12 mm × 12 mm mesh. Each face overlaid to give 6 mm × 6 mm grid on horizontal projection.	.49	.25	123.19
F 3 layers 21 SWG 12 mm × 12 mm mesh. Each face overlaid to give 12 mm × 12 mm grid on horizontal projection.	.774	.387	196.85
G 1 layer 11 SWG 50 mm × 176 mm mesh each face.	.684	.413	55.37

DISCUSSION OF TEST RESULTS

No problem was experienced in placing and compacting the mortar with low water : cement ratios. During the mixing cycle, however, it was found that with water : cement ratios of less than 0.38 to 0.40, balling of the mortar occurred and hence the latter value was used through the tests.

When the ferro-cement panels were subject to flexural loading, the midspan deflexion was recorded in addition to values of strain. Examination of the curve's bending moment vs strain and bending moment vs deflexion indicate only small variations between the two—the mean value between the two being assumed as representative.

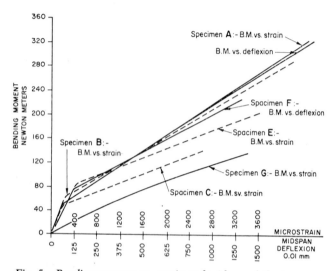

Fig. 5 Bending moment vs. strain and midspan deflexion

It is noticed that for specimens A to F the development of cracks was non-existent up to a strain of 200 to 300 U. Specimen G, however, did not exhibit this characteristic and it is significant that for this specimen a heavy gauge of wire in the large mesh was used, as contrasted with the fine wire and small mesh grid of A to F. It would seem reasonable to assume that the large grid permitted fine cracking to occur during drying shrinkage, whereas the smaller mesh of A to F effectively controlled this aspect. The fine cracking or concentration of stress resulting from drying shrinkage in specimen G immediately became apparent on loading, the member behaving as a reinforced concrete section throughout its loading cycle.

It is possible that the limiting grid size to control drying shrinkage effectively is a function of the depth of the member, but for the ferro-cement panels tested, the upper limit would appear to be a grid not greater than 25 mm × 25 mm.

As noted above, specimens A to F exhibited a crack-free zone to a strain of 200 to 300 U, this portion of the curve was linear and the behaviour of the material was of a homogeneous nature. The first cracks to be observed were very fine but could be seen with equal facility using the unaided eye or observing by microscope, provided a high intensity quartz crystal spot light (2000 watts) was played over the surface to give different values of light incidence. The change from homogeneous

to cracked section was very abrupt and may be noted by the change in slope of the above curves. Cracking was generally sudden and the formation of first to third crack was generally accompanied by an audible cracking sound. With the occurrence of such cracking both the dial gauge and the strain bridge indicated a jump in reading.

The strain at which the specimen first exhibited cracking was to some extent dependent on the type and distribution of reinforcing mesh, but in all cases was significantly close to the ultimate value of strain as determined by the beam flexure test on the mortar samples. Professor P. L. Nervi recommends the use of a safe design stress of approximately 0.400 kgf/mm² in a homogeneous section; this corresponds quite closely to the equivalent stress calculated for the beam specimens tested in flexure (see Table 1). The use of a design stress of this magnitude should therefore result in a crack-free (or limited crack) material suitable as a waterproof barrier.

After the formation of the initial cracks a point was reached where creep was experienced, being indicated by both the dial gauge and strain gauge readings. A fixed time interval of five minutes after the application of loading was, therefore, allowed before recording any readings.

Increasing the area of steel increased the stiffness of the member, this effect being valid in both the uncracked and fully-cracked section. It may be noticed from the curve of bending moment vs deflexion, that the use of smaller diameter wires, although providing slightly less effective area of tensile steel, resulted in a compensating

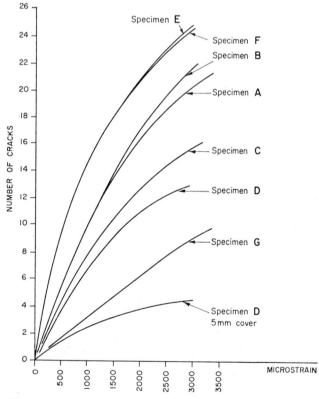

Fig. 6 Strain vs. number of cracks. Note *number of cracks recorded for half span only over distance of 38cm.*

increase in lever arm and hence equivalent increase in stiffness (sample F vs A).

The distribution of cracks in the various specimens was a function of the type of mesh used. In this respect the use of lighter gauge smaller mesh reinforcement was the most effective, as shown by specimens E and F vs A and B. It should be noted that:

(a) Improved control was achieved by the use of the lighter gauge mesh in E and F as compared with A and B. In this respect the area of reinforcement in specimen E was considerably less than for A or B yet a superior crack control was achieved.

(b) No apparent variation in crack spacing between specimen E and F or between A and B, where layers of mesh were staggered.

It would appear, therefore, that in order to exercise control of the crack pattern at the tension face of the ferro-cement members subject to flexure, a limiting maximum size for the mesh grid would be of the order of 25 mm × 25 mm.

Where the layers of reinforcing mesh are overlaid and staggered through the depth of the section to give a smaller grid pattern as projected onto the horizontal plane, very marginal improvement in the control of crack was observed and it would appear that the staggering of the layers of mesh is not very significant.

Reducing the size of the grid of the outer layer of mesh to 12 mm × 12 mm square resulted in a significant improvement in crack control when compared with a large grid (specimens E vs A). This factor, combined with the observation above, would appear to indicate that the major influence in achieving control of the cracking is that exercised by the outer layer of mesh.

When comparing the effect of cross-sectional area vs perimeter of the reinforcing steel, it was found that the latter property was the most effective in controlling crack dispersal. For example, specimen F, with a very much reduced area of reinforcing steel but increased perimeter compared with specimen A or B, achieved improved crack control. The cross-sectional area, however, contributes to the stiffness and also to the ultimate moment capacity of the section and, as such, requires consideration. It would appear, however, that for a particular effective cross-sectional area of steel, the best results are achieved by increasing the perimeter in the outer layers, i.e. by the use of smaller diameter wires at closer centres.

In only one specimen, namely D, was the cover over the reinforcing mesh varied. The results, in terms of crack distribution and control, were significant. At the right-hand end of the specimen, the fixed cover of 2.5 mm was adhered to, whereas at the opposite end this was increased to 5.0 mm. The distribution of cracks at the right-hand end followed the same relationship as with specimens A, B, C and E. At the left-hand end, however, a very limited number of cracks formed, such cracks developing large widths and preventing the even spread of fine cracks along the section. It would appear, therefore, that one of the most significant aspects in limiting the size of cracks is to maintain as small a cover over the mesh as is consistent with protection.

CONCLUSIONS

The most effective control of cracking in the tensile zone of a member subject to bending is obtained where the member develops a multitude of fine cracks spread uniformly along its length, rather than a limited number of large cracks at irregular spacing and of an intensity such as would expose the reinforcement to possible corrosion under working stress conditions.

Within the range of size and distribution of reinforcing mesh used in the ferro-cement specimens tested, and using the above as a criterion of crack control, the following may be concluded:

1. A limiting maximum size for the grid of the reinforcing mesh, which will exercise suitable control of cracking, is of the order of 25 mm × 25 mm.

2. Only marginal improvement in crack control is obtained where the overlaid layers of reinforcing mesh are staggered through the depth of the section (resulting in a reduced grid pattern as projected on the horizontal plane).

3. Reducing the size of the grid of the outer layer of reinforcing mesh to 12 mm × 12 mm resulted in a significant improvement in crack control. This outer layer of mesh should, therefore, have as small a grid size as is practicable.

4. The properties of the outer layer of reinforcing mesh are considerably more important than those of the interior layers and the use of spacer rods or of a larger diameter reinforcement in the internal layers should not result in a significant reduction in crack intensity.

5. The cross-sectional area of the reinforcement contributes to the stiffness and also to the ultimate moment capacity of the section; it is concluded, however, that for a particular effective cross-sectional area of reinforcement the best results are achieved by increasing the perimeter, i.e. by the use of smaller diameter bars at closer centres.

6. The effectiveness of the mesh reinforcement—both in terms of crack control and stiffness of member—falls off rapidly as the neutral axis is approached, the layers of mesh in this vicinity are largely ineffective and for the size of panel tested a satisfactory result may be achieved by using spacer rods overlaid with a minimum of two to three layers of light gauge mesh to each face.

7. The effect of the cover over the outer layer of mesh appeared to be extremely significant. In the one test where the cover had been allowed to increase at one end of the beam, an immediate change in the crack pattern and intensity was observed. The proliferation of fine cracks did not occur at this end but rather limited cracks of high intensity developed. It is concluded that in a member stressed to a level where the concrete has cracked, the provision of large cover will increase the possibility of reinforcement corrosion. The cover should, therefore, be the minimum possible to ensure protection of the mesh. The cover will be a function of the grading and size of the aggregate used in the mortar but the value of approximately 1.5 mm is the logical minimum.

8. Where the level of strain was low (below approximately 700 microstrain) the decrease in crack spacing was almost linear with increase in strain, suggesting a formula of the form:

$$W_{av} = K \cdot \gamma_z \cdot f_s$$

where W_{av} = average spacing between cracks,
K = constant,
γ_z = a function of the perimeter of the reinforcement in the tensile zone.

9. The use of a high strength mortar is significant when considering the properties of the ferro-cement panel and where design is as a homogeneous specimen the cement : aggregate ratio should be not less than 1 part cement : 1.5 parts well-graded sand, and the water : cement ratio should be approximately 0.4.

10. Design may be as a homogeneous material with a safe working stress of 0.4 kg/mm², subject to condition (9) above. The reinforcement should consist of at least three layers of mesh, each face giving a weight of at least 2 kg/m² of projected area per cm thickness of member. The size of the grid of the reinforcing mesh should be as stated in (1) and (3) above.

In view of the limited number of parameters varied in these tests, it is felt that there is scope for more testing to establish the limiting values of relationship between crack distribution and:

(a) the use of different sizes of reinforcing bars in standard grids,
(b) variations in the diameter and perimeter of reinforcement for fixed areas of steel,
(c) variations in level of cover over the reinforcing mesh,
(d) variations in cement : aggregate ratio and water : cement ratio.

No serious attempt has been made to relate the results of the tests to an established mathematical formula; where such attempts have been made in the case of reinforced concrete a large number of different formulae have resulted, with very limited agreement between the various forms proposed.

References

NERVI, P L Il ferro-cemento: sue caratteristiche e possi-
1951 bilità. *L'Ingegnere*, (1). (Also *Ferro-cement: Its characteristics and potentialities*. London, Cement and Concrete Association Library, translation No. 60, 1956.)

NERVI, P L Precast concrete offers new possibilities for design
1953 of shell structures. *J. Am. concr. Inst.*, Feb.

NERVI, P L Concrete and structural form. *The Structural*
1956 *Engineer*, May.

NERVI, P L Thin reinforced concrete members form Turin
1951 Exhibition halls. *Civil Engineering*, 21(1), January.

NERVI, P L *Structures*. New York, USA, F. W. Dodge
1956 Corporation.

S.A.A. Code A 104.
1957

S.A.A. Code CA 2.
1963

Acknowledgement

The investigation was carried out at the University of Sydney, Department of Architectural Science, under Professor H Cowan. The author acknowledges this assistance and the permission to publish the results.

Dynamic Point Loading of Ferro-Cement, Glassfibre-Reinforced Polyester and Plywood H-P Pedersen

Boat structures are usually calculated for static loads. High factors of safety are used to take into account the uncertainty of the loads.

The purpose of the tests here described was to determine the relative strengths of different skin plate materials when subjected to dynamic point loads. It is hoped the results will give some information of how well the skin plates in a boat can withstand collisions with floating objects, quays, etc.

TEST SAMPLES AND TESTING EQUIPMENT DESCRIBED

The test plates had a length of 600 mm and breadth of 500 mm. 100 mm of the shortest sides were clamped. The longest sides were simply supported 25 mm from the edges. Thus the part of the plates between supports was 400 × 450 mm.

Figure 1 shows a test plate with those dimensions and support conditions.

The centre of the plates was hit by a test hammer, which was released from a height of 2.04 m (Fig. 2). The tip of the test hammer was spherical with a radius

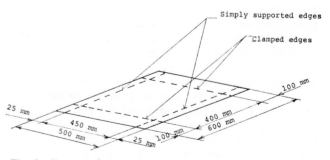

Fig. 1   Test panel

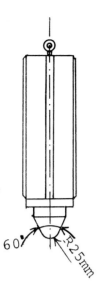

Fig. 2   Test hammer

of curvature of 25 mm and ended in a conical section of 60°.

The breaking load is defined as the dynamic energy of the hammer which gives a hole on the top side of the plate of 50 mm diameter. In order to get a hole of this size into the plates, the weight of the hammer was changed in accordance with results of previous tests. Identical plates were tested two by two with the same load; most results were inside a limit of ± 3 per cent.

The speed of the hammer was kept constant as was the elevation. The hammer hit the test plates only once; after hitting the plates it was thrown upwards in the guiding tube and locked there by automatic mechanism. The distribution of energy, just after the hit, between the test plates and the hammer could be established by means of a photo cell.

Tested panels are shown in Figs. 5 and 6.

TEST SAMPLES

Polyester reinforced by chopped strand mat

6 samples with   2 layers of 450 g/m² mat
6 samples with   6 layers of 450 g/m² mat
6 samples with 12 layers of 450 g/m² mat

The glass content was 29 per cent.

Polyester reinforced by woven roving

6 samples with 3 layers of 800 g/m² woven roving
6 samples with 6 layers of 800 g/m² woven roving
6 samples with 8 layers of 800 g/m² woven roving

The glass content was 66 per cent.

Polyester reinforced by chopped strand mat and woven roving

6 samples with 1 layer of 450 g/m² mat and
                    1 layer of 800 g/m² woven roving
6 samples with 2 layers of 450 g/m² mat and
                    2 layers of 800 g/m² woven roving
6 samples with 4 layers of 450 g/m² mat and
                    4 layers of 800 g/m² woven roving

The glass content was 38 per cent.

Ferro-cement test panels

6 samples reinforced by 1 layer of 6 mm rods of mild steel and 6 layers of $\frac{1}{2}$ in 20 SWG galvanized hexagonal mesh (chicken wire).

Rods are spaced at 50 mm centres and 3 layers of mesh tied on either side of the rod layer. Plates were 17.8 mm thick.

6 samples reinforced by 2 layers of 6 mm rods mild steel, and 8 layers of $\frac{1}{2}$ in 20 SWG galvanized hexagonal mesh. The spacing of the rods was 50 and 100 mm; 4 layers of mesh were tied on both sides of the crossing rods. The steel content of the samples was 19.6 per cent.

Mortar: sand : cement = 2
              water : cement = 0.4

Sand: 100 per cent of the sand passed sieve no. 8
          74 per cent of the sand passed sieve no. 14
          52 per cent of the sand passed sieve no. 28
          22 per cent of the sand passed sieve no. 48
            3 per cent of the sand passed sieve no. 100

Standard Portland cement, PC 300, was used.

Plywood test panels

6 samples 6 mm, 4 layers of mahogany
6 samples 8 mm, 5 layers of mahogany

PRESENTATION OF TEST RESULTS

Comparisons of the strengths of panels on the basis of equal weight per square metre of surface.

For 7.5 kg/m² Fig. 3 shows
    GRP, mat laminate   24.5 kgm (dynamic strength)
    GRP, mat and woven
        roving laminate   40.3 kgm (dynamic strength)
    GRP, woven roving
        laminate   56.5 kgm (dynamic strength)
    Plywood   14.5 kgm (dynamic strength)
    Ferro-cement   about   5 kgm, but this weight
                              represents an impractical
                              ferro-cement panel

The mat-roving laminate is 64 per cent stronger than the mat laminate. Laminate of woven roving is 130 per cent stronger than mat laminate and approximately 40 per cent stronger than mat-roving laminate.

Comparative weights of panels at equal dynamic strength

For a dynamic strength of 50 kgm Fig. 3 gives the following weights:

    GRP, mat laminate   13 kg/m²
    GRP, mat-roving laminate   9 kg/m²
    GRP, woven roving   6.9 kg/m²
    Plywood   about 23 kg/m² (extra-
                                        polated)
    (Test panels of plywood were much lighter)
    Ferro-cement   65.6 kg/m²

Laminates reinforced by woven roving are the lightest. Mat-roving laminates are 30 per cent heavier, and mat laminates are 88 per cent heavier than the roving laminates. Ferro-cement panels are approximately 9.5 times as heavy as the laminates reinforced by woven roving.

23

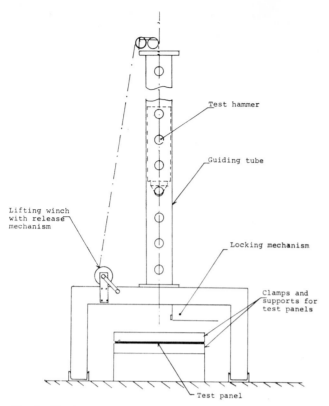

Fig. 3   Testing equipment

Comparative strength of panels at material cost per m²

For a material cost of US$6.93/m², Fig. 4 shows

GRP, mat laminate	30.5 kgm
GRP, mat-roving laminate	47.7 kgm
GRP, woven roving	54.6 kgm
Plywood	about 16 kgm
Ferro-cement	40 kgm

The mat-roving laminate is 56 per cent stronger than the mat laminate. The laminate reinforced by woven roving is 79 per cent stronger than the mat laminate and 14.5 per cent stronger than the mat-roving laminate. Ferro-cement is 31 per cent stronger than the mat laminate. Plywood has about 40 per cent of the strength of ferro-cement.

Comparative material costs for panels of equal dynamic strength

For a dynamic strength of 50 kgm Fig. 4 gives

GRP, mat laminate	61.60 N.kr/m²	= US$9.50/m²
GRP, mat and woven roving laminate	46.70 N.kr/m²	= US$7.20/m²
GRP, woven roving laminate	41.70 N.kr/m²	= US$6.42/m²
Ferro-cement	52.00 N.kr/m²	= US$8.00/m²

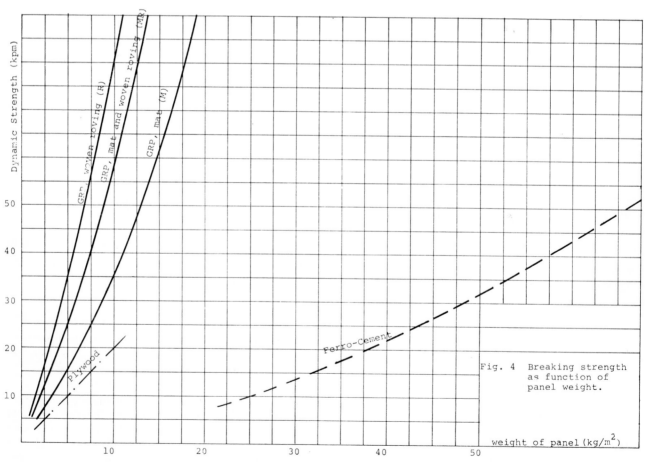

Fig. 4   Breaking strength as function of panel weight.

Fig. 4   Breaking strength as function of panel weight

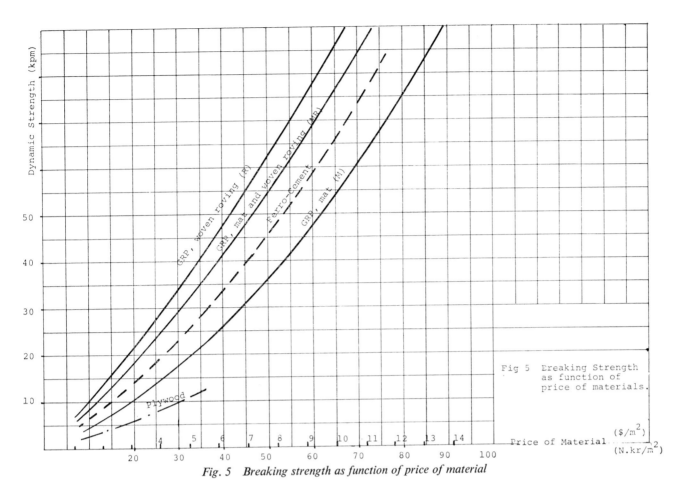

Fig. 5   Breaking strength as function of price of material

Laminates reinforced by woven roving are cheapest. Mat-roving laminates and mat laminates cost 12 per cent and 48 per cent more, respectively. Ferro-cement panels cost 25 per cent more than roving laminates, but are 16 per cent cheaper than mat laminates.

COMPARISON OF HULLS OF GLASS-FIBRE REINFORCED POLYESTER (GRP) AND FERRO-CEMENT

A 50-ft long hull of glassfibre reinforced polyester can be made about one-third as heavy as a hull of ferrocement of the same size. The weight ratios for hull plates of GRP and ferro-cement can, for this size of boat, be approximately 1 : 5 to 1 : 6. The following can be taken as an example of skin plates of the two materials.

Ferro-cement: weight 64 kg/m², thickness 25 mm.
GRP, mat laminate: weight 11.6 kg/m², thickness 8 mm.

Using Fig. 3, the dynamic strength of the ferro-cement plate was 47.5 kgm and 42.5 kgm for the mat laminate. Thus a ferro-cement boat could be about 12 per cent stronger than a GRP-boat made according to the rules of the classification societies. GRP-boats reinforced by woven roving should normally be stronger than conventional ferro-cement boats.

"Conventional" in this case is related to the eight layers of ½ in 20 SWG galvanized hexagonal mesh. Woven roving laminates yield close to the highest possible strength of glassfibre reinforced polyester.

Higher steel content or better steel quality should give a better strength/weight ratio for ferro-cement. Substitution of some layers of galvanized mesh with ungalvanized mesh would give a better strength/price ratio.

A combination of highly tensile steel and flexible mortar seems promising, and tests of such samples should have been carried out to get more information of high strength ferro-cement.

TEST RESULTS IN RELATION TO STRENGTH OF PANELS IN A BOAT STRUCTURE

Test results given are related to the geometry of samples, of supports along the edges of the samples, and to the geometry and speed of the test hammer.

The plates in a hull should in most cases be able to withstand heavier loads than the experiments indicate, because of the spring action of the surrounding structure. Hulls with heavy frames are more vulnerable in this respect than a flexible structure. These remarks on flexibility are not valid, however, if the duration of the load is equal to or longer than the natural frequency.

Fig. 6 to 9   Traces of impact on test panels

Fig. 6a   Topside of mat laminate

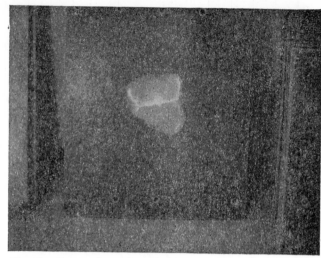

Fig. 6b   Bottom face of mat laminate

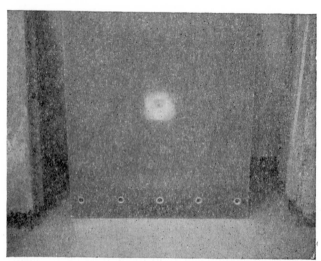

Fig. 7a   Topside of mat-roving laminate

Fig. 7b   Bottom face of mat-roving laminate

Fig. 8a   Topside of ferro-cement panel

Fig. 8b   Bottom face of ferro-cement panel

Fig. 9a Topside of plywood panel

Fig. 9b Bottom face of plywood panel

CONCLUSIONS

Considering plates of same weight per unit of surface, the plates of glassfibre reinforced polyester will be much stronger than ordinary ferro-cement. For plates with the same breaking strength, the weight ratio of GRP and ferro-cement will be around 10 : 1 and 5 : 1.

Displacement hulls of GRP and ferro-cement of the same size will be able to withstand about the same dynamic point loads. For this type of load the GRP-laminates should have a high content of woven roving. More sophisticated ferro-cement, reinforced by heavier mesh, or woven high-tensile wires, for example, is assumed to give much better dynamic strength as regards strength/weight ratio. Use of ungalvanized mesh will give a better strength/price ratio.

Plywood has a much better strength/weight ratio than ferro-cement, but the strength/price ratio is inferior.

Concrete Technology in the Quality Control of Ferro-Cement Vessels   T G Kowalski and B R Walkus

At first, every new shipping material is assessed in terms of other commonly-used media, and in this ferro-cement is no exception. However, what is known already of the properties of this most promising material would suggest that it should be treated as a distinct medium of its own; which means neither as reinforced concrete, nor, still less, as steel.

This article reviews existing guidelines for quality control and proposes their rationalization. The main interest is centred here on the technology of fine-grained concretes used in ferro-cement marine construction.

Quality control of ferro-cement vessels is presently conducted by surveys and tests. The tests, if it is so desired, can also lead to the establishment of design constants, some of which have already been tentatively established by Bezukladow *et al.* (1968). Those constants could now be modified and amplified to suit various local conditions before being adopted by Shipping Registers other than the USSR Registry. The Shipping Registers may well decide that below a certain length of, say, 10 m, extensive testing as well as surveys could be radically curtailed without impairment of safety. Bigger vessels, however, will always require both.

CONCRETE TECHNOLOGY

The object of testing is to obtain specified minimal requirements of compressive strength and volumetric stability with an adequate workability to ensure good compaction. In ferro-cement which is a composite, the concrete part is always the more variable. This means that testing of a few and unrepresentative samples is likely to be more misleading than no testing at all.

At the surveyor's discretion, preliminary tests could be abandoned altogether when sufficient experience and consistency of results has been built up. In practice, due to reasons stated below, marine ferro-cement mortar can only be of one narrowly circumscribed type; namely a mortar which is extremely rich in cement, which is stiff (very low water : cement ratio) and which has only fine aggregate—closely controlled for kind, shape and size.

27

TEST SAMPLES

Most concrete samples taken during ferro-cement vessel construction so far reflect present building and civil engineering practices. The one size which came closest to the thin-wall nature of ferro-cement hulls, which seldom exceed 40 mm in thickness, was the 70 mm-a-side cube. Although the 70 mm sample was more relevant than either the 150 mm (cubic) or 200 mm (cylindric) samples, it still did not reflect the mode of compressive failure of a concrete ship's hull (resembling that of a thin stiffened shell), nor did it bear a suitable relation to the smallness of the aggregate grains, which have to be used in marine mixes. Consequently, apart from the ease of handling on the site, the theoretical reasons pointed to a smaller compressive sample. This led to two proposals.

The first, based on 22 mm (diameter and height), gang mould cylinders was developed by one of the authors in Hong Kong University (Fig. 1). Two moulds, each capable of holding 25 fine-grained concrete cylinders, are shown here: one is completely assembled (bottom left-hand corner); the disassembled parts of another mould show stainless steel baseplate with studs, 6 brass segments and 2 brass yokes.

The second proposal developed jointly in Poland (Kozak, 1970) is more universal in application, and involves less care in the casting and testing of specimens, in comparison with the first and involves only one concrete rod of standard size (160 × 40 × 40 mm). The rod can be used for the tensile rupture test (point load in the middle of a 100 mm span), the concrete compressive crushing test (using the two halves from the previous test or loading across 40 mm square ends) as well as for the measurement of volumetric stability (glued metal nosings and "Demec" type strain gauge). Moreover, under certain conditions (of reinforcing specific surface) it would be even possible to test the sample as a ferro-cement rod subjected to bending.

AGGREGATES

The type and granulometry of concrete aggregates have an important bearing on the mix performance. These maximum or optimum characteristics, have been defined by Kowalski (1972) as the maximum 28-day compressive strength divided by minimum 28-day shrinkage (at constant humidity and temperature). In addition whenever data become available the whole of the previous total value can be again divided by either the minimum 28-day absorption in water and/or the minimum expansion or swelling in water (over a longer period of, say, 90 days). To achieve the optimum characteristics the following notes on aggregates are useful.

Impurities

Clay, salt, vegetable or mineral matter and expanding aggregates are to be avoided. Sources of aggregates

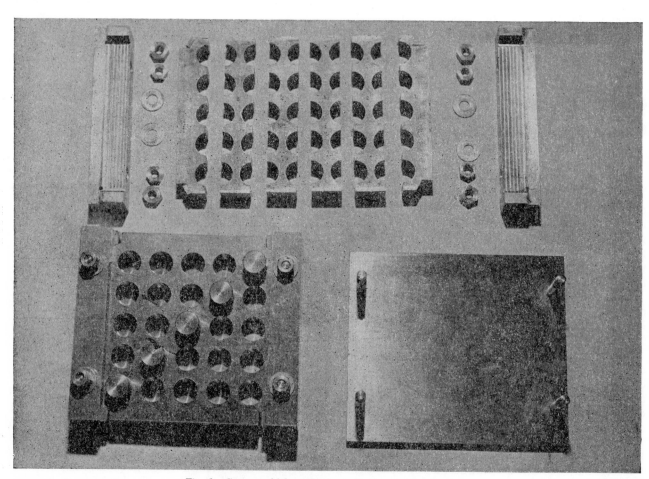

Fig. 1 Gangmould for cylinder concrete compression tests

should be carefully examined to avoid contamination by oil, sewage, etc. The best sources are freshly milled and protectively stored, granitic or basaltic rocks.

Types and sizes

Irregular and sharp milled surfaces give better optimum characteristics than smooth rounded silica, although the latter may be easier to compact. Gap-graded aggregate, or alternatively aggregate of approximately the same size give best results. Too many fines (arbitrarily defined here as all sizes below 0.3 mm mesh opening) will not only step up the water demand to maintain adequate lubrication but may also contain considerable amounts of weathered, weak material as well. If, on the other hand, too many of the larger sizes are used (say, above 0.6 mm) this tends to make the mix harsh and unworkable and affects bond, penetration and, most important of all, compaction. On the basis of previously quoted work (Kowalski, 1972), the optimum aggregate sizes will probably lie in the 1.2 to 0.3 mm range, with a possible narrowing of this range down to 0.3 to 0.6 mm sieve openings.

CEMENTS

Very few cements of the Portland variety produced today seem suited to be used directly in thin-hull marine construction. Present (unpublished) work by one of the authors would indicate that most of the problems could be overcome and a suitable marine Portland cement developed. Incidently, the necessarily high strength and positive volumetric stability characteristics of such a cement would also have ready application elsewhere. Of the cements at present easily available at low cost, the more finely ground rapid-hardening Portland cement offers considerably better characteristics than the ordinary variety (Kowalski, 1972). This fact is more important in warm and humid areas where optimum mix characteristics tend to have a lower value than in temperate climates. So far, the ordinary Portland cements, formulated for low sulphate conditions, have given what appears to be a satisfactory performance in ferro-cement vessels. However, the use of protective epoxy paints may account for this fact. If a protective coating is not envisaged, sulphate resisting Portland cement should be mandatory, although its use may not safeguard against all possible problems, particularly if there is bad concrete compaction.

It must be stated at this point that while short-term negative aspects of a cement's chemical composition become known quite soon (see below), long-term effects require considerably longer periods of study. Consequently, some of the claims of hull durability, based on the excellent past performance of relatively thick hulled concrete vessels, may be premature when projected to ferro-cement hulls in their present stage of development.

ADDITIVES AND WORKABILITY

Most additives are used to improve workability, to lessen water demand and to prolong the concrete setting. In marine mixes, these effects are so valuable that addi-

tives should always be used to improve one or all of these characteristics regardless of climatic conditions. The type of additive may of course vary to suit these conditions.

Of the many types available, Pozzolans are particularly worthwhile because of their versatility, especially in warmer climates where they can promote retardent action, reduce the amount of water necessary for workability as well as remove or neutralize the calcium hydroxide which is sometimes present in cements in excessive quantities (a sign of inferior quality).

Large-scale use of pozzolanic cements could, however, have some disadvantages. Pozzolans are not produced as universally as Portland cements, hence their importation in most localities would raise costs, although these could be reduced by using artificial Pozzolanic material ("Roman" pozzolana, Indian "Surki" or the Egyptian "Homra"). The addition of Pozzolans appears to lower the initial compressive strength, and cause a slight increase in shrinkage and a reduction of the modulus of elasticity.

In view of the importance of compressive strength and volumetric stability the slump cone measurement of workability should not be relied upon, since apart from its unsuitability for very stiff mixes it gives misleading results. For instance, it can be seen that five given ferro-cement mixes can have widely differing optimum properties (through the variation of type and content of cement, additive and aggregate) and yet the same five mixes will apparently have almost identical "slump" of between 70 to 74 mm (Kowalski, 1972). Since the mixes have to be very stiff and only just workable a more relevant measure of workability would be to use a given mix on a trial section of the actual hull material (a mock-up).

CURING

Curing, i.e. the maintenance of set concrete for an initially suitable period in an ambient humidity of at least 85 per cent and over, is essential for cement hydration and the early development of compressive strength. Some points are worth mentioning in this connexion.

Drying out

During the initial curing process of the thin-hull ferro-cement this is a greater danger than in the more robust reinforced concrete members. Surface drying can extend quickly throughout the section and negatively affect the early strength and eventual durability. Ferro-cement hulls should consequently never be allowed to dry-out during this initial curing process.

Steam curing

Although it may mean quicker working for a yard, this ultimately tends to produce less durable, more porous and less strong concrete, as opposed to normal temperature (spray curing) methods. This is particularly true for inexpert steam curing which may damage a hull permanently, without this becoming obvious in the early stages of the hull's life.

Enviromental service humidity

Provided the initial curing has been well done, the relatively high environmental humidity of a ferrocement vessel at sea should in most cases ensure a complete cure for the hull concrete.

Initial curing

The length of initial curing should be governed by the cement type and the ambient temperature. Total maturity (°C × hours) for most ordinary Portland cements in moderate summer ambient temperatures is usually sufficient after approximately seven 24-h periods of continuous wet cure. Rapid hardening cements will require between three to four 24-h periods at these temperatures. To exceed this initial curing period increases subsequent drying shrinkages, although this is not so evident at water cement ratios below 0.40 and will also depend on the cement "freshness" (older cements will require longer periods). Of course, cements which have been stored too long should not be used at all. Preliminary tests should quickly inform the user of this, who should be particularly wary in warmer countries.

CONCRETE DESIGN PARAMETERS

At the present stage of development minimal requirements are difficult to lay down. The difficulties stem from the comparative scarcity of experience and information as well as from the climatically different sources of information available. It is hoped, however, that the following will be useful.

Compressive strength

There is no doubt that a high compressive strength influences positively the optimal mix characteristics. Also, concrete made with the universally available and inexpensive Portland cement forms only a small part of the overall material costs.

It would thus appear to be false economy to save on cement, if only in view of the arduous service conditions of a concrete hull. More important, alternate drying and wetting of a comparatively weak concrete will show up a marked difference of the "wet" and "dry" compressive strength. However, the higher the concrete compressive strength and its associated compaction, the narrower is this strength difference and the sounder and more durable the hull. Moreover, a concrete which has been allowed to dry out before the attainment of sufficient maturity will register a sharp drop of compressive strength, when it has been immersed again. The strength drop is all the more pronounced as the concrete at the time of immersion is weaker and the less mature. A saturated (and presumably absorbent) concrete will also register a lower fatigue performance (Sintzow et al., 1969). The increase of shrinkage normally expected with cement-rich mixes need not automatically happen in the case of marine mixes. Indeed, under conditions of low water content and of a high cement content, the latter will demand more hydration water from the limited total available (Kowalski, 1972). Consequently less "free" water will be left to evaporate and to cause shrinkage.

Minimum calculated value of concrete compressive stress: In view of the above, and the authors' experience this value can be represented by the formula:

$$f_{mc} = 0.45f_c$$

where f_{mc} = minimum calculated value of concrete compressive stress obtained from the testing of basic stress f_c; f_c is the average value of 14 halves, obtained after the completion of the 160 × 40 × 40 specimen test for tensile rupture in bending.[1]

The minimum preliminary test value of f_{mc} should not be less than 200 kg/cm² (works tests can be 15 per cent lower). The maximum fluctuation of results should not be more than ±10 per cent with a corresponding mean standard deviation of 15 per cent.

An approximate value of f_{mc} = 200 kg/cm² for a 70 mm cube is around 600 kg/cm².

Minimum calculated value of concrete tensile stress: This value can be represented by the formula:

$$f_{mt} = 0.40f_{tb}$$

where f_{mt} = minimum calculated value of concrete tensile stress worked out on the basis of bending tests on seven 160 × 40 × 40 mm concrete rods and subject to the same limits as above. The radius of supports and of central joint load applied to determine f_{tb} (tensile stress in bending) is 5 mm. $f_{tb} = M/Z$, where M is the bending moment and Z the section modulus. The minimum value of f_{mt} = 25 kg/cm² (preliminary) and f_{mt} = 20 kg/cm² (works).

Average concrete density: For weigh-batching purposes, the average density of fine-grained concrete made with ordinary (normal stone) as opposed to lightweight (artificial) aggregate, should be taken as 2200 kg/m³. Fluctuations of this value measured on 160 × 40 × 40 mm samples should not exceed ±100 kg/m³. Too little is known at this time to recommend similar figures for lightweight aggregates.

Minimum cement content: Minimum Portland cement content should not be less than 600 kg/m³ of fine-grained concrete, when the average density of that concrete is as given above.

Maximum water : cement ratio: Even under the least favourable conditions of high temperature and evaporation, when additives have to be used, this should not exceed 0.40. In the interests of greater durability but subject to adequate compaction, every effort should be made to bring this figure lower still.

Maximum water absorption: Tests should be conducted on four concrete rods (160 × 40 × 40 mm) 28 days after casting. The rods should be immersed for 3 × 24 h periods in sea water at 20°C, then weighed and dried for another such period at 50°C and 30 per cent maximum relative humidity. The preliminary average value of percentage of absorption in relation to the fully saturated figure should not exceed 5.0 per cent (works = 5.5 per cent) with a maximum fluctuation of results of ±10 per

---

[1] Normal compression testing machines with either 1 or 2 special plattens (62.5 × 40 mm testing area).

cent. Should it be so desired, the samples used for the absorption test could be fitted on their two long (opposite) sides with metal nosings and the shrinkage measured during and after the absorption test.

Maximum swelling strains: Tests should be conducted on four concrete rods ($160 \times 40 \times 40$ mm) 28 days after casting. The rods which should have metal nosings (as above) should be immersed in sea water (at 20°C) for 90 days. The preliminary and works swelling strain figure after this time should not exceed 180×10^{-6}, with no greater fluctuation of results allowed than ± 10 per cent.

Maximum concrete shrinkage strain: The definition of a maximum allowable shrinkage strain is both complex and difficult. Actual service shrinkage strains are likely to be both considerably lower due to closely-spaced reinforcement and uneven, due to scantlings and steel laps. Moreover, any definition of shrinkage strain must allow for the conditions in which shrinkage has been measured (humidity and temperature). In spite of this, the nature of bending behaviour of the material demands an exact knowledge of the crack widths. Indeed, it appears that the proportioning of marine ferro-cement will be governed by crack openings. (These problems have been briefly outlined by Walkus and Kowalski (1971) and will be more broadly discussed in a forthcoming joint publication.) Incidentally, the cracking width under load with a normally adequate protective hull paint should not exceed 0.05 mm. This width should under no circumstances be widened by excessive shrinkage of an unsuitable mix. (As outlined above, hull areas subjected to successive wetting and drying are the most vulnerable.) In view of that, it is tentatively proposed to limit the average value of the 28-day shrinkage strain to 600×10^{-6} "preliminary" and 650×10^{-6} "works" values. (At 85 per cent of relative humidity and 20°C.)

The test can be conducted on the same seven ($160 \times 40 \times 40$ mm) rods which are used after 28 days to determine concrete rupture and compression stresses. The two opposite (long) sides would have the usual (100 mm) base metal nosings glued on to enable "Demec" type strain gauge to be used. Test fluctuation and deviation as for 9.1 (14 no. faces are used for shrinkage strain measurement and the nosings can subsequently be scraped off).

Testing quantities: A total of $15 + 1$ (spare) concrete rods would be required for one testing batch. One test batch would be required for every 3 m³ (or a portion thereof) of the concrete mix. In comparison with, say, one 150 mm (side) cube which requires some 3.5 l of mix, the entire batch of 16 rods requires only 4.5 l of mix. These figures allow for some wastage.

CONSTRUCTION STAGES

To draw attention to points of importance during a survey it is useful to record the construction stages of a ferro-cement vessel. The following stages are based on Lloyds "tentative requirements" (1967) and are amplified by the authors' own observations. It is also thought these stages can be modified to suit methods other than the ones discussed here.

Stage 1. Reinforcement half complete

At this stage, when the hull formers and the longitudinal and transverse steel is in place (together with the inner mesh layers), attention should be given to:

> preliminary hull fairness, stiffness and stability;
> rod and wire mesh lapping;
> rod welding.

Stage 2. Reinforcement complete

When the hull is ready for concreting, the following merit attention:

> inserts and all non-concrete fixtures;
> localized hull stiffness (concreting pressures);
> hull fairness and overall stability during concreting operations;
> all points likely to cause concrete penetration problems;
> walkways for concreting to minimize disturbance to freshly concreted areas;
> capability and suitability of concreting plant, storage and protection of cement, aggregates, water, additives;
> planning of the sequence, timing and breaks in concreting operations;
> emergency provisions to counter the weather, machinery breakdowns, operatives' fatigue or illness and night-time operations;
> operatives' training and experience (particularly relevant with "shotcreting").

Stage 3. Application, compacting and finishing off of hull

In this, the most crucial part of the survey, the following are important:

> correct sequence of placing ingredients in the mixer as well as the time of mixing;
> mix consistency, with particular emphasis on a constant and minimal amount of water and correct amount of additives;
> systematic work to minimize the formation of "cold-joints" in badly compacted places;
> the achievement of the highest possible compaction which should be aided by mechanical means, such as suitably adapted sanding machines;
> proper time lapse between concreting and "finishing off" of the outer surface of the hull, which should be performed so as to avoid creating a weak outer surface crust;
> concrete test samples (works testing) to be taken during concreting.

Stage 4. Framework stripping

Most ferro-cement vessels to date have not used formwork; indeed, the absence of formwork is claimed as one of the principal construction advantages. However, for a better hull fairness which is possible with a stiff temporary mould (which can be quite cheaply made) as well as for better concrete compaction against the rigid backing of the formwork, not to mention development prospects (Kowalski, 1971), construction using formwork should not be disregarded. In this case the following should be noted:

formwork stripping (which should always be expertly and carefully executed) should not commence before completion of a minimum period of concrete maturity (see below);

a vessel constructed upside down using a male mould should be righted—prior to commencement of the stripping process (for stiffness).

Stage 5. At the end of curing

The following are important:

a systematic and painstaking inspection to discover cavities left behind by concreting. This can be done by manual tapping, ultra-sonic or by the local application of vacuum. A method of filling cavities, if detected, is outlined by Eyres (1972);

a second inspection for cavities (looking for damp patches and rust) should take place after the hull has been in the water for 28 days;

painting of the whole hull or of its underwater part only, should follow the second inspection, provided suitable paints are used and the hull is well dried beforehand.

IMPACT

The resistance of ferro-cement to moderate impact is one of its assets in marine use. Its behaviour is unique for in no other material does the fabric remain largely intact after part of the energy of the blow has been absorbed. Of course, one must consider moderate blows only, since every medium can be ruptured by the application of a sufficiently large force. The problems of ferro-cement impact resistance deserve a wider and more rigorous treatment than is given here in the form of these generalized comments. Its inclusion is only justified by the fact that both Lloyds (1967) and ABS (1969) guidelines are including it as part of their quality control. Lately, too, apart from Nervi's initial tests more information has become available. This includes publications by Bezukladow *et al.* (1968), Lessard (1971), Sintzow *et al.* (1969), Kelly and Mouat (1969) and Shah and Key (1971).

Of the above, only Shah and Key appear to present a rational approach to the problem. Instead of measuring the width of cracks due to a variable total potential energy of the blows, they measure the effect of a constant potential energy in terms of flow of water at a constant water head, In the other publications the measurement of the total potential energy of the blows sustained (or Sigma nPh), versus the crack width can lead to contradictory results. This is chiefly due to the variable sizes of impacting bodies employed and the variable interpretations which can be put on the effect of crack width. Moreover, the measurement of the water flow through a damaged panel is more rational, since it can be directly related to the capacities of a given vessel's pumping equipment. Consequently an amendment of the ABS impact test along these lines would clarify the objectives

and methods of such a test. Incidentally, the test panel notching, which is possibly related to steel tests, has in this context little relevance.

CONCLUSION

In comparison with other shipping media, ferro-cement and its quality control is in its infancy. Valuable beginnings made by some major Shipping Registers highlight the continuing need for discussion on the kind and extent of quality control which may be required.

This discussion must be conducted at an interdisciplinary level, between ship-builders, naval architects, concrete practitioners and technologists.

References

ABS (AMERICAN BUREAU OF SHIPPING) *Guidelines for the*
1969   *Construction of Ferro-cement Vessels.* Aug., 12 pp.

BEZUKLADOW, W F, *et al. Korpusa Sudow is Armociemienta*
1968   (*Konstrukcja, Protchnost' i tiechnologia Postroiki*)
[Ferro-cement Hull—Construction, Strength and Technology]. Leningrad, USSR, Izdatielstwo "Sudostroyienie", 189 pp.

EYRES, D J Some notes on the survey of ferro-cement fishing
1972   vessels built in New Zealand. *Report on the Second FAO/Swedish Training Centre on Small Fishing Boat Design and Construction. Seminar for Fisheries Officers, Working Papers and Discussion.* Rome, Italy: FAO/SWE/TF 84, Paper II/4.

KELLY, A M and MOUAT, T W Ferro-cement as a fishing
1969   vessel construction material. *Proceedings, Conference on Fishing Vessel Construction Materials, Montreal, 1968.* Ottawa, Canada: Department of Fisheries and Forestry, Fisheries Service, Fisheries Reports No. 12 : 135–162.

KOWALSKI, T G Ferro-cement in Hong Kong. *Far East*
1971   *Builder*, July, 29–35.

KOWALSKI, T G *Ferro-cement Marine Mixes in Warm and*
1972   *Humid Environment.* Tbilisi, USSR: FIP Symposium on Concrete Sea Structures, 5 pp.

KOZAK, R. (ed.) *Budownictwo Betonowe, tom 8—Badanie Materiałów, Elementów, Konstrukcji* [Concrete Construction, vol. 8—Testing of Materials, Elements and Assemblies]. Warsaw, Poland: Arkady, 523 pp.

LEA, F M *The Chemistry of Cement and Concrete*, 3rd ed.
1970   London, England: Edward Arnold, 727 pp.

LESSARD, Y *Propriétés et Applications du Ferro-Shotcrete*
1971   [Properties and Uses of Ferro-shotcrete]. Thèse de Maîtrise, Département de Génie Civil, Université Laval, Canada, 197 pp.

LLOYD'S REGISTER OF SHIPPING *Tentative requirements for the*
1967   *construction of yachts and small craft in ferro-cement.* Technical Note: FC/REQ/1, Jan., 5 pp.

MISHUTIN, W A *Issliedowanie Sudostroitielnych Bietonow* [The
1967   Investigation of Shipbuilding Concretes]. Leningrad, USSR: Izdatielstwo "Sudostroyienie", 178 pp.

SHAH, S P and KEY, W H (Jr.) Ferro-cement as a material
1971   for offshore structures. *Offshore Technology Conference*, Paper OTC 1465, April, Dallas, Texas, USA, 10 pp.

SINTZOW, G M, *et al. Konstrukcja i Protchnost' zheliezo-*
1969   *bietonnych Sudow* [Construction and Strength of Reinforced Concrete Ships]. Leningrad, USSR: Izdatielstwo "Sudostroyienie", 384 pp.

WALKUS, B R and KOWALSKI, T G Ferro-cement, a survey.
1971   *Concrete*, Feb., 48–52.

Strength and Cracking of Ferro-Cement   S P Shah and M G Srinivasan

Professor Nervi, the inventor of ferro-cement, who also coined its name, observed that ferro-cement behaves like a homogeneous material, capable of withstanding large strains without cracking of cement mortar (Nervi, 1956; Salvadori and Salvadori, 1956).

Since Nervi's demonstration of sea-worthiness of his ferro-cement motor sailor, several investigators have studied the engineering properties of ferro-cement. It has been shown that although ferro-cement is not "crack free", it can be designed to be watertight and that ferro-cement is not a homogeneous material but a composite material similar to reinforced concrete.

An attempt is made in this paper to compare some of the more important investigations and extract information which can be useful in understanding and designing this relatively new composite material.

The following mechanical properties are examined: uniaxial tension and compression, flexure, shear, impact, creep and fatigue. Elastic, cracking and ultimate behaviour are reported for these loadings. Influence of mortar composition and type and volume of mesh reinforcement are studied. Similarities and differences with conventional reinforced concrete are explored.

UNIAXIAL TENSION

Bezukladov *et al.* in Russia (1968), Walkus in Poland (1968 and 1970) and Naaman and Shah (1971) in the United States have studied behaviour of ferro-cement specimens in tension. Typical stress–strain curves

reported by them are shown in Fig. 1, 2 and 3. From these stress–strain curves and from observation of cracks the following conclusions regarding the general behaviour of ferro-cement can be made.

General Behaviour

When a ferro-cement specimen is subjected to increasing tensile stress, three stages of behaviour are observed: (1) *Elastic stage*. The stress–strain curve is essentially

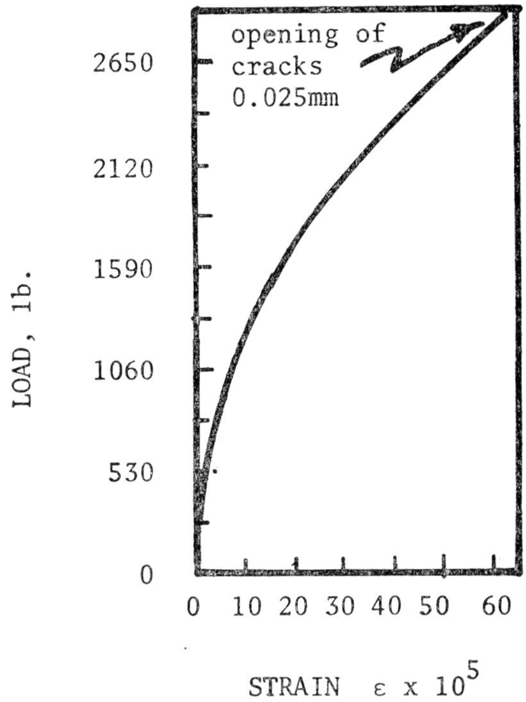

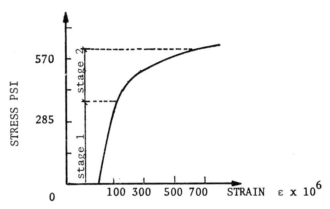

Fig. 2   Behaviour of ferro-cement under tensile load

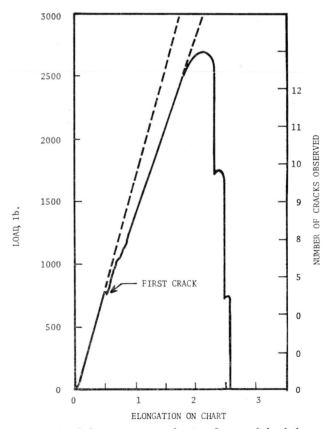

Fig. 1   Load vs. strain of ferro-cement in axial tension. Specimen size: 23.6 in. × 4 in. × 0.79 in. No. of Meshes: 10; Specific surface: 2.52 cm²/cm³; Reinforcement factor: 2.2%

Fig. 3   Load-elongation curve showing first crack-load determination. Specimen size: 12 in × 3 in × 0.5 in; Mesh: 0.5 in × 0.5 in × 16 ga. Welded square mesh—2 layers

linear in this stage. No cracking is observed with magnifications up to 70 times. (2) *Crack formation stage.* Stress–strain curve deviates from linearity and an increasing number of cracks is seen with increasing stress (Fig. 3). The cracks are very fine in this stage (0.005 to 0.05 mm) and increasing mortar strains are due to increasing number of cracks rather than increasing width of cracks. (3) *Crack widening stage.* The maximum number of cracks that are going to develop have already developed before this stage. Increasing mortar strains are thus mainly due to increasing width of cracks.

The end of stage 1 is often referred to as the proportional limit or the stress at first crack. This definition is relative and depends upon the accuracy of the measurements. A better delineation of stages should be based on crack widths such as attempted by Walkus (Table 1). It is desirable to differentiate each stage according to the performance of the structure (e.g. water-tight, or

the volume of reinforcement in the loading direction (V_{RL}) from the formula:

$$E_{C1} = (1 - V_{RL})E_M + V_{RL}E_{RL} = E_M + V_{RL}E_{RL}$$

The slope of the curve during the second stage of behaviour can also be approximated by assuming that $E_M = 0$ as shown in Fig. 4.

Cracking behaviour

Ferro-cement specimens have much finer and more numerous cracks than conventional reinforced concrete. Considerable amount of research has been done in trying to predict crack widths and number of cracks for conventional reinforced concrete structures. For these structures, it has been shown that crack width can be reduced by increasing bond between steel and concrete, by increasing distribution of reinforcement and by

TABLE 1. WORKING PHASES, STRESSES AND ELONGATIONS OF FERRO-CEMENT UNDER TENSILE LOAD

No. of phase	Strength phase	Performance	Permissible width of cracks, μ	Stresses $\sigma_{(20)}$, $\sigma_{(50)}$, $\sigma_{(100)}$, psi	Unit elongation $\varepsilon_{(20)}$, $\varepsilon_{(50)}$, $\varepsilon_{(100)}$, $\times 10^6$
I	Linearly-elastic	water tight	—	—	—
Ia	Quasi-elastic		0 20	470	200
Ib	Nonlinearly-elastic	non-corrosive	20 50	514	290
II	Elastico-plastic		50 100	612	645
III	Plastic	corrosive	>100	—	—

corrosion resistant). For each level of performance, a corresponding average crack width, and related stress-level is determined. The design can then be based on a stress which will produce cracks of certain widths. Knowing the relationship between stress, crack width and the performance of the structure should facilitate more rational design.

Elastic behaviour

Naaman and Shah (1971) have shown that a modulus of elasticity of ferro-cement can be estimated using the law of mixture of composite materials (Fig. 4 and Table 2). In Fig. 4 the slope of the stress–strain curve during the first stage (E_{C1}) can be approximated by knowing the modulus of elasticity of mortar (E_M), of mesh reinforcement in longitudinal direction (E_{RL}) and

TABLE 2. DESCRIPTION OF SPECIMENS TESTED BY NAAMAN AND SHAH

Series	Specimen size (inches)	Mesh size	No. of layers of Mesh
A	12 × 3 × 0.5	0.25 × 0.25 × 23g	1 to 9
D	12 × 3 × 0.5	0.5 × 0.5 × 19g	2, 4, 6
L	12 × 3 × 0.5	0.25 × 0.25 × 23g	1, 2, 4, 6
M	12 × 3 × 0.5	0.5 × 0.5 × 19g	1, 2, 3, 4
N	12 × 3 × 0.5	0.5 × 0.5 × 16g	2
		1 × 1 × 16g	2
		2 × 2 × 16g	2

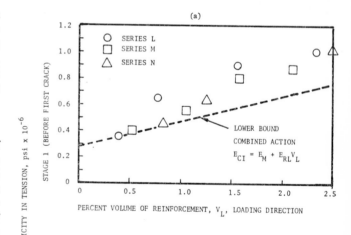

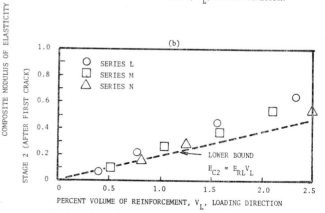

Fig. 4 Composite modulus of elasticity in tension

reducing cover (crack width is nearly zero at the interface between steel and concrete and increases as you go away from the interface towards the surface; thus, the smaller the distance between the interface and surface of the structure, i.e. the cover, the smaller the crack width). All these factors are favourable for ferro-cement. A parameter, which combines all these factors is the specific surface of reinforcement. It is defined as the total surface area of reinforcement per unit volume of the composite.

Bezukladov *et al.* (1968) have shown that stress and strain at first crack increase with increasing specific surface, up to a point, as can be seen from Table 3. Naaman and Shah results are shown in Fig. 5 which shows a similar trend.

The total number of cracks increases with the increasing surface as can be seen from Naaman and Shah's results in Fig. 6. They derived an analytic relationship between crack spacing and specific surface based on some simple consideration involving bond strength and

TABLE 3. RESULTS OF TESTS IN AXIAL TENSION
(From Bezukladov *et al.*)

Comp. strength of mortar kg/cm²	Specific surface of reinforcement cm²/cm³	Reinforcement factor in one direction %	Stress at first crack[1] (σ_{cr}) kg/cm	Rupture stress kg/cm²	Strain at first crack (ε_{cr}) (10^{-5})	Secant modulus at first crack $(\sigma_{cr}/\varepsilon_{cr})$ kg/cm²
650	1.2	1.85	39	48	45	86,000
650	2.08	1.80	42	48	55	76,000
650	3.04	1.75	45	50	70	64,000
650	1.8	2.80	59	80	60	98,000
650	3.12	2.70	73	90	100	73,000
750	3.12	2.70	82	90	100	82,000
650	4.50	2.68	50	80	100	50,000

[1] Width of crack up to 0.04–0.05 mm.

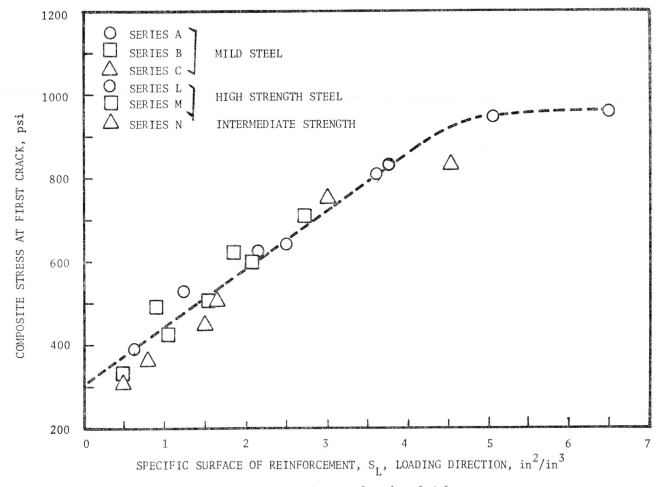

Fig. 5 Stress at first crack vs. specific surface of reinforcement

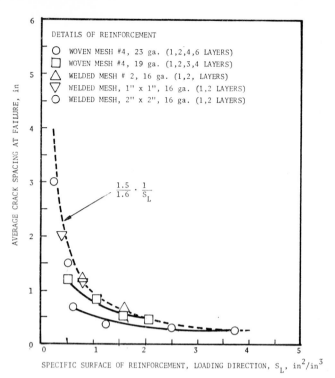

DETAILS OF REINFORCEMENT
○ WOVEN MESH #4, 23 ga. (1,2,4,6 LAYERS)
□ WOVEN MESH #4, 19 ga. (1,2,3,4 LAYERS)
△ WELDED MESH # 2, 16 ga. (1,2, LAYERS)
▽ WELDED MESH, 1" x 1", 16 ga. (1,2 LAYERS)
○ WELDED MESH, 2" x 2", 16 ga. (1,2 LAYERS)

$$\frac{1.5}{1.6} \cdot \frac{1}{S_L}$$

AVERAGE CRACK SPACING AT FAILURE, in

SPECIFIC SURFACE OF REINFORCEMENT, LOADING DIRECTION, S_L, in^2/in^3

Fig. 6 Observed average crack spacing at failure vs. specific surface of reinforcement

the tensile strength of mortar. It is interesting to note that their theoretical prediction compared favourably with experimental results not only of ferro-cement but also for conventionally reinforced prisms. The main distinction between the two is that ferro-cement has higher specific surface and transverse wires which result in much smaller crack spacing and crack widths. The optimum value of specific surface including reinforcement in both directions, appears to be about 8 in^2/in^3 or about 3.2 cm^2/cm^3.

The relationship between specific surface and crack width is primarily valid within the second stage of behaviour. The crack width during the final stage depends also on the ductility of mesh. The more ductile the mesh or lower its yield strength, the higher the crack width (Shah and Key, 1972).

Fracture strength

The tensile strength of ferro-cement depends chiefly on volume of reinforcement and the tensile strength of the mesh (Table 3, and Fig. 7 from Bezukladov *et al.*, 1968 and Naaman and Shah, 1971, respectively). Types of sand, normal weight or light weight, and ratio of sand and water have little influence on the tensile strength of ferro-cement.

Type of mesh

The above comments apply only to woven or welded square meshes. Hexagonal or chicken wire mesh were not found very satisfactory (Naaman and Shah, 1971). Specimens with chicken wire mesh exhibited mortar spalling before the maximum tensile stress was reached. Also, at the maximum tensile stress, wires did not fracture as in square meshes. Premature mortar spalling was also observed for square meshes with relatively large weaving angles.

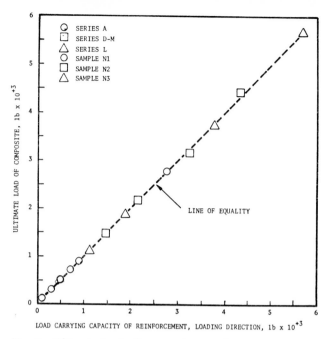

○ SERIES A
□ SERIES D-M
△ SERIES L
○ SAMPLE N1
□ SAMPLE N2
△ SAMPLE N3

LINE OF EQUALITY

ULTIMATE LOAD OF COMPOSITE, lb x 10^{+3}

LOAD CARRYING CAPACITY OF REINFORCEMENT, LOADING DIRECTION, lb x 10^{+3}

Fig. 7 Ultimate load of composite vs. ultimate capacity of reinforcement

UNIAXIAL COMPRESSION

Studies by Bezukladov *et al.* (1968), Shah (1972), Kelly and Mouat (1968) and by Rao and Gowder (1969) show that the compressive strength of ferro-cement depends primarily on that of cement mortar and is independent of the specific surface or volume of reinforcement. This is because at the failure, mortar splits longitudinally and meshes buckle. Close tying of meshes should partly prevent this phenomenon. Some of the results from Rao and Gowder are shown in Figs. 8, 9 and 10. The modulus of elasticity of ferro-cement in compression is directly dependent on those of mortar and meshes, and on volume of reinforcement. Thus, similar to tension, elastic behaviour of ferro-cement in compression can be predicted by using the law of mixture of composite materials.

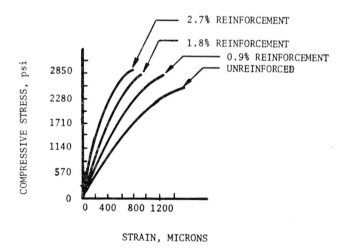

2.7% REINFORCEMENT
1.8% REINFORCEMENT
0.9% REINFORCEMENT
UNREINFORCED

COMPRESSIVE STRESS, psi

2850
2280
1710
1140
570
0

0   400   800 1200

STRAIN, MICRONS

Fig. 8 Stress-strain curve of ferro-cement in axial compression Specimen size: 12 in × 4 in × 1.5 in; w/c Ratio: 0.5; c/s Ratio: 0.37; Reinforcement: 0.0246 in diameter wires, 0.25" apart

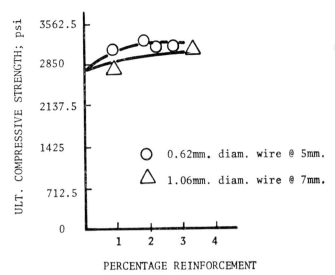

Fig. 9 *Steel content vs. compressive strength. Specimen size: 12 in × 4 in × 1.5 in; w/c Ratio: 0.5; c/s Ratio: 0.37*

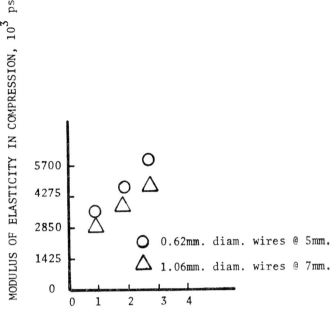

Fig. 10 *Steel content vs. modulus of elasticity in axial compression. Specimen size: 12 in × 4 in × 1.5 in; w/c Ratio: 0.5; c/s Ratio: 0.37*

FLEXURE

The behaviour of ferro-cement in flexure has been studied by several investigators (Tancreto and Haynes; Chang *et al.*; Collen, 1960; Scott, 1971). Bezukladov *et al.* observed that the tensile zone of ferro-cement beams behave similarly to the uniaxial tensile specimens. The flexural tensile stress at first crack ($\sigma = M/Z$) increases with increasing specific surface up to an optimum value of the specific surface (Table 4). They also observed that the moment–extreme tensile fibre strain (Fig. 11) and the moment deflection curve (Fig. 12) has a similar shape to the load–strain curve in axial tension. The failure of the beam was due to fracture of extreme meshes in the tensile zone followed by the crushing of mortar in the compression zone.

Similar conclusions were reached by Tancreto and Haynes, who observed that the flexural stress at first crack increases with wire density (the number of longitudinal wires per unit of reinforced area) as shown in Fig. 13. Based on their results, they have developed an empirical equation, shown in Fig. 13, for the stress at first crack divided by the flexural strength of mortar. They also note that the ultimate flexural stress can be

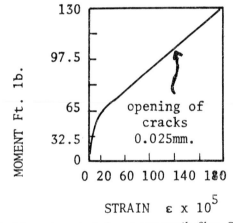

Fig. 11 *Moment vs. strain in extreme tensile fibre. Specimen size: 39.4 in × 7.25 in × 0.825 in; No. of Meshes: 10; Specific surface: 2.52 cm²/cm³; Reinforcement factor: 2.2%*

TABLE 4. RESULTS OF TESTS IN PURE FLEXURE
(From Bezukladov *et al.*)

Comp. strength of mortar kg/cm²	Specific surface of reinforcement cm²/cm³	Reinforcement factor in the direction of flexure %	Stress at first crack kg/cm²	Strains at first crack		Secant modulus at first crack	
				Extreme tensile (10^{-5})	Extreme compr. (10^{-5})	In tension kg/cm²	In compr. kg/cm²
650	1.20	1.85	100	110	55	91,000	182,000
650	2.08	1.80	120	150	70	80,000	171,000
650	3.04	1.75	130	170	100	76,000	130,000
650	1.80	2.80	160	150	65	107,000	246,000
650	3.12	2.70	190	215	90	88,000	210,000
750	3.12	2.70	215	230	100	94,000	215,000
650	4.56	2.65	120	225	95	53,000	126,000

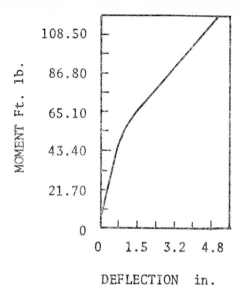

Fig. 12 Load vs. deflection of ferro-cement in pure flexure. Specimen size: 39.4 in × 7.25 in × 0.825 in; No. of Meshes: 10; Specific surface: 2.52 cm²/cm³; Reinforcement factor: 2.2%

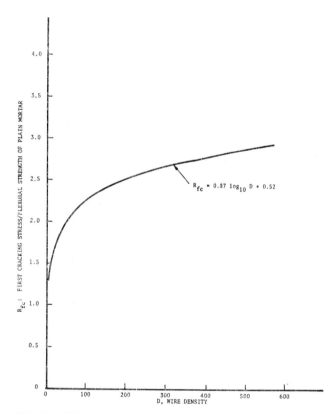

Fig. 13 Wire density vs. strength ratio

very approximately predicted by the flexural capacity of the tensile mesh reinforcement alone

$$M_{ult} = \frac{\text{(Tensile strength of the mesh)} \times \text{(Moment of inertia of the reinforcement)}}{\text{Half the depth of the beam}}$$

The flexural strength can be more accurately predicted by using the ultimate strength theory developed for conventional reinforced concrete. This theory rationally takes both the tensile and compressive properties of the composite beam. Chang *et al.* have shown that the complete moment–curvature relationship can be predicted by using such theory.

Chang *et al.*, as well as Collen (1960), found that expanded metal is not as efficient as square wire mesh. Similarly, a report issued by the Canadian Fisheries Service (Scott, 1971) also notes that square meshes gave higher flexural strength than hexagonal meshes or expanded metal.

SHEAR

Bezukladov *et al.* (1968), performed a series of tests on ferro-cement plates to observe its behaviour in pure planar shear. The shear stress–shear strain relationship was found to consist of two straight line segments, giving rise to two different shear moduli, each corresponding to one stage of loading (Fig. 14). The initial

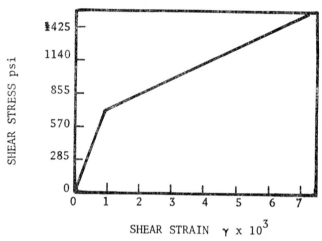

Fig. 14 Shear stress vs. shear strain of ferro-cement in plane shear

shear modulus is linearly dependent on the specific surface of wires oriented in the direction of the diagonal of the plate whereas the shear modulus in the second phase is the same for all values of specific surface.

Rupture of the ferro-cement plates occurred by way of formation and opening of cracks perpendicular to the tension diagonal. This cracking apparently causes the plates to behave anisotropically after tensile cracking begins.

IMPACT

The extent of localized damage due to impact loads on ferro-cement plates is of direct concern in its marine applications. Bezukladov *et al.* (1968) conducted impact tests on ferro-cement panels, with falling weights. They conclude that the only significant results that could be obtained from these tests are in the form of a qualitative comparison of the nature of breakdown of ferro-cement and conventional reinforced concrete plates. The dispersion of reinforcement promotes increase in the impact strength. While reinforced concrete plates have large cleavages, the crushed concrete in ferro-cement is held back by the meshes from disintegrating.

Shah and Key (1972) concluded, by measuring the flow of water through a small panel of ferro-cement after it was subjected to impact load, that the higher the specific surface of reinforcement, or the higher the yield strength of reinforcement the lesser the damage (that is, leakage rate) due to impact loading. The impact loading was applied with the double pendulum method and the amount of energy absorbed by the specimen was compared with the leakage rate (Fig. 15).

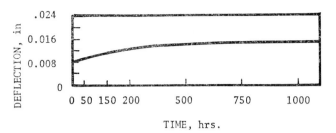

Fig. 16   Time vs. deflection under prolonged load for ferro-cement under pure flexure

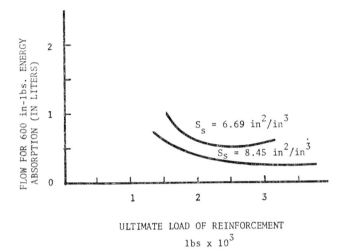

Fig. 15   Effect of specific surface and ductility of reinforcement on impact damage

Chang *et al.*, from their dynamic tests on ferro-cement beams, found that when subjected to impact loads, no large fragments fall out from the specimens, since the multiple layers of mesh hold the fragments together.

The Report on Ferro-cement for Canadian Fishing Vessels (Scott, 1971), states that the impact resistance of ferro-cement panels tested, was less than expected. While the failure for panels with two to four layers of mesh was typically by cracking at comparatively low loads, that for panels with six or more layers of mesh was by punching shear at higher loads.

It may be noted that it is difficult to generalize the quantitative results of various impact tests conducted by different investigators because of the widely differing sizes of specimen, method of applying the load and the lack of precise definitions for evaluating damage as well as for measuring loads.

CREEP

Bezukladov *et al.* (1968) studied the effects of prolonged loads on the deflection of ferro-cement beams. It was found (Fig. 16) that under constant load (equal to 0.7 times the instantaneous load causing appearance of cracks of 0.01 mm width, which corresponded to a flexural stress of 50 kg/cm^2) the deflection increased with time. The beams were 2 months old at the time of application of sustained load. The rate of increase in deflection is greatest during the initial period of applica-

tion of load and with increasing time the rate decreased. The increase in deflection was accompanied by the formation of new cracks with the width of about 0.005 mm.

FATIGUE

Although there is very little information available on fatigue strength of ferro-cement, fatigue may be a critical property for ferro-cement ship hulls. It is known that for reinforced and prestressed concrete structures, the fatigue resistance of the reinforcement is often the controlling property for the fatigue characteristics of the composite structure. This should also be true for ferro-cement. This is so because the wire mesh reinforcement has been considerably cold worked and in case of welded meshes, welding may also reduce the fatigue resistance of the reinforcement.

DESIGN RECOMMENDATIONS

Based on the information gleaned from the various investigations, the following design recommendations are made:

1. Tensile strength of the composite, ferro-cement, depends solely on the strength of the reinforcing mesh. Knowing the volume of reinforcement and the tensile strength of the wire mesh, one can calculate the fracture strength of ferro-cement.
2. The compressive strength of ferro-cement depends primarily on that of the matrix. Knowing the water–cement ratio of the Portland cement mortar one can estimate the compressive strength of the composite.
3. The moduli of elasticity in tension and in compression (prior to the matrix cracking) can be calculated from those of the mortar and of the mesh by simply using the law of mixture of composite materials ($E_C = E_M V_M + E_P V_P$).
4. The flexural strength of ferro-cement can be quite accurately estimated by using the "ultimate strength theories" which are developed for conventional reinforced concrete.

The main difference between ferro-cement and conventional reinforced concrete is in the nature of matrix cracking. For ferro-cement, mortar cracking starts at a higher stress and strain, the width of the cracks is an order of magnitude smaller and the cracks are numerous as compared to conventional reinforced concrete. This is the reason why ferro-cement can be designed to be waterproof under operating conditions.

References

BEZUKLADOV, V F, *et al.* *Ship Hulls Made of Reinforced*
1968 *Concrete.* Navships Translations No. 1148. Washington, DC, USA: Scientific Documentation Division (205), US Department of the Navy, 229 pp.

CHANG, WEN F, GIBSON, D W and GIBBONS, N R Flexural Behavior of Ferro-cement Panels. In *Civil Engineering in the Oceans*, **2**, 1023–44.

COLLEN, L D G Some experiments in design and construction
1960 with ferro-cement. *Transactions of the Institution of Civil Engineers of Ireland*, Dublin, Ireland, January (86): 39–56.

KELLY, A M and MOUAT, T W Ferro-cement as a fishing
1968 vessel construction material. *Proceedings, Conference on Fishing Vessel Construction Materials.* Montreal, Canada: Fisheries Service, Department of Fisheries and Forestry, Fisheries Report No. 12, 135 pp.

NAAMAN, A E and SHAH, S P Tensile test of ferro-cement.
1971 *J. Am. Concr. Inst.*, Sept.: 693–698.

NERVI, P L *Structures.* New York, USA: F. W. Dodge
1956 Corporation.

RAO, K A and GOWDER, K C S A study of behaviour of
1969 ferro-cement in direct compression. *Cement and Concrete*, Oct.–Dec.: 231–237.

SALVADORI, G and SALVADORI, M. *Structures by Pier Luigi*
1956 *Nervi.* New York, USA: McGraw-Hill.

SCOTT, W G (ed.) *Ferro-cement for Canadian Fishing Vessels.*
1971 Ottawa, Canada: Industrial Development Branch, Fisheries Service, Department of the Environment, Project Report No. 42.

SHAH, S P Evaluation of ferro-cement as a construction
1972 material. *Proceedings, Conference on New Materials in Concrete Construction.* Chicago, Illinois, USA: University of Illinois, Extension Division.

SHAH, S P and KEY, W H Impact resistance of ferro-cement.
1972 *J. Struct. Div. Am. Soc. Civ. Engrs.*, January.

TANCRETO, J E and HAYNES, H H Flexural strength of ferro-cement. *Technical Report R-Z-Roll*-01-01-34. Port Hueneme, California 93043, USA: Naval Civil Engineering Laboratory.

WALKUS, R State of cracking and elongation of ferro-cement
1968 under axial tensile load (I). *Buletinul Institutului Polytehnic*, Iasi (14).

WALKUS, R State of cracking and elongation of ferro-cement
1970 under axial tensile load (II). *Ibid.* (16).

Mechanical Properties of Ferro-Cement S-L Lee, M Raisinghani and R P Pama

Ferro-cement as a structural material is not new. In the form that it is known today ferro-cement was developed by Nervi (1943) whose original work consisted of coating several layers of wire mesh with cement mortar. The concept of ferro-cement evolved from the observation of the behaviour of concrete which can undergo considerable deformation in the immediate proximity of the reinforcement. When wire mesh reinforcements are dispersed in the matrix, the resulting material behaves as a homogeneous composite with greatly improved mechanical properties compared with ordinary reinforced concrete. The impact tests conducted by Nervi (1943) showed that when the slabs failed, the impacting weight did not penetrate through them. When the mortar cracked and the wire meshes yielded, the slabs did not disintegrate and remained appreciably impervious.

On the basis of experiments performed on ferro-cement slab elements in bending, Muhlert (1969) concluded that standard methods of analysing reinforced concrete are applicable. He further suggested a method for predicting its ultimate strength. Naaman and Shah (1971) investigated the properties of ferro-cement in direct tension by varying the type, size and volume of the wire mesh. They observed that the ultimate strength of ferro-cement in axial tension is the same as that of the wire mesh alone and that its modulus of elasticity can be predicted from those of the mortar and wire mesh by the law of mixtures (Broutman and Krock, 1967). They also observed that specific surface of the reinforcement strongly influences the cracking behaviour of ferro-cement. The high resistance of ferro-cement to impact loading has been observed by Shah and Key (1972) from a series of pendulum impact tests performed on slab elements. Bezukladov *et al.* (1968) have conducted exhaustive experimental investigation on ferro-cement in connexion with its application in ship building.

A great deal of interest has lately developed in Southeast Asia on the possible use of ferro-cement in vessel building, grain silos, liquid container construction and as a material for low cost housing. This interest in ferro-cement as a construction material in developing countries where labour cost is cheap is generated by the fact that it is labour intensive and the materials used are all available locally.

The present study was primarily aimed at investigating the mechanical properties of ferro-cement slab elements in pure flexure, torsion, axial compression and tension to enable designers to analyse ferro-cement structures based on a more rational approach. A typical cross-section of commonly constructed ferro-cement slab in Thailand is shown in Fig. 1. The reinforcement consists of a skeletal grid of ordinary mild steel bars sandwiched at the centre by equal layers of wire mesh on both sides.

PROPERTIES OF FERRO-CEMENT

In a composite material consisting of a matrix reinforced with uniformly dispersed undirectional continuous fibres, it is assumed that when stressed the fibres are

40

firmly bonded so that no slippage occurs at the interface of the fibres and the matrix. The load acting on a composite section per unit area carried by the matrix and the fibres is expressed by

$$\sigma = \sigma_m A_m + \sigma_f A_f \tag{1}$$

in which σ, σ_m and σ_f denote average stress in the composite section, the stresses in the matrix and the fibres respectively, and A_m and A_c are the area fractions for the matrix and the fibres respectively. Multiplying Eq. (1) by unit length in the direction of the load leads to

$$\sigma = \sigma_m V_m + \sigma_f V_f \tag{2}$$

where V_m and V_f denote the volume fractions for the matrix and the fibres respectively. For a composite material with n types of fibres oriented at an angle with the loading direction, Eq. (2) may be generalized by

$$\sigma = \sigma_m V_m + \sum_{i=1}^{n} F_i \sigma_i V_i \tag{3}$$

in which F_i is the cosine of the angle between fibre i and the loading direction.

Since no slippage occurs at the interface, the strains in the matrix and the fibres are equal to the average strain in the composite, for which Eq. (3) may be rewritten in the form

$$E = E_m V_m + \sum_{i=1}^{n} F_i E_i V_i \tag{4}$$

in which E, E_m and E_f denote the modulus of elasticity of the composite, the matrix and the fibres respectively.

Modulus of elasticity of ferro-cement

Uncracked range: Fig. 1a shows a typical cross-section of the ferro-cement slab under consideration and Fig. 1b depicts the type of hexagonal wire mesh used which is oriented alternately in two orthogonal directions. If λ_1 and λ_2 denote the length fractions of the two segments, the modulus of elasticity for the upper segment $\lambda_1 L$ is

$$E' = E_m V_m + F E_f V_f \tag{5}$$

where F denotes the direction cosine of the wire mesh with respect to the direction of the load. For the lower segment $\lambda_2 L$ in which only half of the wire is oriented in the direction of the load, the modulus of elasticity is

$$E'' = E_m V_m + \tfrac{1}{2} E_f V_f (1 + F) \tag{6}$$

The effective modulus of elasticity E_c of a typical segment L is obtained by considering the total strain of the segment, i.e.

$$\frac{1}{E_c} = \frac{\lambda_1}{E'} + \frac{\lambda_2}{E''}$$

which yields

$$E_c = E' \left[\frac{1}{\lambda_2 + \lambda_1 (E'/E'')} \right] \tag{7}$$

Eq. (7) defines the modulus of elasticity of this particular type of ferro-cement in the uncracked range.

The contribution of the skeletal steel in the above discussion is neglected due to the fact that, unlike the wire mesh, it is not dispersed sufficiently in the matrix. The poor dispersity renders it ineffective by slippage.

This fact is verified by the experimental results discussed later.

Cracked range: The effective modulus of elasticity is obtained by dropping the term $E_m V_m$ in Eqs. (5) and (6) for which Eq. (7) becomes, in this case,

$$E_t = E_t' \left[\frac{1}{\lambda_1 + \lambda_2 [2F/(1+F)]} \right] \tag{8}$$

where E_t is the effective modulus of elasticity in the cracked range and E_t' is defined by

$$E_t' = F E_f V_f \tag{9}$$

Ultimate strength in axial tension and compression: When fibres of relatively high strength and modulus are embedded in a brittle matrix such as the mortar commonly used in ferro-cement, the ultimate tensile strength of the ferro-cement slab is contributed mainly by the wire mesh. In other words, the first term in Eq. (3) is negligible when the fibres reach their ultimate strength and the ultimate tensile strength of ferro-cement using a single type of wire mesh is given by

$$\sigma_t = F \sigma_{ft} V_f \tag{10}$$

where σ_t and σ_{ft} are the ultimate strength of ferro-cement and the wire in tension respectively. It should be observed that the skeletal steel does not contribute to Eq. (10) because of its low specific surface which results in premature bond failure.

Experimental results indicate that the ultimate strength of ferro-cement in compression is controlled by the mortar only and Eq. (3) becomes

$$\sigma_c = 0.85 f_c' V_m \tag{11}$$

where σ_c denotes the ultimate strength in compression and $\sigma_m = 0.85 f_c'$ is the ultimate compressive strength of the mortar. Since $V_m < 1.00$, the ultimate strength in axial compression of ferro-cement is lower than the strength of the mortar. This is borne out by experimental results discussed later.

BENDING OF FERRO-CEMENT

Bending stress: The load deflection curve of a ferro-cement slab element subjected to monotonically increasing bending moment is approximately trilinear as shown in Fig. 2.

Uncracked range: The ferro-cement slab can be treated as a homogeneous isotropic elastic slab and the stress and strain distribution, as shown in Fig. 3a, can be determined from classical beam theory. The modulus of elasticity in tension and compression can be assumed equal as given by Eq. (7).

Cracked range: The stress and strain distribution in the cracked range are shown in Fig. 3b where the neutral axis shifts upward relative to that of the uncracked range. The more accurate stress distribution curve on the left may be replaced with very little loss of accuracy by the simpler one on the right for ease of calculation.

It can be shown that the position of the neutral axis is defined by

$$\frac{h_t}{h_c} = \sqrt{\frac{E_c}{E_t}} = \beta \tag{12}$$

where h_t and h_c denote the depth of the tension and compression zone respectively. The tensile and compressive

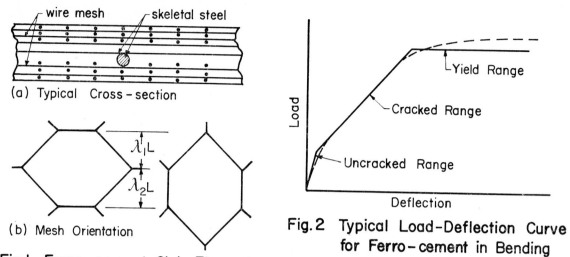

(a) Typical Cross-section

(b) Mesh Orientation

Fig.1 Ferro-cement Slab Element

Fig. 2 Typical Load-Deflection Curve for Ferro-cement in Bending

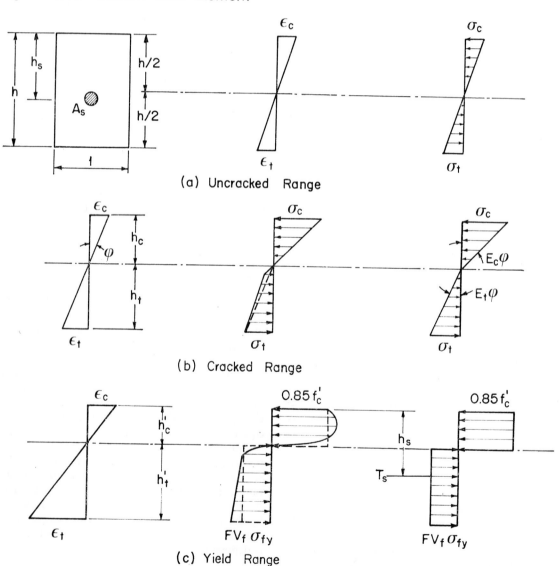

(a) Uncracked Range

(b) Cracked Range

(c) Yield Range

Fig. 3 Stress-Strain Distribution

stresses are respectively

$$\sigma_t^* = \alpha_1 \frac{6M}{h^2} \tag{13}$$

$$\sigma_c^* = \alpha_2 \frac{6M}{h^2} \tag{14}$$

in which

$$\alpha_1 = \frac{1+\beta}{2\beta} \tag{15}$$

$$\alpha_2 = \frac{1+\beta}{2} \tag{16}$$

and σ^* and σ^* denote the tensile and compressive stresses in bending respectively, h the thickness of the slab and M the bending moment per unit width of section. For use in the experimental investigation, Eqs. (13) and (14) can be restated in terms of ε_t and ε_c, the tensile and compressive strains at the extreme fibres, in the form

$$\sigma_t^* = \frac{3M}{h^2}\left(1 + \frac{\varepsilon_c}{\varepsilon_t}\right) \tag{17}$$

$$\sigma_c^* = \frac{3M}{h^2}\left(1 + \frac{\varepsilon_t}{\varepsilon_c}\right) \tag{18}$$

Yield range: The stress and strain distributions in the yield range are shown in Fig. 3c. Again the more accurate stress distribution curve shown on the left can be replaced with sufficient accuracy by the simpler rectangular stress block on the right.

In the tension zone the total tensile force T' per unit width is obtained by following similar argument as in the derivation of Eq. (10) but, in this case, superimposing the contribution of the skeletal steel which becomes effective due to the frictional bond developed as a result of large curvature. Thus

$$T' = T_f + T_s = F\sigma_{fy}V_f h_t' + A_s\sigma_{sy} \tag{19}$$

where σ_{fy} and σ_{sy} denote the yield stress of the wire and the skeletal steel respectively, A_s the area of the latter per unit width of slab section and h_t' the depth of the tensile zone.

The total compressive force C per unit width of the section is

$$C = 0.85f_c'h_c' \tag{20}$$

where h_c' is the depth of the compressive zone. In Eq. (20), as in the discussion of Eq. (11), the fibre reinforcement is assumed to be ineffective at failure.

The equilibrium conditions on the section yield

$$h_c' = \frac{A_s\sigma_{sy} + F\sigma_{fy}V_f h}{0.85f_c' + F\sigma_{fy}V_f} \tag{21}$$

$$M_0 = A_s\sigma_{sy}\left(h_s - \frac{h_c'}{2}\right) + F\sigma_{fy}V_f\left(\frac{h}{2}\right)(h - h_c') \tag{22}$$

where M_0 is the ultimate moment per unit width and h_s the depth of the skeletal steel from the extreme compressive face of the slab.

Elastic rigidities of slab elements: In the uncracked range, the bending of ferro-cement is governed by the plate equation (Timoshenko and Woinowsky, 1959)

$$\frac{\partial^4 w}{\partial x^4} + 2\frac{\partial^4 w}{\partial x^2 \partial y^2} + \frac{\partial^4 w}{\partial y^4} = \frac{q}{D} \tag{23}$$

in which w denotes the displacement normal to the undeformed middle plane, q the transverse load per unit area and D the flexural rigidity of the plate given by

$$D = \frac{E_c h^3}{12(1 - v^2)} \tag{24}$$

and E_c is as defined by Eq. (7).

Cracked range: On the bending properties in the cracked range and the corresponding strain and stress distribution shown in Fig. 3b, it can be shown readily by similar derivation that Eq. (23) remains valid in this range provided that the flexural rigidity is defined by

$$D = \frac{\alpha_3^2 E_c h^3}{12(1 - v^2)} \tag{25}$$

in which

$$\alpha_3 = \frac{2}{1 + \sqrt{E_c/E_t}} = \frac{2}{(1 + \beta)} \tag{26}$$

and E_c and E_t are as defined by Eqs. (7) and (8) respectively. Observe that $\alpha_3^2 \leq 1$ and, for the uncracked section, $E_c = E_t$ for which Eq. (26) becomes unity and Eqs. (24) and (25) are identical.

The torsional rigidity of the slab is $D(1 - v)$ where D is defined by Eq. (24) or (25) as the case may be and v is Poisson's ratio.

EXPERIMENTAL INVESTIGATION

Ferro-cement slab elements were tested in flexure, direct tension and compression. Fifteen samples for each of the above series were cast. An additional five square slabs were also cast for the determination of the various flexural rigidities. The only variable in all the samples cast was the number of layers of galvanized hexagonal wire meshes (chicken wire). The skeletal reinforcement for all these specimens consisted of 6 mm diameter mild steel bars, 75 mm on centres in the two orthogonal directions.

Pertinent details of these test samples are shown in Table 1 and Fig. 4. The letters F, T, C and S in the tables denote flexure, tension, compression and slab series. The number preceeding these letters denotes the number of layers of wire mesh in that particular sample.

Materials and preparation of test specimens

Skeletal grids consisting of 6 mm diameter steel bars spaced at 75 mm centre to centre each way were formed to conform with the desired dimensions of the samples. Two to six layers of galvanized hexagonal wire mesh, Gauge 19, were tied on both sides of the grid. To obtain a homogeneous composite mat and to avoid the effect of weaving of the wire mesh, the layers were arranged in alternate directions. Each layer of the wire mesh was firmly tied to the skeletal grid with small strips of these wire meshes as spacers. In larger slabs the different layers of wire mesh were provided with an overlap of 125 mm to get a stronger joint. Care was also taken to stagger all such joints evenly throughout the slab. A typical cross-section of ferro-cement slab element is shown in Fig. 1.

The mortar used for all the test samples has a cement : sand ratio of 1 : 1.75 by weight with a water : cement

43

TABLE 1. DETAILS OF TEST SPECIMENS

Series No.	Number of samples	Thickness mm.	Volume fraction		Total volume fraction of reinforcement	Specific surface of wire mesh
			Skeletal steel	Wire mesh		
4F	3	26.98	0.0240	0.0122	0.0362	0.0488
6F	3	28.57	0.0230	0.0173	0.0403	0.0693
8F	3	28.57	0.0230	0.0231	0.0461	0.0925
10F	3	30.48	0.0214	0.0275	0.0489	0.1082
12F	3	30.48	0.0214	0.0325	0.0539	0.1299
4T	3	26.67	0.0244	0.0124	0.0368	0.0492
6T	3	26.67	0.0244	0.0180	0.0424	0.0728
8T	3	27.68	0.0236	0.0238	0.0474	0.0952
10T	3	28.95	0.0225	0.0283	0.0510	0.1141
12T	3	30.48	0.0214	0.0326	0.0540	0.1299
4C	3	26.41	0.0247	0.0125	0.0372	0.0500
6C	3	26.67	0.0244	0.0180	0.0424	0.0728
8C	2	28.44	0.0230	0.0232	0.0462	0.0929
10C	3	27.30	0.0240	0.0302	0.0542	1.2080
12C	2	28.95	0.0225	0.0343	0.0568	0.1370
4S	1	28.57	0.0230	0.0116	0.0346	0.0439
6S	1	26.98	0.0230	0.0177	0.0407	0.0732
8S	1	28.57	0.0230	0.0231	0.0461	0.0925
10S	1	30.16	0.0220	0.0274	0.0491	0.1904
12S	1	31.35	0.0210	0.0316	0.0526	0.1263
8S63	1	28.57	0.0230	0.0231	0.0461	0.0925

ratio of 0.35. Type II Portland cement (ASTM Standards 150-62) and natural fine sand of graduation shown in Fig. 5 were used throughout the investigation. Plastet II was used as admixture to control the quality of the mix (350 cc/bag of cement). The above mix proportion was recommended by Daranandana *et al.* (1969).

Normally no formwork is required in applying the mortar on the wire mesh but, to get the exact dimensions and true surfaces, machine finished plywood moulds were used in casting the samples. Wet mixing of mortar was done in pan-type mixer for about $2\frac{1}{2}$ min. The moulds were oiled properly and the reinforcements were positioned in place. The mortar was pressed manually inside the mesh. The moulds were vibrated for 20 to 30 seconds to obtain uniform compaction. Four control cylindrical specimens (100 mm × 200 mm high) were also cast from each batch of mixes. The specimens were removed from the moulds after 24 hours and were cured in the fog room. The larger slab specimens were cured with wet gunny bags. All specimens were cured for 21 days. The compression specimens and control cylinders were capped after allowing them to dry for one day.

Electrical resistance strain gauges and Demec points were attached to the various test and control specimens at strategic points as shown in Fig. 4.

Control specimens

The mechanical properties of the wire mesh were determined from standard tension tests. To avoid slippage of the wires during the tests, special snub type grips (ASTM: A318-56) were provided. The 6 mm diameter steel bars used as skeletal reinforcement were tested in tension up to ultimate load. In both cases, the elongations were measured by Demec gauges. A typical stress–strain curve for No. 19 wire (1 mm diameter) taken from the wire mesh used is shown in Fig. 6. The curve is the average of three specimens tested. The modulus of elasticity, ultimate strength, tensile strength and Poisson's ratio of the mortar were determined from cylindrical control specimens. The Brazilian test (ASTM: C496-69) was used in determining the tensile strength of mortar. The relevant mechanical properties of the various control specimens are given in Table 2.

TABLE 2. PROPERTIES OF CONTROL SPECIMENS (MEAN VALUES)

Cylinder crushing strength of mortar	576.98 kg/cm²
Poisson's ratio of mortar	0.185
Initial tangent modulus of mortar	30.94 × 10⁴ kg/cm²
Tangent modulus of mortar at 50% strength	23.56 × 10⁴ kg/cm²
Tensile strength of mortar (Brazilian test)	34.17 kg/cm²
Yield strength of wire	2180.18 kg/cm²
Ultimate strength of wire	3755.53 kg/cm²
Modulus of elasticity of wire	96.70 × 10⁴ kg/cm²
Yield strength of 6 mm bars	2756.87 kg/cm²
Ultimate strength of 6 mm bar	4008.72 kg/cm²
Modulus of elasticity of 6 mm bars	210.98 × 10⁴ kg/cm²

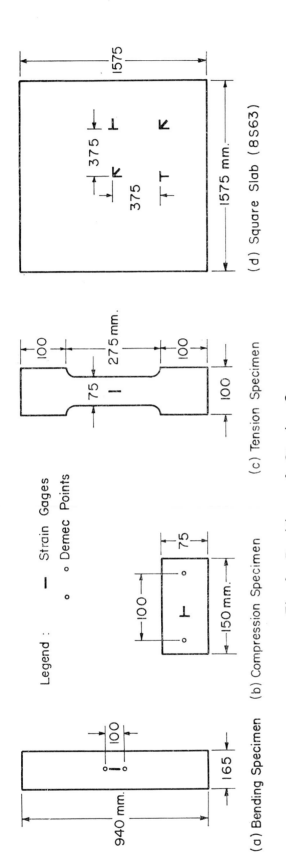

Legend :   —   Strain Gages

              o   o Demec Points

(a) Bending Specimen   (b) Compression Specimen   (c) Tension Specimen

Fig.4 Position of Strain Gages

(d) Square Slab (8S63)

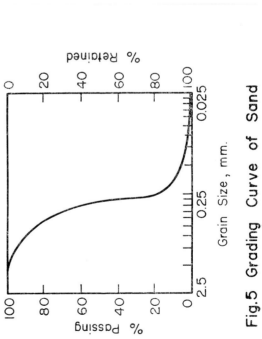

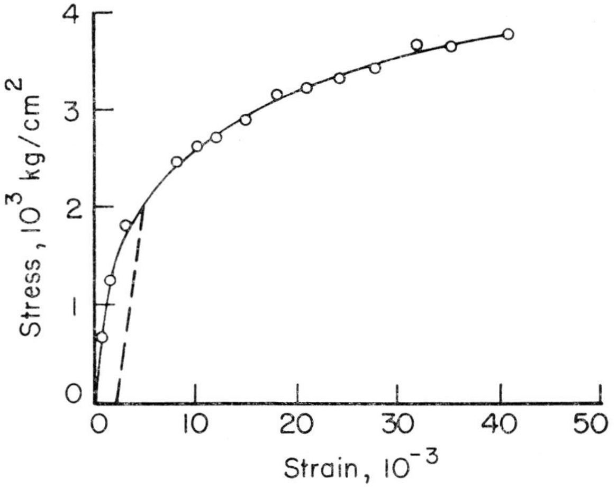

Fig.6 Stress–Strain Curve for Gage #19 Wire

Fig.5 Grading Curve of Sand

Direct tension tests

In the direct tension tests, special grips designed to clamp the 30 mm thick specimen were used. It is extremely difficult to measure strains in the uncracked range since the tension specimens twist at initial application of load causing almost immediate cracking of the mortar. The stress levels at the appearance of the first visible crack are plotted against specific surface of the wire mesh in Fig. 7. It is seen that increasing the specific surface increases the stress level at which first cracks appear. The stress levels obtained are lower than the true ones since a portion of the load is required to align the specimen. The elastic moduli reported in Table 3 are for the cracked range of loading only which are in reasonable agreement with theoretical values predicted by Eq. (8).

TABLE 3. MODULUS OF ELASTICITY FROM TENSION TESTS

Specimen	Modulus of elasticity, 10^4 kg/cm² (Cracked range)	
	Theoretical	Experimental
4T	0.9107	1.1252
6T	1.3432	1.5401
8T	1.7722	1.8988
10T	2.1168	2.1942
12T	2.4192	2.6162

Fig. 8 shows good agreement between the experimental and theoretical ultimate loads calculated by Eq. (10) which does not include the contribution of skeletal steel due to premature bond failure. The skeletal steel slips clearly from the tension specimen.

Axial compression tests

The results of the axial compression tests are shown in Table 4 in which the theoretical ultimate strengths predicted by Eq. (11) and the moduli of elasticity calculated by Eq. (7) are also included. Reasonably good agreement was obtained in the moduli of elasticity.

The comparison of ultimate strengths is also good. As discussed earlier in the derivation of Eq. (11) which does not include the contribution of both the wire mesh and skeletal steel, the ultimate strength of ferro-cement in compression is actually lower than the mortar strength. A comparison of the stress–strain curves of the mortar

and ferro-cement is shown in Fig. 9. Laminated longitudinal cracks, induced by the wire mesh layers, develop in the compression specimen at failure. This as well as the influence of the volume fraction in Eq. (11) account for the lower ultimate strength.

Poisson's ratios, also shown in Table 4, are in agreement with the results quoted by Bezukladov et al. (1968). It appears that Poisson's ratio decreases with increasing volume fraction of the wire mesh. These values are used in the calculation of the flexural rigidities. The moduli of elasticity shown in Table 4 are the initial tangent modulus.

Bending tests

The flexure specimens were simply supported and subjected to third-point loading. The extreme fibre strains and deflexions at midspan were measured by strain and dial gauges respectively. Figure 10 shows a typical load–deflection curve predicted by means of the moduli of elasticity defined by Eqs. (7) and (8). It can be seen that the experimental points are reasonably close to the theoretical curves. Two typical stress–strain curves are shown in Figs. 11 and 12. Table 5 summarizes the theoretical and experimental values of the moduli of elasticity for the complete series of bending tests, the flexural rigidities obtained experimentally together with values calculated from Eqs. (24) and (25). The overall agreement between the theoretical and experimental results is good.

The kink in the load–deflexion curve of Fig. 10 is initiated by the cracking of the mortar predicted from the modulus of rupture obtained from the Brazilian test. Following the suggestions of Ramakrishnan et al. (1967), the rupture strength of the mortar was taken as 1.5 times the value given by the Brazilian test.

The appearance of the cracks in the middle third of the span were observed carefully during the test. When one or a small number of cracks appeared, the additional deformation due to an increase in the load was accompanied by the formation of new cracks while the width of the old cracks remained roughly the same. Figure 13 shows the uniform crack patterns of the bending specimens at failure. Observe that the cracks coincide with the diagonal segments of the wire mesh. No crushing in the compression zone of the specimens were observed up to collapse.

A comparison of theoretical and experimental collapse loads in bending of the complete bending series are tabulated in Table 5. The experimental collapse loads

TABLE 4. ULTIMATE STRENGTHS AND MODULUS OF ELASTICITY FROM COMPRESSION TESTS

Specimen	Cylinder crushing strength (f'_c), kg/cm²	Ultimate strength of specimen, kg/cm²		Modulus of elasticity, 10^4 kg/cm²		Poisson's ratio, v
		Theory	Exper.	Theory	Exper.	
4C	559.11	457.13	457.13	30.69	28.58	0.173
6C	604.82	492.29	511.99	30.82	27.14	0.153
8C	604.82	485.26	479.64	31.04	29.53	0.135
10C	580.27	500.74	500.74	31.26	31.36	0.122
12C	530.97	426.19	425.48	31.41	32.07	0.135

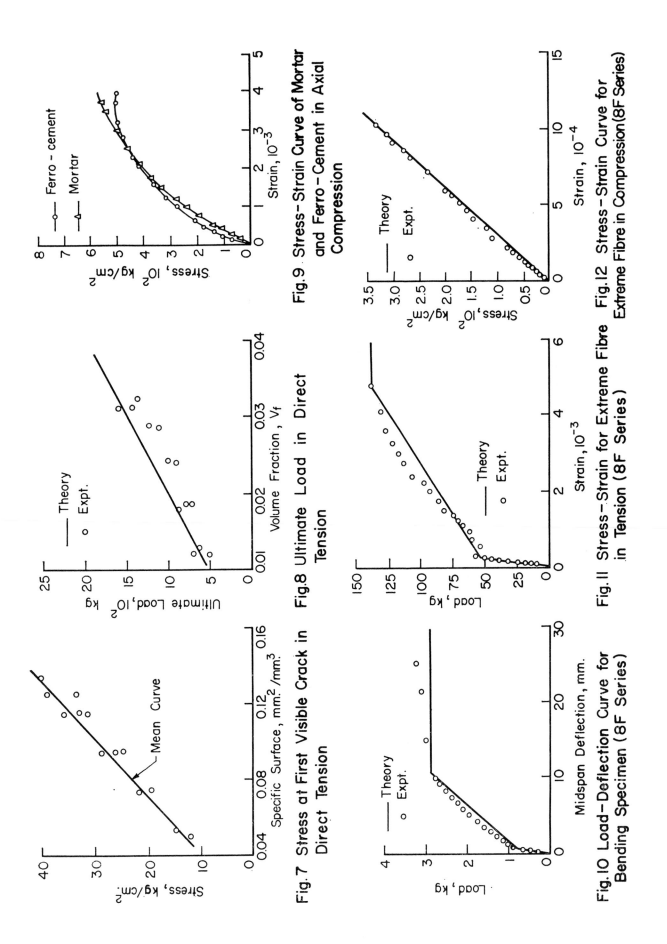

Fig.7 Stress at First Visible Crack in Direct Tension

Fig.8 Ultimate Load in Direct Tension

Fig.9 Stress-Strain Curve of Mortar and Ferro-Cement in Axial Compression

Fig.10 Load-Deflection Curve for Bending Specimen (8F Series)

Fig.11 Stress-Strain for Extreme Fibre in Tension (8F Series)

Fig.12 Stress-Strain Curve for Extreme Fibre in Compression(8F Series)

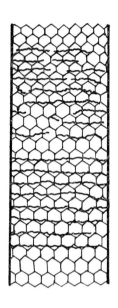

Fig.13 Crack Patterns of Bending Specimens

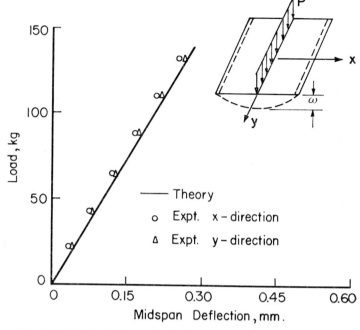

Fig.14 Typical Load-Deflection Curve Under Cylindrical Bending (IOS Series)

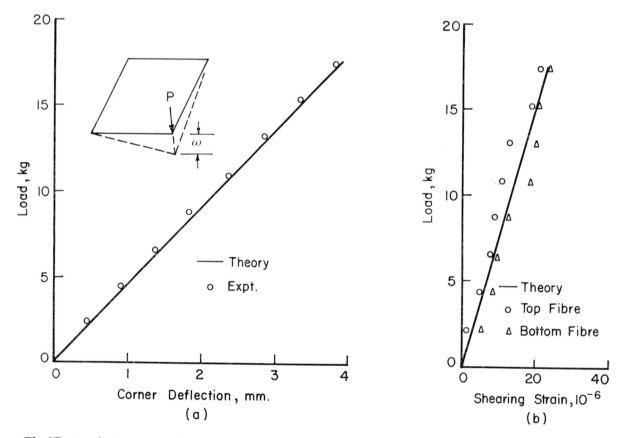

(a)

(b)

Fig.15 Typical Load-Deflection and Load-Strain Curves under Anticlastic Test (8S63)

TABLE 5. MODULI OF ELASTICITY, RIGIDITIES AND ULTIMATE LOADS FROM BENDING TESTS

Specimen	Modulus of elasticity, 10^4 kg/cm^2 (theoretical)			Modulus of elasticity, 10^4 kg/cm^2 (experimental)		
	E_t		E_c	E_t		E_c
	Uncracked	Cracked	Initial	Uncracked	Cracked	Initial
4F	30.69	0.9072	30.69	17.58	0.7876	27.21
6F	30.82	1.3221	30.82	30.59	1.8566	30.66
8F	31.04	1.7160	31.04	34.24	2.3138	35.51
10F	31.26	2.0676	31.26	29.04	3.0311	30.52
12F	31.41	2.5247	31.41	34.18	3.0170	37.27

Specimen	Theoretical rigidities, 10^6 kg/cm		experimental rigidities, 10^6 kg/cm		Ultimate load kg	
	Uncracked	Cracked	Uncracked	Cracked	Theory	Exper.
4F	0.5172	0.0438	0.4746	0.0388	218	181
6F	0.6117	0.0723	0.5437	0.0829	254	272
8F	0.6128	0.0887	0.5875	0.0979	288	295
10F	0.7464	0.1238	0.6566	0.1147	340	340
12F	0.7522	0.1497	0.7395	0.1566	415	408

were taken as the load at the second kink of the load–deflection curves. It is seen that close agreement exist between the experimental values and those predicted theoretically from M_0 based on Eq. (22). On the whole, the theoretical values are on the conservative side.

Elastic rigidities

The bending rigidities of the slabs, simply supported on 850 mm span along two opposite edges with the other two free, were determined by subjecting them to cylindrical bending under line load at midspan. These tests were done in both orthogonal directions to determine the bending rigidities in both directions independently. Figure 14 shows a typical load–deflexion curve obtained from these series of tests which are summarized in Table 6. It is evident that the predicted values of the bending rigidities from Eq. (24) are in good agreement with the experimental results. A study of Table 6 shows that the slabs behave isotropically in the uncracked range.

All slabs in this series were also subjected to anti-clastic corner loads and Fig. 15 shows typical load–deflexion and load–strain curves obtained from these tests. The experimentally obtained torsional rigidities are also summarized in Table 6 along with the theoretical predictions computed by the expression $D(1 - v)$. Here again good agreement is obtained although the latter are slightly higher.

CONCLUSIONS

From this study, the following conclusions can be drawn regarding the behaviour of ferro-cement slab elements:

1. The mechanical properties of ferro-cement can be determined from the law of mixtures of composite materials with the mortar acting as the matrix and the wire mesh as the fibre reinforcement.

2. In the uncracked range, ferro-cement can be treated as a homogeneous isotropic composite elastic material.

TABLE 6. BENDING AND TORSIONAL RIGIDITIES FROM SLAB BENDING TESTS (UNCRACKED RANGE)

Specimen	Theoretical		Experimental		
	Bending rigidity, 10^6 kg/cm	Torsional rigidity, 10^6 kg/cm	Bending rigidity, 10^6 kg/cm		Torsional rigidity, 10^6 kg/cm
			x-direction	y-direction	
4S	0.6048	1.0598	0.5241	0.5425	0.9054
6S	0.5137	0.9216	0.4320	0.5921	0.9054
8S	0.6163	1.0771	0.6658	0.7130	1.1773
10S	0.7257	1.2672	0.7257	0.7603	1.2096
12S	0.8179	1.4515	1.0713	1.1404	1.6704
8S63	0.6163	1.0771	0.7315	0.7511	1.1151

3. After the mortar has cracked in a ferro-cement slab element subjected to bending, the slab behaves as a two-layer plate with different modulus of elasticity in the compression and tension layer.

4. The presence of wire mesh does not influence the rupture strength of the matrix in bending but increases considerably the resistance of the mortar to crack propagation. The crack arrest mechanism is considerably influenced by volume fraction, specific surface and the mechanical properties of the wire mesh.

5. In axial compression, local buckling of the wire mesh causes premature spalling of the matrix. The ultimate strength of ferro-cement in axial compression is less than the ultimate strength of the mortar.

6. The ultimate strength in direct tension is controlled by the strength of the wire mesh only, with no contribution from the skeletal steel due to its premature bond failure.

7. The ultimate moment of ferro-cement slabs in bending can be accurately determined by assuming that the mortar alone resists the compressive force and the tensile force is resisted by both the wire mesh and the skeletal steel.

References

BEZUKLADOV, V F, et al. *Ships Hulls Made of Reinforced*
1968   *Concrete*. Navships Translations No. 1148. Washington, DC, USA: Scientific Documentation Division (205), US Department of the Navy, 229 pp.

BROUTMAN, L J and KROCK, R H   *Modern Composite*
1967   *Materials*. London, England: Addison-Wesley, 581 pp.

DARANANDANA, N, SUKAPADHANADHI, N and DISATHIAN P
1969   *Ferro-cement for Construction of Fishing Vessels*. Bangkok, Thailand: Applied Scientific Research Corporation of Thailand, Report No. 1.

MULHERT, F H   *Analysis of Ferro-cement in Bending*. Mon-
1969   treal, Canada: Eastern Canadian Section, Society of Naval Architects and Marine Engineers.

NAAMAN, A E and SHAH, S P   Tensile tests on ferro-cement.
1971   *J. Am. Concr. Inst.*, 68(9): 693–698.

NERVI, P L   Il ferro-cimento: Sue Caratteristiche e possi-
1951   bilità. *L'Ingegnere* (1). Milan, Italy. (Also *Ferro-cement, its Characteristics and Potentialities*. London, England: Cement and Concrete Association Library, Translation No. 60.)

RAMAKRISHNAN, V, ANANTHANARAYANA, Y and GOPAL, K C
1967   The determination of tensile strength of concrete, a comparison of different methods. *Indian Concrete Journal*, May: 202–206.

SHAH, S P and KEY, W H, Jr.   Impact resistance of ferro-
1972   cement. *J. Struc. Div. Am. Soc. Civ. Engrs.* 98(ST1): 111–123.

TIMOSHENKO, S and WOINOWSKI, S K *Theory of Plates and*
1959   *Shells*. New York, USA: McGraw-Hill.

Acknowledgement

The research upon which this paper is based was supported in part by the Construction Material Marketing Co. Ltd., Bangkok, Thailand.

Practical Ferro-Cement Design, Reinforced and Post-Tensioned   P E Ellen

The design of ferro-cement must be related to the type and content of the materials used to form the composite material.

Since the early concepts of ferro-cement as envisaged by Professor Nervi, various studies have indicated the practical aspects but very limited information is available on design.

Various graphs have been published such as Fig. 1.

It is now proposed that ultimate load design methods could be used to analyse the physical properties of ultimate tensile and flexure strengths.

From Table 1, concretes reinforced with steels having a wide range of ultimate tensile strengths must change their composition to suit the reduced diameter of the reinforcement, which is necessary to give the required bond values to obtain adequate crack control and waterproofness.

With many layers of mesh and congested rods or cables the mixture must be of sufficient workability to be fully compacted into place, whether it be done in one or more operations.

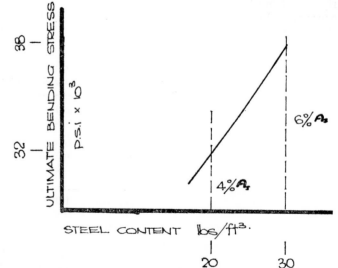

Fig. 1   Steel content vs. ultimate bending stress

TABLE 1. RANGE OF PROPERTIES OF REINFORCED CONCRETE

A AND B ARE CLASSIFIED AS REINFORCED CONCRETE
C, D, E AND F ARE CLASSIFIED AS FERRO-TYPE CONCRETE
ALL TYPES MAY BE PRESTRESSED EITHER BY PRETENSION OR POST-TENSION METHODS

			Reinforcing steel %
A	Placed concrete aggregate size ranging down to $\frac{1}{2}$ in	Unreinforced concrete reinforcing bars and rods reinforcing mesh	0–1 % for slabs 1–4 % for beams
B	$\frac{3}{8}$ in max. size aggregate	Less than 3 in spacing	
C	$\frac{3}{16}$ in aggregate concrete placed by gun application, vibration or render	Reinforced mesh less than 1 in for micro concretes	0.5 to 3 %
D	Coarse sand render. Cement aggregate ratios 1:2 to 3	Reinforced mesh not less than $\frac{1}{2}$ in limited number of layers (say 4)	1 to 4 %
E	Fine sand render. Cement aggregate ratios 1:1 to 2	Reinforced mesh not less than $\frac{1}{2}$ in but several layers (say 8–10)	3 to 8 %
F	Very fine cement pastes pumped into place under pressure or hand applied renders. Cement aggregate ratios 1:$\frac{1}{2}$ to 1	Reinforced mesh not less than $\frac{1}{2}$ in but combined with rods, bars and cables in greater thicknesses	3 to 20 %

It should also be noted that prestressed concrete may be superimposed over these materials to further change the physical characteristics. This may be done by pretensioned, post-tensioned or chemical prestressing methods.

TYPES OF REINFORCEMENT

Bars, wire mesh and cable for thin shell concrete

Due to the small size (usually less than $\frac{3}{8}$ in (9.52 mm) diameter), reinforcing bars are not usually deformed and therefore have low bond values but are available in a wide range of ultimate tensile and yield point strengths.

It is possible to combine the best properties of each material into ferro-cement type concretes to give the desired final property to the material. For example, hexagonal wire mesh is easily moulded into shape and in doing so raises the yield point from, say, 40–50 ksi* to over 60–70 ksi while still retaining a very large ultimate extension capacity.

Now if this mesh (B) is combined with high carbon high-tensile rods (C) the composite material exhibits the ductility of the mesh and the high yield point of the rods. It may therefore be severely deformed and will, due to its inherent ductility without yielding want to return to its shape prior to deformation.

Alternatively, by combining high tensile mesh with soft rods we obtain a material rigid in its outside skin and ductile in the interior.

These two material combinations will differ widely in apparent yield point strength for flexure and impact shear values.

The low yield point of the ductile soft woven mesh can be dramatically altered by post-tensioning which in

* Where the symbol k or the name kip appear in the text this refers to the US kip = 1000 lb.

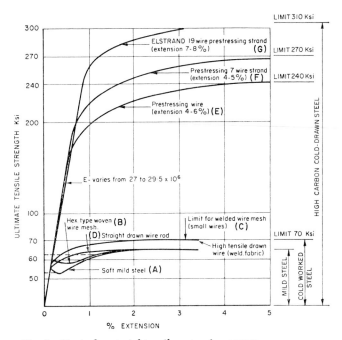

Fig. 2 *Typical material tensile-extension curves*

effect raises the apparent yield point of the combined materials to any desired design level. This is due to the shallow dome arching effect generated by the eccentric post-tension forces. These dome-arch effects can be calculated to give a "load to flatten" which may be well in excess of the apparent yield point of the composite materials without post-tensioning. Some test specimens have been designed and built which have no defined yield point and permanent deformation begins at about 90 per cent of ultimate load.

51

CONCRETES

Concretes can be manufactured using a wide range of cement contents to change the compression and tensile strengths as well as the bond and strain capacities both in compression and tension.

Figure 3 shows a typical range of stress–strain characteristics for various concretes. Low strength concrete has a low "E" value and a high strain capacity while high strength concretes have a higher "E" value but tend to

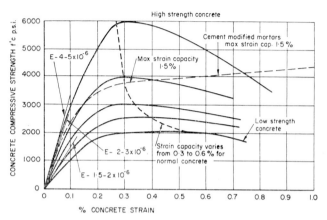

Fig. 3   Stress strain characteristics of various concretes

have a low strain capacity and hence are classified as brittle materials. In ferro-cement design the object of increasing the steel reinforcing content is to provide a greater overall material strain capacity but this effect is reduced by the brittleness of high strength concretes. On the other hand, high strength concretes usually have higher tensile and bond strengths, leading to better crack control, if adequate bond area on the reinforcement is provided.

More recently cement-modified concretes have indicated considerable benefits are to be obtained from their greatly improved bond and strain capacities, allowing considerably higher steel tensile stresses to be adopted.

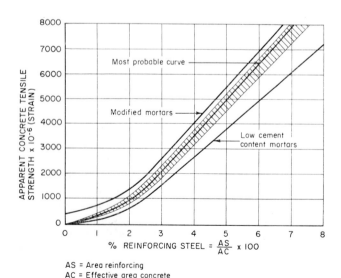

AS = Area reinforcing
AC = Effective area concrete

Fig. 4   Relationship between ultimate tensile concrete strength and % of reinforcing steel

52

Providing of course that deflexions due to these stresses are controlled.

It should be noted that one such concrete indicates an "E" value of $2-3 \times 10^6$ psi, a compressive strength of over 4000 psi and an ultimate strain capacity of 1.5 per cent; over five times that of normal high strength concretes.

STRENGTH DESIGN - BENDING FLEXURE

Concrete having low reinforcement percentages

Assume the normal stress block for ultimate load design (Fig. 5).

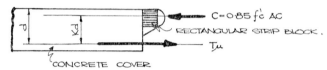

Fig. 5

$T\mu$ = reinforcing Y.P. or ultimate tensile at about 1 per cent extension
$M\mu = kd\,T\mu$
$M\mu$ = ultimate bending moment
K = constant
Ac = effective concrete area
$f'c$ = concrete cylinder strength

Concrete having compression reinforcement (Fig. 6)

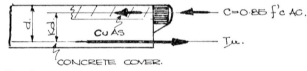

Fig. 6

$$M\mu = Kd\,T\mu_{AS}$$

kd in this case depends on the location of the compression reinforcement. The combined value of concrete thrust ($C = 0.85f'c\,Ac$) and the compression reinforcement C_{AS} is always considerably in excess of the tensile requirement $T\mu_{AS}$.

This latter value controls the ultimate bending moment capacity of the section.

Concrete having compression and tensile mesh and spacing rods (Fig. 7)

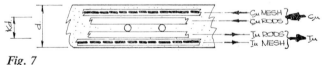

Fig. 7

As the percentages of reinforcement increases the compression component becomes

$$\Sigma\,C\mu = C\mu \text{ mesh}$$
$$+ C\mu \text{ concrete}$$
$$+ C\mu \text{ rods}$$

and the tension component becomes

$$\Sigma T\mu = T\mu \text{ mesh}$$
$$+ T\mu \text{ rods}$$

Hence the ultimate bending moment capacity $M\mu = \Sigma T\mu \times kd$ assuming that the strain capacity of the lower mesh is large enough to enable the sufficient rotation to occur and generate full tensile components of the lower rods and mesh.

The spacing and the tensile strength of the combined rods and mesh plays a very important part in determining the effectiveness of the above assumptions. From tests, these assumptions appear to be effective if the ultimate tensile strength inbond of the mesh is greater than the tensile strength of the mesh and rods combined.

Where the mesh is less than this value the effective rod tensile strength must be proportioned from linear strain across the section and from the allowable capacity for bond crack control (Fig. 8).

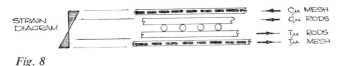

Fig. 8

If the concrete did not contribute to the compressive thrust C the neutral axis would be central in the section as in the case of steel beams with equal compression and tension flanges, and the strain would vary linearly.

However, the concrete, when adequately bonded to the mesh, will strain so that the full ultimate compression capacity of the steel is effective and the neutral axis will be raised toward the top of the compression zone, magnifying the strain capacity needed in the tensile mesh component. In general this requires the mesh to have a strain capacity of at least 8 to 10 per cent.

Concrete having compression and tensile mesh and central spacing rods (Fig. 9)

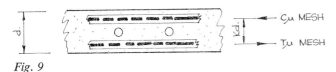

Fig. 9

The ultimate moment capacity $M\mu = kd\,T\mu$ where kd is approximately the C of G of the mesh layers. This will apply in directions parallel or normal to the spacing rods.

CRACK CONTROL

From various tests and the building of a wide range of structures using ultimate load methods, ferro-concrete can be designed for a given crack control by assuming:

(a) The ultimate tensile strength of the mesh component of the reinforcement expressed as an ultimate tensile bond capacity $T\mu$ (bond) must be at least equal to or greater than the ultimate tensile strength of that same mesh and any other rod component. (Note modification for the case when the section is post-tensioned.)

(b) If the mesh bond value $T\mu$ (bond) is in excess of the mesh $T\mu$ $(_{As})$ then rod or bars may be added to increase the ultimate tensile strength until the limit of (1) above is reached.

TENSION BOND VALUES

Various authorities have recommended average tensile bond values for small wires. We have found that the following values offer suitable design solutions. (This does not mean that these are accurate values but the results using these values appear to be consistent.)

(a) Small wires to 0.1 in diameter bond stress = 2000 psi;

(b) larger wires between 0.1 and 0.15 in diameter bond stress = 1500 psi;

(c) larger wires between 0.15 and 0.2 in diameter bond stress = 1000 psi.

An arbitrary spacing of 0.5 in has been adopted for crack spacing. This means that the mesh wires must have sufficient bond value over 0.5 in without an assumed contribution from any cross wires or welds. When sections are loaded in ultimate bending moments cracks usually occur at the cross wires and effectively debond some wires, in such cases the weld or weave cross-over may be necessary to develop bond, but it is considered that this should not be included in the calculation. Also shrinkage cracking, if it occurs, will be most prominent at the cross wires.

SPACING OF MESH LAYERS

To increase the bending moment capacity the mesh layers may be separated by "spacing rods" providing the requirements of bond and reinforcing steel percentage criteria are met (Fig. 10).

Fig. 10

This means that for thicker types of ferro-cement the "inside" mortar contains lower steel percentages than the outer layers and having a low surface area bond value, will probably be cracked, while the outer layers or shells are still capable of larger strains.

When these thicker "shells" are subjected to ultimate bending moments, cracking occurs as shown in Fig. 11.

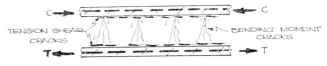

Fig. 11

If the member is then subjected to direct tension the horizontal shear forces can separate the two outer shells and lamination is possible. Also such a section usually has a low impact value (see test methods).

In these cases sufficient transverse ties must be placed to join the two shells together.

In fact, the inner concrete is of no advantage except to act as a spacer for each shell or mesh layer and can often be replaced with another lighter material such as foam styrene.

SECTIONS IN PURE TENSION

The rules given for ultimate bending moment equally apply to ultimate tension:

    (a) The desirable crack spacing assumed to be 0.5 in;
    (b) the ultimate bond tensile value $T\mu$ (bond) measured between cracks must be greater than the ultimate tensile stress value $T\mu_{AS}$.

Combinations of mesh and rods must meet these requirements.

When large tensile forces are to be accommodated the space between each skin must be reduced to an absolute minimum to allow the bond values between interior rods to be transferred to the outer mesh, or the whole section may be post-tensioned with high tensile steel cable.

SECTIONS SUBJECT TO BENDING MOMENTS AND TENSILE FORCES

Combined bending and tension is treated similarly to the foregoing. The rules apply to the tension face layer. If alternate positive and negative bending moments occur then each face layer must be considered separately.

IMPACT AND SHEAR VALUES OF HIGHLY REINFORCED SLABS

When a panel of concrete is subjected to a series of impacts such as the dropping of a heavy steel ball, a compression failure will usually occur on the upper surface at the point of contact and if the impact load exceeds the ultimate bending moment of the slab, then compression and tension failures, together with a local shear cone failure will occur in the slab.

The effects of these impacts on the failure shear cone will vary widely, depending on the type of section reinforcement.

In slabs having a low reinforcement percentage (less than approximately 2 per cent), the angle of the shear cone failure (slope of cone at (C)) appears to range from $Tan\ \theta = 0.34$ to 0.40.

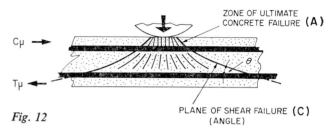

Fig. 12

As the reinforcement percentage increases the $Tan\ \theta$ angle reduces to approximately 0.25 to 0.3. Further, if the member is post-tensioned to at least 300 psi on the gross concrete section then the $Tan\ \theta$ angle falls to 0.16 to 0.20.

Test results indicate that the major factors effecting impact shear value are the physical combinations of mesh and its reinforcing properties and whether or not the member is post-tensioned.

Suggested impact test procedure

A typical impact failure pattern is shown below. The equipment consists of a 15 lb "steel ball" supported at a height of 5 ft above the specimen.

Upper surface: Progressive failure will occur due to a series of impact blows of the 15 lb ball acting on the same point.

Lower surface: The first failure indications are a form of combined local bending punching shear failure progressively spreading across the surface finally resulting in a "punch through" failure and often combined with a bending failure. The sample panel supporting the test equipment is shown in Fig. 13.

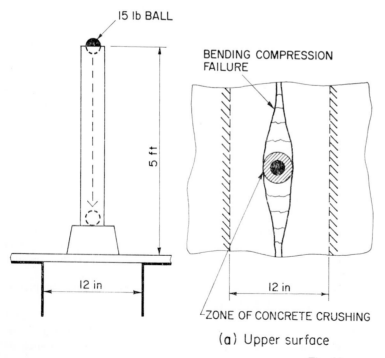

(a) Upper surface   (b) Lower surface

Fig. 13

Test procedure: The equipment is set up on the sample to be tested and the ball dropped 10 times. The following are recorded after each impact:

(a) The diameter of upper surface damage;
(b) the diameter of lower surface damage including tapping for hollow spots or lamination of the "ferro-cement shells" as previously described;
(c) water test to damaged area to observe any leakage within a 10-sec period.

Comments

This test is severe and reveals several important features:

(a) The ability of the ferro-cement to absorb impact;
(b) the combined bending and impact effects;
(c) the waterproofness of the impact area;
(d) the susceptibility of the ferro-cement to lamination;
(e) the response of various materials and their properties to impact.

From a limited series of tests we have concluded:

(a) That soft woven wire mesh absorbs impact with the minimum of damage.

(b) That soft mild steel longitudinal rods do not contribute to impact resistance whether they be combined with soft woven wire mesh or high tensile welded mesh.

(c) That high tensile weld mesh causes severe damage to the ferro-cement due to lamination on the underside. The area of damage was almost twice the area of soft woven mesh.

(d) That high tensile 240 ksi rods located in the centre of the ferro-cement offer the greatest resistance to impact whether they be combined with soft woven wire mesh or welded wire mesh.

(e) That post-tensioning greatly improved impact in all cases and generally by a factor of 3 to 5 times untensioned slabs of the same thickness and materials.

(f) That the greatest impact resistance was achieved with the least physical damage when the combination of materials was:

1. Soft woven hexagonal wire mesh
2. 240 ksi longitudinal rods
3. Two-way post-tensioning varying from 300 to 500 psi on cross sections.

Design impact values

The above test was derived to show that certain combinations of materials offer better impact values than others. When designing large vessels the best possible values are required consistent with the lightest possible structural weight. Further, the test can relate ferro-cement materials to other forms of construction such as plywood, timber, steel or glass reinforced plastic and relative design values chosen.

The following criteria were used in designing a 72 ft racing hull:

(a) after two impacts the member should be waterproof;
(b) after five blows the member should not disintegrate;
(c) a further five blows will clearly indicate the form of failure and whether the materials are ductile or prone to lamination;

(d) the area of damage should be as small as possible:
top surface diameter of damage = 4 in
Lower surface diameter of damage = 8 in.

BASIC HULL DESIGN

The design of ferro-cement hulls offers a considerable challenge to structural engineers, even to those familiar with concrete "shell" design. Two basic approaches are available:

(a) The hull acts as total shell for longitudinal bending and torsion and secondary transverse bending. Composite action occurs uniting the deck, hull-sides, keel, etc., into one structural unit. The effect of ribs or stiffeners is only nominal, while the effect of large holes such as deck openings for cargo or access is extremely important as these greatly reduce the torsional stiffness;

OR

(b) The hull acts as a frame waterproofed with a ferro-cement skin. In this case the design of the ferro-cement membrane as a tension member is similar to the design of a steel plate skin.

Clearly, combinations of the two basic approaches may offer suitable structural solutions depending on the size, shape and use of the ferro-cement hull. Post-tensioning by the use of flexible high tensile multi-strand steel cable offers a simple approach to structural design.

The technique can easily solve many difficult structural problems and as the cost factor is relatively low compared to the overall cost of the hull, its use is strongly recommended.

POST-TENSION DESIGN

"Post-tensioning forces can usefully be applied to change the state of stress within the member so that when applied loads occur the member is better able to resist these loads."

As most stresses that occur in hull design are reversible, many authorities see no advantage in post-tensioning ferro-cement hulls. However, we have developed a special form of post-tensioning for hulls by the use of eccentric cables relative to the concrete section which cause the concrete to camber and produce a dome action. This dome action preloads the member and offers considerable resistance to applied loads.

Our example compares reinforced ferro-cement using weld wire mesh and hard drawn central wires and post-tensioned ferro-cement using soft woven wire mesh and 240 ksi rods with two-way eccentric prestress at about 500 psi each way. Each was designed to have approximately the same bending moment capacity over a 30 in span (see Table 2).

The Elstress post-tensioned ferro-cement is greatly superior in strength at working loads and has 40 per cent less weight. Two basic approaches are possible when applying post-tension forces:

(a) eccentrically applied forces causing "dome" action;
(b) concentrically applied forces.

TABLE 2. DESIGN COMPARISONS OF REINFORCED AND POST-TENSIONED FERRO-CEMENT FOR APPROXIMATELY EQUAL BENDING MOMENT CAPACITIES

Based on a S.S. span of 2′ 6″	Typical reinforced ferro-cement	Elstress method post-tensioned ferro-cement
1. Thickness	$1\frac{1}{4}$–$1\frac{3}{8}$ in	0.8 in
2. Applied load to flatten surface	0	550 lbs/ft²
3. Bending moment at maximum design stress (0.6 Mμ)	5.9 kips ft $f_t = 1900$ psi	5.1 kips ft $f_t = 3500$ psi
4. Load applied to reach maximum design stress (cracks just forming) (0.4–0.45 Mμ)	580 lb/ft²	1050 lb/ft²
5. At load (4) % of ultimate	30%	50%
6. Ultimate load as U.D.L.	1930 lb/ft²	2120 lb/ft²
7. Maximum stresses when considered as a homogeneous material		
(a) Bending moment f_t (cracking value)	1900 psi*	3500psi†
(b) Ultimate B.M. $f_b\mu$	3180 psi	7900 psi
(c) Ultimate tension $T\mu$	3200 psi	8700 psi

* Assumed to be 0.4 to 0.45 Mμ.
† Assumed to be 0.6 to 0.65 Mμ.

The methods adopted will depend on the hull shape and the loads to be resisted. The concentrically applied cable will contribute most to the moment capacity of the ferro-cement and it can be shown that if 500 psi (equivalent to an ultimate load of 7.1 k/ft) prestress is applied to the previous example of eight layers of soft wire mesh and 0.25 in diameter rods, the following property changes occur.

TABLE 3. LONGITUDINAL STRENGTHS

Longitudinal strength	reinforced mesh	Post-tension effect	Predicted post-tension ferro-cement
Ultimate tensile strength	40 kip/ft	+7.1	47.1 kip/ft
Ultimate tensile stress on concrete section	4300 psi	+770	5070 psi
Total reinforcement %	4.8%	+(equivalent mesh)	6.65% Equivalent
Weight of steel per cu ft	23.5 lb	+(equivalent mesh)	32.5 lb Equivalent
Ultimate bending strength	3.16 kips in	+2.12	5.28 kips in
Ultimate bending stress on concrete section	2620 psi	+1830	4450 psi
Actual wt. of steel per cu ft of concrete—wt	1.53	cable only .14	1.67 lb sq ft
lb/cu ft	23.5	+2.5	26.0

The application of post-tension forces greatly improves the flexure capacity in the longitudinal direction while in the transverse direction, the flexural capacity is similarly increased and the ultimate tensile capacity is increased by 75 per cent due to there being no transverse rods to assist the mesh.

For example, post-tensioning can be applied in a local area where greater strength is required, eliminating increased structural thickness involving heavy ribs or frames.

For boats of, say, up to 100 ft (30 m) length post-tensioning enables a considerable reserve of strength to be built in at no apparent extra cost. For larger hulls the methods are equally applicable and offer simple structural analysis of the otherwise difficult problems.

ADDITIVES TO CONCRETE

Many additives can be used with concrete but our research has been confined to the type representing micro fine wax emulsions about which we know a great deal, especially with regard to the hydration process.

Workability and Waterproofness

Concretes may be modified in several ways to increase workability by inclusion of the above micro fine wax emulsions which also offer greatly reduced permeability due to the surface tension increase of the cement-wax hydration components. Suitable micron waxes may be introduced up to 15 per cent by weight of cement. These waxes also aid the curing process by greatly restricting moisture movement during hydration. However, care should be exercised with the surface finish effects as a smooth steel trowelled finished may be difficult to paint. This can be overcome by sand blasting or other roughening processes after curing.

Cement modified mortars

Considerable advances are being made with the addition of synthetic rubber emulsions of the styrene butadiene acrylic types. These emulsions can vary the properties of concrete to greatly improve the bond value of the reinforcement and the apparent concrete strain at ultimate load. With suitable modification the concrete strain at failure can be increased up to about five to six times that of plain concrete. Where lower compression strengths are permissible even greater strains are possible. Also the concrete tensile strength is improved by at least 50–150 per cent for the same compressive strength.

The inclusion of these emulsions will greatly reduce cement paste permeability and offer improved curing. If sufficient emulsion is used, the concrete may be dry-cured, for moisture is effectively trapped within the concrete and no volume change takes place.

Shrinkage control

The use of higher cement content concretes necessitates the use of shrinkage control procedures. Prolonged high speed mixing of cement and water as a paste will greatly reduce the drying and plastic shrinkage of the cement paste so that when aggregate is added, the total concrete drying shrinkage is reduced over that of lower cement concretes mixed in the usual manner.

Also, cement expansion agents can be used to counteract the effect of shrinkage following the initial cement hydration expansion. These products must be used with caution as they greatly increase the SO_3 content of the cements, often leading to greater plastic cracking if moisture is suddenly lost due to rapid hydration or sudden drying.

The greatest problem in their use is the control of moisture loss after placement of the concrete and this must be prevented by adequate curing or using cement modified mortars.

COMMENTS ON DESIGN

The design of ferro-cement hulls begins with the method of construction. Due to the many and varied construction methods and opinions developed in the industry over the last few years the time has approached for serious specification writing to draft codes of practice which will be of use to the industry and not a hindrance.

In our view the end result or requirement must be clearly established so that the "design" and "construction" limitations can be defined. At the present time specifications acceptable to one authority could well be unacceptable to another while it may not even be possible to actually achieve in practice what the specification calls for.

In summary, ferro-cement hulls must:

(a) be able to be designed to specific strength criteria, with realistic factors of safety;
(b) be able to be constructed to meet these criteria;
(c) be waterproof;
(d) be durable and free from corrosion;
(e) be able to be repaired if damaged.

CONCLUSION

This paper summarizes years of basic applied research and construction practice into ultimate load design problems and the understanding of material properties. This brief outline indicates that ferro-cement design may be adjusted to a wide range of material properties. On this basis materials may be selected which when combined give ferro-cement the best advantages of each material. If this can be achieved, ferro-cement has an enormous potential in ship construction.

APPENDIX 1
ANALYSIS OF THE PROPERTIES OF FERRO-CEMENT TYPE REINFORCEMENT

Properties of 0.5 in soft woven hexagonal mesh

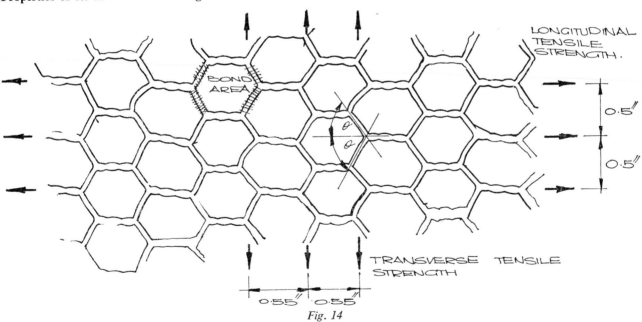

Fig. 14

Weave angle θ	$= 55°$
Diameter wire—19 g	$= 0.04$ in
Cross section area	$= 0.00125$ in
Ultimate tensile strength $f_{s\mu}$	$= 55$ ksi
Cold worked tensile strength $f_{sc\mu}$	$= 70$ ksi
Tensile strength per wire	$= 70$ lb (approx.)

The longitudinal tensile strength per ft width, calculate as follows:

$T\mu_{AS}$ per ft width = 44 wires × 70 lb × cos 55°
$$= 1.75 \text{ kips}$$
Effective cross section $A_s = 44 \times 0.00125$
$$\times (\cos 55° = 0.57)$$
$$= 0.0313 \text{ in}^2$$
Effective bond area of wire between mesh over a length of 0.55 in

$$\text{Bond area } U_B = 44\pi \begin{bmatrix} 0.04 \times 0.3 \cos \theta = 0.94 \text{ in} \\ 0.08 \times 0.3 \quad = 1.55 \\ \hline = 2.49 \text{ in}^2 \end{bmatrix}$$

Assume an ultimate bond stress of 2 ksi

Then total ultimate load in bond $T\mu_B = 2.49 \times 2$ ksi
$$= 5.0 \text{ kips}$$

Similarly the transverse strength may be calculated:

$T\mu_{AS}$ $\qquad = 21$ wires $\times$ 70 lb
$$\times (\sin 55 = 0.82)$$
$$= 1.2 \text{ kips}$$

Bond area U_B $\qquad = 21$ wires $\times \pi \times 0.04$
$$\times 0.6 \sin 55°$$
$$= 1.3 \text{ in}^2$$

Ultimate tensile
strength in bond $T\mu_B = 1.3 \times 2$ ksi $= 2.6$ kips

Properties of soft woven hexagonal mesh per layer

	Effective steel area	TμAS (55 ksi)	Effective Tμ (2 ksi)	
			Bond area	Bond
Longitudinal	0.0313 in²	1.75 kips	2.49 in²	5.04 kips
Transverse	0.0216 in²	1.2 kips	1.3 in²	2.6 kips

Typical mesh arrangement

Assume four layers of mesh clamped tightly together have an effective thickness = 0.2 in per layer group.

Place two layers either side of a 0.25 in diameter rod with the longitudinal strength parallel to the rod (Fig. 15).

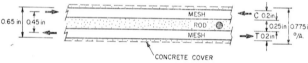

Fig. 15

Bending moment capacity

The ultimate properties can be calculated as follows:
From the assumed thrust components:
$$M\mu = T\mu \times 0.45 = 4 \times 1.75 \times 0.45$$
$$= 3.16 \text{ kip in}$$

Also the equivalent solid section stresses can be calculated from $M = fz$
where M = B.M., f is equivalent fibre stress, z is section modulus.
1.2 in³ for an equivalent section thickness of 0.775 in
Then equivalent fibre bending stress
$$f\mu b = \frac{3.16}{1.2} = 2620 \text{ psi}$$

Tension capacity

Let it be assumed that the pure tension capacity is controlled by the mesh bond capacity to limit cracks to a spacing of approximately 0.5 in. Then we must equate this bond tension capacity to the ultimate tensile strength of the composite materials.

The mesh only offers
$$T\mu_{AS} = 1.75 \text{ kips} \times 8 \text{ layers} = 12.00 \text{ kips}$$

But we have an ultimate bond tensile capacity of
$$T\mu_B = 5.0 \text{ kips} \times 8 \text{ layers} = 40 \text{ kips}$$

Hence rods may be added to provide the tensile load difference, i.e.
$$40 - 12.0 = 28 \text{ kips}$$

In the calculation the effective bond from the rods may be included but for this approximate design is neglected.

Further, it is assumed that the mesh bond capacity will allow the concrete to strain sufficiently to allow the steel to strain and develop load. The rods used to develop this 28 kip load may be mild, medium grade or high tensile steel.

(a) If it is assumed that soft mild steel 0.25 in diameter rods are used $fs = 34$ ksi and $T\mu_{AS}$ per rod $= 0.05 \times 34 = 1.7$ kips per rod.

Then the number of rods required to balance the mesh is $\dfrac{28}{1.7} = 16.5$ per ft width.

This spacing is obviously too close and hence either the number of mesh layers could be reduced or the tensile capacity of the rods increases.

(b) A more usual steel type is the drawn wire $Fs\mu \simeq 70$ and $T\mu_{AS}$ per rod $= 3.5$ kips, which has an $fs = 70$ ksi and $T\mu_{AS}$ per rod $= 3.5$ kips.

Then the number of rods required $= \dfrac{28}{3.5}$ or 8 per ft width.

(c) It is known that the effective steel reinforcing percentage greatly effects the apparent concrete strain capacity and hence the steel tensile stress.

From Fig. 4 and assuming the total reinforcing steel percentage exceeds 4.5 per cent then the effective tensile stress could exceed 135 ksi. The rod tensile capacity would then be about 6.7 kips and number of rods required $= \dfrac{28}{6.7} = 4.2$ per ft width.

Assume 0.25 in diameter rods at 3 in centre to centre were used. Then

As per ft width (rod) $0.05 \times 4 = 0.20$ in²
As per ft width (mesh)
$$8 \times 0.0313 = \underline{0.25 \text{ in}^2}$$
$$0.450 \text{ in}^2$$

The concrete area per ft width $= 0.775 \times 12$
$$= 9.3 \text{ in}^2$$

Hence the apparent tensile
stress across the section $= \dfrac{40}{9.3}$ kip
$$= 4400 \text{ psi}$$

Weight of steel reinforcement
per ft² $= 0.45 \times 3.4 = 1.53$ lb

Percentage of reinforcement $= \dfrac{0.45}{9.3} \times \dfrac{100}{1} = 4.8\%$

Weight of steel reinforcement
per ft³ of mortar $= 23.5$ lb

From Fig. 4 maximum apparent concrete strain is approximately 4700×10^{-6} and maximum steel stress therefore which could be used and concrete crack control still maintained is about $29 \times 10^6 \times 4700 \times 10^{-6} = 135$ ksi.

Similarly, the effective ultimate tensile force may be calculated for the transverse direction.

$$T\mu_{AS} \text{ (mesh)} = 1.2 \text{ kips} \times 8 \text{ layers} = 9.6 \text{ kips}$$

No transverse rods would be placed between the mesh if minimum thickness was required.

Hence the apparent tensile strength is

$$\frac{9.6 \text{ kips}}{9.3 \text{ in}^2} \simeq 1040 \text{ psi}$$

Ultimate bending moment $M\mu = 4 \times 1.2 \times 0.45$
$$= 2.16 \text{ kip in}$$

$$\text{Equivalent } fb = \frac{2.16}{1.2} = 1800 \text{ psi}$$

Summary

Material soft woven wire mesh 8 layers
High tensile steel rod at 2 in centres

	Longitudinal strength	Transverse strength
Ultimate tensile strength	40 kips/ft width	9.6 kips/ft width
Ultimate tensile stress on concrete section	4300 psi	1040 psi
Total reinforcement	4.8%	2.7%
Weight of steel per ft³ of concrete	23.5 lb	13 lb
Ultimate bending strength	3.16 kip in	2.16 kip in
Ultimate bending stress on concrete section	2620 psi	1800 psi

Note: The reduced transverse strength is in hull design compensated for by the increased transverse rib strength or forming, or placing mesh in the opposite direction.

Properties of 0.5 in welded wire fabric

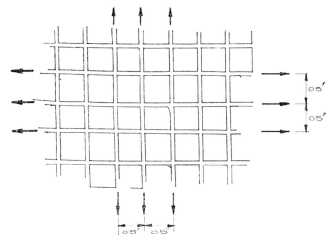

Fig. 16

17 g wire after galvanizing diameter = 0.056
Less galvanizing = 0.004
0.051 in

Steel area As per wire	= 0.00204 in²
As per ft width	= 0.049 in²
Bond area per 0.5 in length	= 0.085 in²
Ultimate tensile strength of material	= 70 ksi
Ultimate tensile strength per wire	= 143 lb
Ultimate tensile strength per ft width	= 3.43 kips
Bond area per ft width	= 24 × 0.085 in²
	= 2.04 in²
Total ultimate load in bond at 2 ksi per in²	= 2.04 × 2 ksi
	= 4.08 kips
Assume hull thickness as before	= 0.75 in (approx.)

With 0.25 in diameter rods for longitudinal spacing (Fig. 17).

Fig. 17

Maximum number of layers of welded wire mesh to fit into 0.2 in thickness is 2 layers.

Then ultimate bending moment $= 2 \times 3.43 \text{ kips} \times 0.45 \text{ in}$
$$= 3.1 \text{ kip in}$$

Apparent ultimate fibre stress on concrete section 0.75 in thick = 2580 psi

Maximum tensile load due to wire ultimate tensile stress = 4 × 3.43
$$= 13.72 \text{ kips}$$

Maximum tensile bond load $T\mu_B = 4 \times 4.08$
$$= 16.3 \text{ kips}$$

Hence to take advantage of the excess bond capacity 0.25 in diameter rods can be added to increase the tensile strength.

Soft mild steel rods 0.25 in diameter $T\mu_{AS}$ per rod = 1.7 kips

Number of rods to balance these capacities $= \dfrac{16.3 - 13.72}{1.7}$
$$= 1.5 \text{ rods}$$

Any further increase in rod number will not necessarily increase the ultimate tensile strength due to the crack control bond requirement governing the form of failure.

The added rods will give longitudinal tensile strength of 16.3 kips/ft.

The following is a summary of properties:

	Longitudinal strength	Transverse strength
Ultimate tensile strength	16.3 kips	13.72 kips
Ultimate tensile stress on concrete section	1800 psi	1480 psi
Total reinforcement	3.2%	2.1%
Mesh 4 × 0.049	0.196 in²	
Rods 2 × 0.05	0.10 in²	
	0.297 in²	
Concrete area	9.3 in²	
Weight of steel reinforcement per ft³ of concrete	15.7 lb	10.5 lb
Ultimate bending strength	3.10 kip in	3.10 kip in
Ultimate bending stress on concrete section	2580 psi	2580 psi
Maximum steel stress for 0.5 in crack spacing and steel reinforcing %	72 ksi	32 ksi

From Fig. 4 assuming a longitudinal steel reinforcing content of 3.2 per cent the apparent concrete strain is approximately 2500×10^{-6} and the equivalent steel stress is 72 ksi but as the bond values are low relative to the mesh tensile strength available there is no advantage to use steel rods of higher tensile strength than 34 ksi. (This stress provides adequate rod tensile strength to make up the deficiency) unless the bond areas and hence ultimate bond tensile capacity are increased.

Similarly, an analysis of four layers of mesh on each side of 0.25 in diameter rods would give the following properties (Fig. 18).

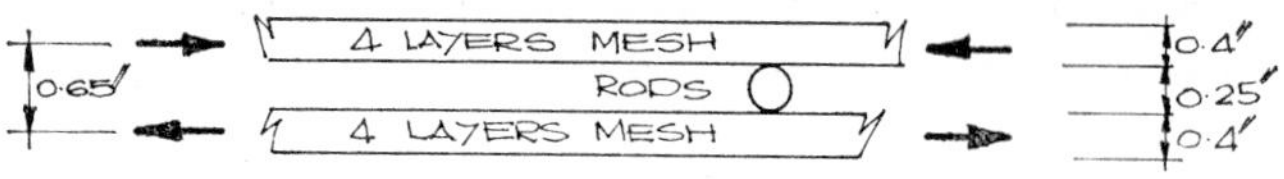

Fig. 18

	Longitudinal strength	Transverse strength
Ultimate tensile strength	32.64 kips	27.5 kips
Ultimate tensile stress on concrete section ft	2320 psi	1950 psi
(Rods 0.25 in diameter 34 ksi)	3 ft width	—
Total reinforcement	3.85%	2.8%
Mesh 8 × 0.049	0.392	
3 × 0.05	0.15	
	0.542	
Concrete area	14.1 in²	14.1 in²
Weight of steel reinforcement per ft³ of concrete	18.8 lb	13.7 lb
Ultimate bending strength	8.95 kip in	8.95 kip in
Ultimate bending stress on concrete section	3240 psi	3240 psi
Maximum steel stress for 0.5 in crack spacing and steel reinforcing %	95 ksi	58 ksi

The total weight of steel per ft³ of concrete is the sum of that weight in each direction.

Definition of Ferro-Cement   G W Bigg

To the best of the writer's knowledge there is no generally understood technical definition of ferro-cement. The American Bureau of Shipping defines ferro-cement as: "A thin, highly reinforced shell of concrete in which the steel reinforcement is distributed widely throughout the concrete, so that the material under stress acts approximately as a homogeneous material. The strength properties of the material are to be determined by testing a significant number of samples . . ."

This statement immediately prompts a number of questions from a technical point of view.

How thin is thin?
What does highly reinforced mean?
Does the word concrete mean the same to everyone?
What are the limits on an "approximately homogeneous material"?
How many samples are significant?
When does this material behave like reinforced concrete, a material which has received a great deal of attention?

From a descriptive point of view the definition has meaning, but from a technical point of view the answers to the above questions and many others must be quantified and widely adopted in order that designers, builders, classifiers and researchers might communicate their results to one another unambiguously.

SCOPE

This paper will be restricted to discussion of the definition of ferro-cement which is in common usage. Specifically, the author is concerned with the mechanical definition of hull layups comprised of multiple layers of steel mesh and discrete rods tied into a tight fair skeleton and embedded in a hydraulic cement "mortar". A mortar is considered to be a hydraulic cement–sand–water–admixture combination in which the sand particles are of a size consistent with the mesh opening but do not exceed 3 mm.

No attempt will be made to include discrete fibre reinforced concrete, glass reinforced concrete, composite structures, polymer mortars, or traditional reinforced concrete in the definition. It is considered likely that some of these hold a great deal of promise in the future development of fishing vessel materials; however, they will require their own particular mechanical definition. It is reasonable to expect that some of the ideas presented here will be readily adapted.

To define ferro-cement too precisely is to run the risk that the material might become classified to a point which restricts development. It is the writer's opinion that ferro-cement must be considered an experimental material from an engineering point of view and it is suggested that the many combinations of mesh, rod, mortar, plastics, etc., be given a fair appraisal. It is presumptuous to think that ferro-cement as commonly conceived is optimized in its application. Builders have tried many different combinations but as the material is seldom discussed in accurate engineering terms, a quantitative assessment of relative merits cannot be obtained.

The subject of impact cannot be discussed quantitatively at this time. Although it is a major cause of hull failures, little is known about the relative merits of ferro-cement with respect to other materials. The answer is quite beyond analysis so it is suggested that comparative testing would be appropriate.

To characterize ferro-cement it is important to understand the nature of concrete mortar; the mechanisms of material failure; the properties of the reinforcement; the bond characteristics between the mortar and the reinforcement; the essential parameters which might distinguish one type of ferro-cement from another; and appropriate methods of testing to ascertain the mechanical properties of the material.

USE OF ENGINEERING TERMINOLOGY

It is common, when reading existing published work on ferro-cement, to find confusing or inappropriate words used to describe the mechanical behaviour of ferro-cement. Stress and strain, for example, are not the same as load and deformation; however, they have been used interchangeably. Many writers report strength data in terms of load–deformation curves. These are qualitatively very useful; however, unless information about the geometry of loading and material dispersement is very complete, the transfer to a stress–strain characterization can be impossible, yet it is on the basis of stress–strain that various types of ferro-cement of different reinforcement geometries, mortars and dimensions can be compared. One area of great confusion, at least in the writer's mind, is in the use of the term "modulus of elasticity". Modulus of elasticity is not synonymous with stiffness. The modulus of elasticity is a material property, while stiffness is a geometrical and material property. In addition, when presented, the term modulus of elasticity must be defined carefully as ferro-cement has a non-linear behaviour. With reference to Fig. 1, three distinct modulii of elasticity can be defined from a simple tension test. In addition, the work of Chiang and Thiruvillakatt (1972) and others point to the fact that

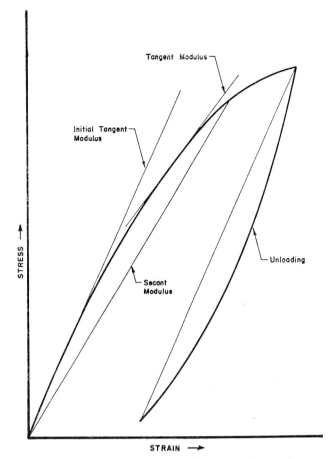

Fig. 1 Typical stress–strain curve for concrete (mortar)

once ferro-cement has cracked, the modulus will decrease upon reloading if the specimen has been unloaded. Further confusion exists when the modulus of elasticity is quoted from a bending test of a ferro-cement panel. The derived modulus will be effective in establishing deflexions but it is only approximate for establishing fibre stresses as the neutral axis shifts with the onset of cracking.

The term "strength" is seldom useful without a modifier. When characterizing ferro-cement the strength parameter mentioned usually requires definition (e.g. ultimate strength, yield strength, design strength, strength at a crack of corrosive size, etc.). The units of strength are usually the units of stress (kg/cm^2) rather than load (kg).

NATURE OF CONCRETE MORTARS

The designer of ferro-cement vessels must have an intimate knowledge of the concrete mortar which constitutes the major bulk of the hull. The mechanical and chemical behaviour of mortar is very complex and is not completely understood even by experts. In most important respects the behaviour of mortar is similar to that of plain concrete. The major distinction is the size of the aggregate used. In general, a good quality mortar is stronger and more durable than good quality concrete; however, their basic response to the environment is essentially the same. As a consequence much can be learned about mortar from studies performed on plain concrete.

As a boat-building material, good quality mortar has some desirable properties, including:

within limits mortar is compatible with sea water;
it is relatively easy to fabricate and maintain;
if properly placed and cured, good quality mortar does not deteriorate appreciably with age;
it is cheap and readily available in most parts of the world.

Unfortunately mortar has some serious disadvantages which must be understood. These include:

1. Mortar is brittle. Its tensile ultimate strength is roughly one-tenth of its compressive ultimate strength;

2. On the basis of a weight/useful strength ratio, concrete mortar and consequently ferro-cement as presently conceived is heavy in comparison with all traditional boatbuilding materials. The designer must be realistic about this when establishing the displacement of the vessel;

3. As stated by Philleo (1971): "Of all the materials used in a marine environment none undergoes volume changes as large as those endured by concrete (read mortar) and none is so ill equipped to deal with these changes. Concrete shrinks and swells with changes in moisture content. It experiences large creep strains under sustained loads. Improper mix, design and curing can cause extensive shrinkage cracking which will affect its durability;"

4. The overall quality of mortar depends primarily on the water : cement ratio. Durability, ultimate strength, creep response and permeability are sensitive to this ratio. The best-designed vessel can be rendered useless if the water : cement ratio is allowed to vary outside that prescribed in the design;

5. Mortar is susceptible to freeze-thaw deterioration and appropriate steps must be taken in temperate and northern climates;

6. Mortar is not impermeable. Water is continually migrating through the material in response to humidity changes. For practical purposes it is watertight;

7. The strength and stiffness properties of mortar are statistical as well as time, load history, specimen size and humidity dependent.

Neville (1963) contains a wealth of information on the basic properties of the various cements used in making mortar and of hardened mortar. Figs. 2 to 6 are presented from Neville to show how properties of mortar are affected by various parameters. With suitable reinforcing systems, mix design and quality control the disadvantages of concrete mortar as a shipbuilding material can be brought under control.

DEFINITION OF FERRO-CEMENT MORTAR

The properties of the mortar which goes into the fabrication of ferro-cement are dependant upon a number of important variables. Many of these are superficially described in literature. To interpret the results of a researcher or to estimate the probability of success of a design a reasonably complete description of the mortar

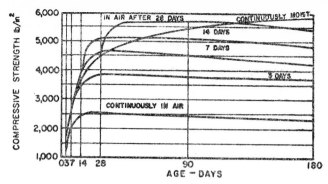

Fig. 2 The influence of moist curing on the strength of concrete with a water : cement ratio of 0.50

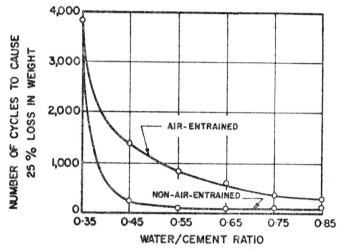

Fig. 3 Influence of water : cement ratio on the frost resistance of concrete moist cured for 28 days

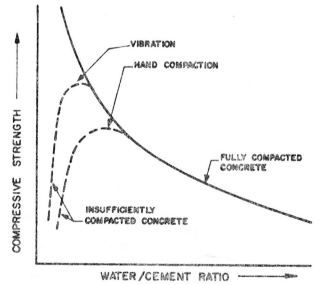

Fig. 4 The relation between strength and water : cement ratio of concrete for various compaction types

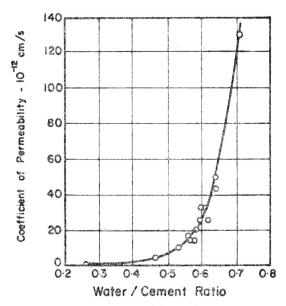

Fig. 5 *Relation between permeability and water : cement ratio for mature cement pastes*

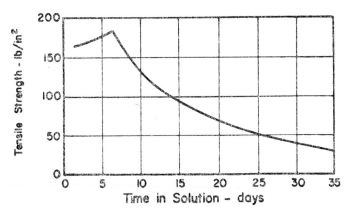

Fig. 6 *Effect of a 0.15 molar solution of sodium sulphate on mortar tensile strength*

used or proposed is required. As a minimum it is suggested that the following information is required to define a ferro-cement mortar adequately.

Details of mix design, placement and strength properties
The specification of the mix design should include:

water : cement ratio by weight;
sand : cement ratio by weight;
grading, shape, source, purity and chemical composition of sand;
quality, age and type of cement;
quality of water;
type and amount of admixtures.

The ultimate quality of mortar is highly dependent upon its placement. The available information should include:

type of mixer;
mixing time;
estimate of the type and amount of vibration or compaction;
environment at time of mixing (wind, humidity, temperature);
curing (temperature, duration, type).

Standard mechanical properties of the mortar must be established as follows:

Ultimate tensile strength at 28 days as determined by a flexure test (ASTM C-348 or equivalent is suggested). There are three standard methods of estimating the tensile strength of mortar and each yields a different magnitude. The problem here is to establish a consistent testing procedure.

Ultimate compressive strength at 28 days (ASTM C-349 is suggested as the standard as it uses the mortar pieces created in ASTM C-348) and at the time of any ferro-cement panel tests.

Modulus of elasticity in compression. For consistency, it is suggested that the secant modulus of elasticity be used defined to a stress level of 90 per cent of the ultimate strength.

The statistical significance of the above information. It is useful to consider a general statement which ASTM makes concerning the reliability of mortar test results done to standard. "Specimens that are manifestly faulty or that give strengths differing more than 10 per cent from the average for all test specimens made from the same sample and tested at the same period shall not be considered in determining the (. . . . .) strength. After discarding strength values, if less than two strength values are left for determining the (. . . . .) strength at any given period a retest shall be made."

It is suggested that three specimens of a given mortar mix represent an absolute minimum for a test series.

The above properties of the design, placing and strength of the mortar are considered to be a minimum. Water permeability tests, tensile elastic modulus tests and sulphate attack tests are examples of further additions which might be made. It is felt, however, that with co-ordinated experience the above list will suffice in the long term.

FERRO-CEMENT AS A COMPOSITE MATERIAL

In general terms, ferro-cement is considered to be a mortar highly reinforced with steel mesh and rods. It is applied to thin shells and shell-like structures. From an engineering point of view this material has not been adequately defined. From the nature of the reinforcing system ferro-cement cannot be considered a homogeneous isotropic material. As is the case for glass reinforced plastic (GRP), ferro-cement would appear to be decidedly anisotropic, and at best orthotropic in the plane of the layup. As reported by Greenius and Smith (1972), Figs. 7 and 8 indicate a markedly different load deflexion behaviour which depends upon the orientation of the rods and/or mesh with respect to the direction of load application. For highly optimized GRP applications such as in the Aerospace industry, full consideration must be given to the effect of anisotropy on the mechanical properties of the material. If one wishes to optimize ferro-cement to the same extent then cognizance of its full composite nature will be required. Simple compression, tension and beam bending tests are not sufficient to characterize the mechanical properties of the material.

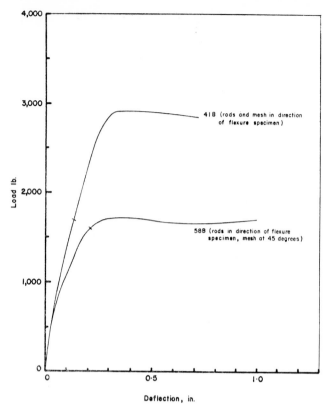

Fig. 7   Effect of mesh orientation on flexural strength

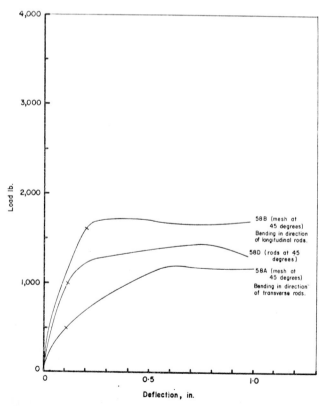

Fig. 8   Effect of rod and mesh orientation on flexural strength

64

With specific reference to small marine and fishing vessels, there is an almost total lack of information concerning the environmental loadings that the vessel might reasonably expect in its life time. For this reason, it is considered unnecessary in a small vessel application to consider the full composite behaviour of ferro-cement at this time. As vessels grow larger or as refinements in weight proceed the picture will change. It is useful at this time to consider some properties of a unidirectional fibre-reinforced composite and these will be discussed subsequently. The relationship between ferro-cement and traditional reinforced concrete requires some discussion. Traditional reinforced concrete in application is a well-developed engineering material. It is not considered to be a synergistic composite material as the two constituent materials, concrete and steel, are considered to act largely independent of each other. There would appear to be a difference of opinion as to the synergistic nature of ferro-cement. For the levels of reinforcement used in current practice the ultimate strength of the material would appear to behave more like reinforced concrete than as a new material. Shah (1970) suggests that ferro-cement is not synergistic. From his test results, the basic ultimate compressive strength depends solely on the mortar and the tensile strength at first crack is controlled by the amount of steel and its surface bonding area. Professor Lachance, in a private communication, reported that he tested a number of ferro-cement panels in bending and found that the results up to first crack compared favourably with standard analysis for reinforced concrete. The ultimate modulus of rupture, however, was conservatively estimated by reinforced concrete analysis.

Bezukladov *et al.* (1968) and Walkus and Kowalski (1971) define ferro-cement in terms of the ratio of the surface area of reinforcement to the volume of the composite (specific surface). This is implicit recognition of the importance of cracking control on the service behaviour of the material. Bezukladov *et al.* delineate between reinforced concrete and ferro-cement at a specific surface of 0.5 cm^2/cm^3, but consider 2.0 cm^2/cm^3 as true ferro-cement. Design stresses have been proposed which vary linearly with specific surface to 2.0 cm^2/cm^3 and then remain constant. Bezukladov *et al.* suggest that the practical limit on specific surface (because of poor penetration) is around 3.5 cm^2/cm^3. Walkus and Kowalski suggest that a specific surface of 2.0 cm^2/cm^3 should be the minimum value for ferro-cement. These authors intimate that the values chosen were somewhat arbitrary as the properties changed gradually.

General remarks on composite materials

With reference to Broutman and Krock (1967) some general remarks on composite materials are in order. A composite material consists of a matrix and a reinforcement which together form a new material with superior properties to either of its constituents. There are three basic types of composite materials: dispersion (0.01 to 0.1 micro inch particles representing 1–15 per cent of the volume); particle (> 1.0 micro inch particles representing > 25 per cent of the volume); fibre (particles with one long dimension with cross-sectional dimensions from micro inches to mils, representing 1–70 per cent of the volume).

Concrete has been considered as a particulate composite with sand and gravel as the reinforcing particles and hydrated cement gel as the matrix. The modulus of elasticity of concrete falls below that predicted by the law of mixtures for a composite. The law of mixtures states:

$$E_c = V_m E_m + V_p E_p$$

where E_c = elastic modulus of the composite
E_m = elastic modulus of the matrix
E_p = elastic modulus of the particles
V_m = volume of matrix
V_p = volume of particles

Ferro-cement can be considered as a fibre-reinforced composite whose matrix is assumed to be homogeneous. For fibrous reinforcement an analysis can be established based on the assumptions that the fibres are unidirectional, fully bonded, continuous and uniformly dispersed. If it is assumed that the load is shared by the matrix and the fibres and that both carry the same strain, then in uniaxial loading:

$$\sigma_c = [E_m V_m + E_f V_f] \varepsilon_c$$

or

$$\sigma_c = E_c \varepsilon_c$$

where σ_c = stress carried by the composite
V_f = volume fraction of the fibre in the composite
E_c = elastic modulus of the composite as determined by the law of mixtures
E_f = elastic modulus of the individual fibres
ε_c = strain in the composite

The ratio of the load carried by the fibres to that carried by the matrix is:

$$\frac{\text{Fibre load}}{\text{Matrix load}} = \frac{E_f}{E_m}\left(\frac{V_f}{V_m}\right)$$

This ratio is plotted in Figs. 9 and 10.

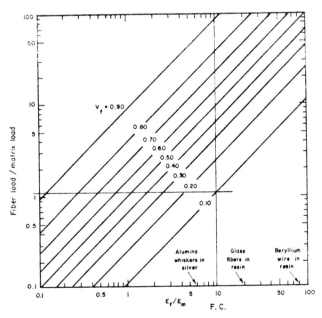

Fig. 9 Elastic moduli ratio vs. load ratio for various fibre volume ratios

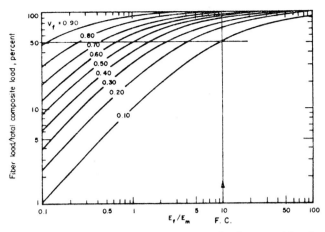

Fig. 10 Elastic moduli ratio vs. percent load assumed by the fibres for various fibre volume ratios

The deformation stages associated with a fibre-reinforced composite are:

(a) both fibres and matric deform elastically;
(b) fibre deformations continue elastically and the matrix behaves in some non-linear fashion;
(c) both deform non-linearly;
(d) fibres fail, followed by immediate composite failure.

With respect to ferro-cement, the mortar matrix is very brittle, consequently stage (b) consists of progressive cracking of the matrix while the mesh reinforcement continues to deform first elastically and then plastically. In stage (a), E_c can be predicted conservatively by the law of mixtures. In stage (b), the law of mixtures is still considered valid for plastically deforming matrices, however, for cracked systems the influence of the matrix can be ignored (Shah, 1970).

The critical volume of fibres necessary so that the composite strength exceeds the matrix strength is given by:

$$V_{\text{crit}} = \frac{\sigma_{mu} - \sigma_m}{\sigma_{fu} - \sigma_m}$$

where σ_{mu} = ultimate matrix strength
σ_m = stress in matrix when fibres are stressed to ultimate
σ_{fu} = ultimate fibre strength.

For a ductile fibre in a brittle matrix (i.e. ferro-cement) $\sigma_m = 0$ as the matrix will have long since cracked, therefore,

$$V_{\text{crit}} = \frac{\sigma_{mu}}{\sigma_{fu}}$$

When the fibres are discontinuous the critical volume is increased as the transfer of load to the fibres is not immediate.

Table 1 represents a summary of different characteristics of composites. It is most interesting to observe in item (6) that for composites in general the composite strength varies linearly with V_f.

With regard to fracture behaviour, the mechanics of composites involves relationships between geometry, loads, deformations, crack initiation, flaw and crack growth leading to partial or complete failure of the material. Failure is initiated in two stages. Initially there

TABLE 1. COMPARISON OF DISPERSION, PARTICLE, AND FIBRE-STRENGTHENED MATERIALS*

Item compared	Dispersion strengthened	Particle-strengthened	Fibre-strengthened
(1) Role of matrix	Principle load-bearing constituent	Intermediate load-bearing constituent	Main purpose to transmit load to fibres
(2) Matrix work hardening	Major strengthening mechanism; rate of work-hardening depends on particle shape and spacing	Major strengthening mechanism; increases possibility of maximum constraint leading to ductility	Minor strengthening factor
(3) Role of dispersed phase	Impedes dislocation motion (slip)	Constrains matrix; deforms in ductile composites; provides hardening in brittle composites	Principal load-bearing constituent also impedes dislocation motion, but of less importance
(4) Maximum stress on dispersed phase	$\sigma_p \ll \sigma_{pu}$ (spherical particles)	$\sigma_p \le \sigma_{pu}$	$\sigma_f \le \sigma_{fu}$
(5) Strengthening parameters	$\sigma_c = (f)D_p, d_p, l_p,$ where $D_p = 0.3$ to 0.01μ, $d_p = 0.1$ to 0.01μ, $V_p = 0.01$ to 0.15	$\sigma_c = f(D_p, d_p, V_p)$ in brittle particulates. $\sigma_{cv} \propto 1/\sqrt{D_p}$ or $\log(l/D_p)$ in brittle particulates. $\sigma_{cy} \propto$ constrained particle flow stress in ductile composites. $D_p = 1$ to $25.0\ \mu$, $d_p = 1$ to $50.0\ \mu$, $V_p = 0.35$ to 0.90	$\sigma_c = (f)L_c, L/d_f, V_c,$ fibre orientation. $\sigma_c =$ relatively independent of fibre spacing. $L/d_f = 2$ to ∞. $V_f = 0.01$ to 0.91
(6) Composite strength, σ_c	Varies linearly with V_p at lower volume fractions (where $0.0005 < V_p < 0.2$)	Composite strength, σ_c, increases linearly with decreasing V_m and mfp until very low values where it decreases in brittle composites. Independent of volume fraction in ductile composites	Varies linearly with $V_p = 0.01$ to 0.90
(7) Composite strength, σ_c Room temperature Elevated temperature	$\sigma_c/\sigma_m = 2$ to 15 T.C.† $= 0.75$ to 0.79	$\sigma_c/\sigma_m = 2$ to 25 T.C. $= 0.75$ to 0.85	$\sigma_c/\sigma_m = 2$ to 50 T.C. $= 0.80$ to 0.98
(8) High-temperature stability (long-term strength)	Depends (a) on ability of dislocations to move around particle barriers, and (b) on particle agglomeration	Depends on constrained flow properties of matrix and somewhat less on high-temperature properties of particles	Depends on retention of fibre strength; low chemical activity and diffusion between matrix and fibres necessary
(9) Composite stress-strain relationship	Exhibits yield-point; fracture elongation: 0.1 to 15%	May exhibit yield point or continuous flow-curve; fracture elongation 0 to 30%	May fracture elasticaly or exhibit yield point; this depends chiefly on V_f, fibre properties, and fibre orientation

	Isotropic	Isotropic	Anisotropic
(10) Composite properties			
(11) Interfacial bond (matrix-dispersed phase)	May be important, but not critical to σ_c	Critical for ductile and nonductile composites	Critical for discontinous fibres, not as critical for continous fibres
(12) Fabrication methods	(a) powder metallurgy (b) internal oxidation (c) electrochemical (d) solidified from melt (e.g., Mo.TiC)	(a) powder metallurgy (b) infiltration (c) casting	(a) powder metallurgy (b) vacuum infiltration (c) solidified (fibres) from melt (d) electrochemical (e) filament winding, high-pressure molding
(13) Where used	(a) elevated-temperature strength and stability (b) elevated-temperature electrical and thermal conductivity	(a) electrical contacts (b) weights, counterbalances (c) spark-machining electrodes (d) structural parts (e) cutting tools and drilling bits (f) turbine blades (g) resistance-welding electrodes (h) dies and punches	(a) tailor-made properties and applications (b) highest strength: weight material (c) high strength: weight at elevated temperatures (d) matrix can be selected on basis of desired properties, i.e., oxidation resistance, chemical corrosion, hardness, ductility, etc., while fibres carry load (e) motor cases (f) boat hulls (g) helicopter blades (h) building materials

* Based on the assumption that dispersed articles and fibres are hard, chemically inert, and well bonded to matrix. Particles are coarser than those formed by precipitation, $d_p \approx 0.01\ \mu$, and all fibres are discontinuous and parallel to the direction of applied load.

† T.C.—temperature capacity $= T/T_m$, where $\sigma_c = 20{,}000$ psi at T.

is a slow or intermittent growth of subcritical flaws, followed by rapid growth and joining of critically-sized flaws. It is most important that there be continuous bonding of the matrix to the fibres, otherwise a set of built-in flaws is available to initiate cracks. In addition the fibres act as crack arresters.

Under compressive loadings the fibres can be considered as long slender columns supported by an elastic foundation. The contribution of the fibre can probably be neglected without serious error for small volumes of fibres as is the case for ferro-cement.

Ferro-cement

In summary, the following points can be made concerning ferro-cement as a composite material.

Typical ferro-cement designs involve between 2–10 per cent steel mesh by volume and the approximate ratio of the moduli of elasticity is $E_f/E_m = 10$.

Figures 6 and 7 indicate that the relatively low percentage of steel inhibits the full utilization of the material. The relatively weak brittle matrix is carrying approximately 50 per cent of the load before cracking.

For $\sigma_{mu} \sim 42.2$ kg/cm² and $\sigma_{mu} \sim 4220$ kg/cm² the critical volume of steel for continuous fibres would be 1 per cent. This is almost always exceeded; moreover, for the composite to be sufficiently strong as to be practical the critical volume must be greatly exceeded.

In general, fibre reinforced composites are not synergistic. Ferro-cement would appear to be no exception. In order to improve the strength properties there are two approaches. Either the volume of fibre is substantially increased by going to finer mesh systems or alternate reinforcements, or the properties of the basic mortar matrix is altered. In the second case it would be advantageous for the mortar to have a lower modulus of elasticity and a higher ultimate strength in tension than is presently available.

With all fibre reinforced composites the bond between the matrix and the reinforcement must be continuous. Otherwise, small cracks can initiate and grow under repeated loads into major failures. This is not quite so critical for ferro-cement as the fibres (steel) are not as likely to fail abruptly as might be the case in GRP. This statement may not be true as far as long-term corrosion might be a problem.

In most commercial composites a relatively brittle, high strength and high stiffness fibre is encased in a relatively ductile low strength and stiffness matrix. The failure mechanism consists of progressive failure of the fibres due to stress concentrations resulting from flaws until the matrix and the remaining fibres can no longer sustain the load. The failure occurs usually without warning and it is usually a destructive cleavage.

In ferro-cement the reverse would appear to be the case; a relatively high strength ductile fibre is encased in a low strength brittle matrix. Consequently failure will invariably initiate in the matrix. Providing sufficient steel is present to sustain useful loading, the cracking of the mortar provides the operator with a visual indication that repair or modification is necessary. A catastrophic failure is not as likely to occur. The one exception to this reported by Bezukladov et al. (1968) concerns instability under direct compression.

It can be shown by dimensional analysis that the fibres perform an important crack arrest function which can be stated as follows: For geometrically similar reinforcement arrangements the average tensile stress necessary to extend a crack beyond a fibre spacing varies inversely as the square root of that spacing. This result was stated by Irwin (private communication from J. A. Neal). In other words, the more finely dispersed the fibre for a given volume, the higher the stress necessary to propagate a crack.

There is sufficient experimental evidence to conclude that the volume percentage of steel and the specific surface area of steel in the mortar are important parameters in the characterization of ferro-cement.

Authors working with brittle fracture of fibre reinforced concrete have suggested that the resistance to first crack is proportional to $1/\sqrt{a}$, where a is the fibre spacing. The results of some experiments with the percentage volume of steel-fibre V_f as a variable have shown that the stress at first crack is insensitive to this parameter. These results corroborate the work of Shah and Bezukladov et al. in ferro-cement.

It is proposed that any definition of ferro-cement should include a statement of the following parameters.

Specific surface of reinforcement, K.

With reference to a square grid mesh, the specific surface of reinforcement K is defined as the total surface area of the wire in contact with the mortar, divided by the volume of the composite.

$$K = 2\frac{\pi\, d.n}{a.t}$$

where d = wire diameter
n = number of layers of mesh
a = wire spacing
t = specimen thickness.

This definition reflects the specific surface in both directions of the grid. Bezukladov et al. quote an equation $K \sim 5.65(d.n/a.t)$ without comment. It is noted that 5.65 is 10 per cent less than 2π, which suggests an empirical definition of an "effective" specific surface. This might reflect the use of woven wire mesh. Shah (1970) and Walkus and Kowalski (1971) define specific surface as the effective surface area of reinforcement in the loaded direction divided by the volume of the composite (i.e. $\pi(d.n/a.t) = \frac{1}{2}K$).

Reinforcement factor, V_f

Reinforcement factor V_f is defined as the cross-sectional area of the mesh reinforcement in the loaded direction divided by the cross-sectional area of the element.

$$V_f = \frac{\pi}{4}\left(\frac{d.n}{a.t}\right)d = 0.125K.d$$

The reinforcement factor is equivalent to the fractional volume of steel in ferro-cement in the loaded direction. Some authors describe the weight of reinforcement per unit volume. This is essentially the same parameter as the reinforcement factor and can be found by multiplying $2V_f$ times the weight density of steel. This definition could be somewhat more useful in assessing non-rectangular mesh configurations.

Although there is a unique mathematical relationship between K and V_f, they are quite different in their effect on the physical behaviour of ferro-cement. K would be a measure of the resistance to first crack while V_f is a direct measure of the ultimate strength of the material.

REINFORCEMENT CONFIGURATION SPECIFICATION

The mechanical behaviour of ferro-cement is highly dependent upon the type, quantity, orientation and strength properties of the mesh and rod. It is considered important that the reinforcement configuration be defined in detail. The results from the British Columbia Research Council, Greenius and Smith (1972), point to the influence of the reinforcement on the strength. For the reader's information, Figs. 7 and 8 are two examples of their results. Although qualitative, they give a clear example of the anisotropy of ferro-cement.

It is suggested that whenever test results are presented or whenever a design is specified the following parameters should be supplied:

Apparent tensile elastic modulus of the mesh and rod.

Apparent yield strength and ultimate strength of the mesh and rod.

Accurate rod spacing and location. (In a vessel or test panel which rods, if any, are transverse.)

How are the rods lapped and tied together?

Surface condition and/or preparation of the rod and mesh reinforcement.

Bond strength of the rod in the mortar by a standard test.

Specific surface K for the mesh at the outer layers.

Method of tying up mesh. Method of attaching adjacent strips and darts,

Thickness of the mortar cover on both sides of the reinforcement configuration.

Final thickness of the panel with a description of the surface waviness and roughness.

Reinforcement factor, V_f, for the section.

Geometrical description of the mesh and rods.

If any testing is done the layup of the ferro-cement test panels must realistically effect the proposed or actual layup in the hull. It should be noted that it is impossible to relate load-deformation information to stress-strain information without a complete description of the reinforcement configuration and its location within the ferro-cement.

DEFINITION OF FERRO-CEMENT

The definition of the mortar and the reinforcement configuration is relatively straightforward. To properly define the combination, in the opinion of the writer, can only be done at this time by test. The designer must test to verify as far as possible the potential of his design as well as to establish the safe working stresses for the design. The builder must test in order to provide quality assurance and in some instances regulatory bodies must test as an independent verification of the design and the construction. In order that the testing can be done in a

spirit of mutual enlightenment the preceding information must be available concerning the mortar and the reinforcement configuration. In addition, standard tests are required for the final product testing.

Problems in testing

The realistic testing of ferro-cement is an extremely difficult problem. The reasons for the difficulty can be summarized as follows:

The structure is basically loaded in two dimensions (shell structure); however, the simple tests are all uni-dimensional. Since ferro-cement is at least orthotropic, the interpretation of results is difficult.

In small vessels, the real service loads are not well defined so the question of which tests to conduct is raised. Clearly, it is not practical to cover all possibilities. Ultimately the designer would like to be able to predict performance by analysis using data obtained from a minimum of testing. The feedback of service experience is essential; however, there is little that is available. The only definitive report known to the author is a paper by Eyres.

An accepted definition of service failure is required for ferro-cement. Notwithstanding extravagant claims, the long-term durability of ferro-cement is not well known. In particular, the access of sea water to the reinforcement coupled with current leakage from the vessel's electrical system could conceivably disintegrate large portions of the hull reinforcement. Also, the ferro-cement could crack under load in service to the point where the bilge pumps might be overwhelmed and yet from a load-carrying point of view, the structure might still have reserve capacity. It would appear reasonable that the stress required to open a crack to a given size would be a most useful definition of failure. Walkus (1970) suggests that cracks of the order of 100 microns might be considered non-corrosive. Whatever the crack size chosen might be, it influences the type of testing required.

As mortar is an inherently flawed material, the test results will be dependent on specimen size; the larger the test piece, the lower the stress that can be expected at first crack.

The geometry of load application and the geometry of the specimen influence the mechanic properties. The author has seen numerous results described as pure bending test results where the failure initiated at the point of load application. The state of stress in this area is a combination of transverse shear and bending and consequently it is not clear as to the stress state which caused failure. Tension specimens are very difficult to grip so that failure doesn't initiate at the grip.

Much can be learned from other fibre composite technologies (Broutman and Krock, 1967), and the brittle material technology (Duke, 1971) as there are many similarities between ferro-cement and other composite materials. It is interesting to note that methods of test, quality control, statistical nature of results, among others, present common problems.

Specification of ferro-cement

Tentatively, with the present state of the art, a definition of ferro-cement would include, in addition to the mortar and reinforcement specifications:

The stress–strain–cracking behaviour in tension and pure bending to the ultimate strength of the composite. It is seldom sufficient to present the load–deformation characteristics.

The direct tensile stress and the pure bending composite tensile stress to produce a crack of a specified width. The author suggests that the standard crack width be tentatively set at 25 microns.

The stress–strain cracking behaviour of ferro-cement in transverse shear to structural failure.

The secant modulus of elasticity in tension and the reduced modulus of elasticity in tension and the reduced modulus of elasticity in pure bending to the stress which opened a crack of 25 microns at the steel. The values should be established on specimens which have been loaded, unloaded and then reloaded for the modulus test. As reported by Chiang and Thinivillakatt (1972) this modulus is lower in bending than the initial secant modulus.

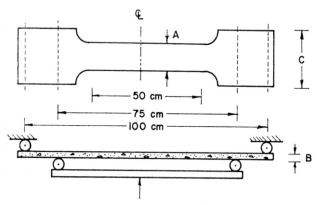

Fig. 11. Recommended type of bending specimen

LEGEND FOR BOTH FIGURES
A . . 3 longitudinal rod spacings
B . . Panel thickness to suit
C . . 6 rod spacings
D . . Sufficient length to develop
 the shear strength
E . . 6 transverse rod specimens

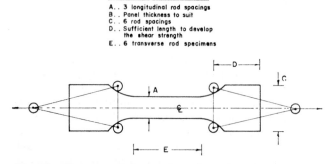

Fig. 12. Recommended type of tensile specimen

Complete details of the loading fixtures, location of initial failure and specimen geometry. The recommended pure bending specimen is shown in Fig. 11 and the recommended tensile specimen is shown in Fig. 12. It is appreciated that these specimens are more difficult to fabricate than rectangular sections cut from flat panels and might properly be considered as research specimens, but as stated previously, the author considers this material to be experimental insofar as design criteria are concerned. Correlation studies with rectangular panel

specimens could be most instructive. The bending panel dimensions are proportioned to increase the ratio of bending moment to shear force in the hope of initiating failure in the 50 cm region.

CONCLUSIONS

The foregoing thoughts on the definition of ferro-cement can be used to establish a rational definition of a marine quality ferro-cement. Such a definition would quantify the limits to be placed on many of the parameters. The author does not presume to place definitive limits on these as the material must be free to develop.

Although many parameters have been mentioned, it is expected that when sufficient experience has been gained with this material, its character will be satisfactorily judged on the basis of:

 specific surface of the mesh;
 reinforcement factor of the mesh and rod;
 ultimate compressive strength of the mortar at 28 days;
 precise geometrical description of the reinforcement configuration;
 composite stress and stiffness to first crack of a corrosive size in tension, shear and bending. In this connection, it is important to know accurately the mortar cover on the reinforcement and the surface condition of the specimens.

The writer thinks most of the remaining mechanical properties of the material will be inferred from the above list.

In order to gain the necessary experience, it is recommended that a comprehensive study of existing ferro-cement craft, layups, mixes, and known mechanical properties be undertaken by a responsible agency with a view to correlation of prediction techniques with known test results. The Industrial Development Branch of the Fisheries Service of Canada is proceeding in this direction in collaboration with the British Columbia Research Council and the author.

References

BEZUKLADOV, V F, *et al.* *Ship Hulls Made of Reinforced*
1968 *Concrete.* Navships Translations No. 1148. Washington, DC, USA: Scientific Documentation Division (205), US Department of the Navy, 229 pp.

BROUTMAN, L J and KROCK, R H *Modern Composite*
1967 *Materials.* London, England: Addison-Wesley, 581 pp.

CHIANG, F P and THIRUVILLAKATT, N *On Pure Bending of*
1972 *Ferro-Cement Beams.* Report 223. Stony Brook, NY, USA: Department of Mechanics, SUNY.

DUKES, W H *Handbook of Brittle Material Design Tech-*
1971 *nology.* AGARDograph No. 152.

EYRES, D J *Some notes on the survey of ferro-cement fishing*
1972 *vessels built in New Zealand. Report on the Second FAO/Swedish Training Centre on Small Fishing Boar Design and Construction, Seminar for Fisheries Officers, Working Papers and Discussion.* Rome, Italy: FAO/SWE/TF 84, Paper II/4.

GREENIUS, A W and SMITH, J D *Ferro-cement for Canadian*
1972 *Fishing Vessels*. Ottawa, Canada: Industrial Development Branch, Fisheries Service, Department of the
Environment, Project Report 98, vol. 2.
NEVILLE, A M *Properties of Concrete*. London, England:
1963 Pitman, 532 pp.
PHILLEO, R E *Cracking Phenomenon in Concrete*. IMCYC
1971 Int. Seminar, Mexico City, April.
SHAH, S P *Ferro-cement as a New Engineering Material*.
1970 Chicago Circle, USA: University of Illinois, Department of Materials Engineering, Report 70–11.

WALKUS, R State of cracking and elongation of ferro-cement
1970 under axial load (II). *Buletinul Institutului Politehnic*,
Iasi, vol. 16.
WALKUS, R and KOWALSKI, T G Ferro-cement: a survey.
1971 *Concrete*, February: 48–52.

Acknowledgements
The assistance of Cdr H A Shenker, RCN, Ret., Chief
of the Vessels and Engineering Division of the IDB is
acknowledged in the preparation of this paper.

Ferro-Cement—The Design of its Properties for Marine Usage   H M Moar

Ferro-cement has often been described as a "completely new material" possessing entirely different properties to those of reinforced concrete, from which it is derived. Investigators have sought to establish the inherent properties of this new material, but this cannot be done any more than it can be for reinforced concrete. Like concrete, its properties depend on those of mortar, reinforcement, the absolute dimensions of the member and the spatial arrangement of the reinforcement in the member. This paper discusses the problem of producing a composite material of mortar and steel reinforcement that will have predictable strength and durability characteristics.

DESIGNING FOR MANUFACTURE

This section emphasizes the need to remember the practical requirements of the manufacturer so far as they limit design. These requirements are material availability and ease of manufacture.

Materials

The worldwide requirement for sound durable concrete has made available to the ferro-cement user good quality ordinary Portland cement suitable in every way. There is no advantage in specifying any other type but care should be taken to purchase only good quality cement.

Sand is commonly available but it may be necessary to wash out impurities such as salt and silt, and to grade the sand by sieving. These precautions are more necessary for durability than for strength. The designer must therefore take the best commercial sand available, process it to the extent acceptable and then have it chemically checked for inertness.

Various additives have been recommended; three that give any real benefit are water-reducing agents, chromium trioxide and air entraining agents. Water-reducing agents may be employed if difficulty is experienced in making a workable mix having a minimum water : cement ratio of 0.4 by weight. A lower ratio than this is not recommended as it does not allow complete hydration of the cement (Powers, 1965). In warm climates the use of a combined retarder–water reducing agent may be neces-

sary to allow plastering to be completed. Chromium trioxide, or chromate (Hofsoy and Gukild, 1969), has a definite beneficial effect if the reinforcement is galvanized and if the locally available cement does not already have sufficient quantities of this compound.

Selection of reinforcing steel is again somewhat limited by availability. Practical requirements dictate a mesh that can be moulded in two directions, a property that welded mesh does not have, and it should consist of fairly high yield strength steel to enable a fair surface to be achieved without too much difficulty. Although hexagonal mesh does have excellent moulding properties it is too soft to maintain its shape between stations. Also it is difficult to lap without causing a high spot in the ferro-cement surface which increases total thickness. Woven mesh has advantages as it can be moulded easily and be made of high yield steel; however, under extreme loading conditions it tends to straighten out causing local spalling of the mortar. For the same reason, expanded metal meshing is entirely unsuitable. Ideally, therefore, a mesh for ferro-cement boat building should consist of straight high tensile wires, be able to be moulded in two directions, be able to be lapped within its own thickness and preferably be able to be galvanized. A mesh that meets these requirements has recently been developed in New Zealand. Until this becomes generally available, however, a suitable compromise is to use welded mesh on the flatter sections of the hull and to use hexagonal mesh on the areas where welded mesh cannot be moulded satisfactorily.

Manufacture

Other problems consist mainly of the need for a rigid structure that can support the weight of wet mortar to be applied. The number of layers of mesh that can be attached to this rigid structure is limited by the requirement of complete penetration of these mesh layers by the mortar. Allowance must also be made for the necessity to lap the mesh, or alternatively if it is butt jointed, the designer must recognize that strength at that point will be significantly affected. Mortar penetration is closely related to mortar mix but this has also to be related to the need for producing a mortar that has low shrinkage characteristics and high strength and durability. In practice, it has been found that a sand : cement ratio of about 2 combined with a water : cement ratio of a little more than 0.4 is a suitable compromise. Controlling the mix (once decided on) is something the designer should take an interest is, as most professional plasterers think in terms of workability only, gauge this by guess-work, and are therefore reluctant for any other mix to be imposed. Consistent and thorough mixing combined with careful curing is essential to produce a crack-free strong durable hull. Careful attention to mix and control should yield a mortar having a compressive strength on a 50 mm cube of approximately 60 N/mm² under labora-tory conditions. The designer has to assess how much of this strength is lost under production conditions where vibration, or the lack of it, and the problem of adequately curing large areas of thin ferro-cement will probably reduce this labortory result by at least 25 per cent.

DESIGNING FOR STRENGTH

Scrivener and Carr (1971) analysed two hulls and pro-duced values for bending, tension and compression that appear to agree with the strength requirements of hulls as determined by experience. Their analysis confirms what is guessed by intuition, that well-rounded hulls are imperative and that concave outward sections are highly stressed both in bending and in tension. Unfortunately it is difficult to arrive at quantitative values for stresses in small hulls subjected to service conditions because it is impossible to determine at all accurately just what conditions will be met with in service. Local areas of high impact caused by the slapping action of waves and the dropping of the hull off large waves have been known to cause hull failure and can only be allowed for by learning from experience. Another more common cause of damage, however, arises from impact against rocks, wharves and other boats. This damage can be avoided by careful handling and is usually very local, but it is the major problem encountered by ferro-cement craft in service and the designer has the task of maxi-mizing needed resistance.

Resistance to local impact

Experience in service is the only way to determine whether or not a given design will withstand the day-to-day knocks that come its way. For work boats and in particular, fishing boats it is simply a case of the stronger the better. Resistance to local impact damage improves with hull thickness and mortar strength and also depends on reinforcement type and quantity. Shear steel in the form of wires placed at an angle to the ferro-cement surface at close intervals would also be beneficial but is difficult to apply in practice. The mesh recently deve-loped in New Zealand also provides a solution.

With mortar strength and steel content already at a practical maximum, the only real variable left is hull thickness. This should be the maximum that weight restrictions allow and certainly not less than the minimum thicknesses established by experience. For work hulls this thickness is greater than that required for bending stresses (both primary and secondary).

Resistance to bending stresses

The analyses made by Scrivener and Carr make a significant contribution to understanding the distribution of stresses through a hull and also provide a quantitative answer to the question of "how strong", albeit for a somewhat theoretical loading situation. Further work in this direction would seem worth while, combined with evaluating more closely the loadings of small hulls in service.

It would also be interesting to know what the differ-ences in analyses would be if widely varying loading applications were assumed. Such analysis is valuable in that it can pinpoint areas of high stress and allow modifications to the lines of the hull if necessary. Another interesting outcome is the finding that maximum bending moment in the perpendicular direction is of the same magnitude as that in the longitudinal direction. This confirms the author's opinion that too many ferro-cement craft are being built with far too little transverse steel.

Analysis of bending strength

The application of ordinary reinforced concrete analysis techniques to ferro-cement sections is acceptable only where the reinforcement can clearly be classified as tension or compression steel. In practice this means thick (30 mm or greater) sections reinforced only by a thin layer of mesh placed adjacent to each surface. Distributing the mesh throughout the thickness of the section, or placing steel rods between the mesh layers makes the accurate application of reinforced concrete analysis techniques difficult or impossible and if approxi-mations are made the bending capacity of the section tends to be grossly underestimated.

The difficulty of applying these techniques lies in the fact that very often a reinforcing bar will straddle the neutral axis having part of its area in the compression zone and part in the tension zone. If the contribution this bar makes to the tensile reinforcement is neglected a conservative answer for the bending strength of the ferro-cement section is obtained. A method of analysis is therefore required that takes into account the steel reinforcing placed close to the neutral axis of the section. One such method recently proposed by the author has been found to predict the ultimate strength of ferro-cement sections to within 10 per cent of the tested result. This method can be termed "The equivalent steel girder analysis technique". It has so far been used only for predicting ultimate strengths but it is probable that it accurately predicts the behaviour of ferro-cement sections throughout the elastic range as well. It is essential in applying this or any other mathematical model to the analysis of ferro-cement that the principle on which the model is based be thoroughly understood and that a complete understanding of what is actually happening in the section is maintained throughout the analysis.

The equivalent steel girder analysis technique

This method consists of converting the ferro-cement section into an equivalent steel girder which is made up of all the steel reinforcement and in addition a com-pression flange consisting of all the ferro-cement in the compression zone. The effective width of the ferro-cement compression flange is, of course, the width of the section divided by the modular ratio of the steel to the mortar. Figure 1 illustrates a typical ferro-cement section and the equivalent steel girder derived from it. The two layers of steel mesh on each face have a combined area in the longitudinal direction of 18 mm². A steel : mortar modular ratio of 10 has been assumed. It is also assumed that the ferro-cement provides sufficient shear strength to connect all the elements of the girder into one.

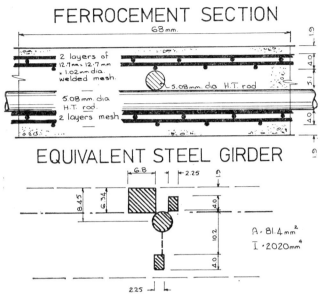

Fig. 1 The derivation of equivalent steel girder from typical ferro-cement section

The yield point of the mesh steel is approximately 510 MPa. This stress is reached at a bending moment of approximately 88 Nm. At this stage the stress distribution in the mortar is no longer triangular, but even if this were assumed to be the case the peak stress of 28 MPa is well below that at which failure would occur. The tested strength of this section was 95 Nm, approximately 8 per cent higher than that predicted by the theory. It is interesting that for this section the initial cause of failure is the yielding of the tension steel. In fact, for bending in the opposite direction, where the high tensile bar is more effective in tension, the same condition still applies, although yielding of the mesh is closely followed by compressive failure in the mortar, so that the high tensile rod is not able to develop anything like its potential strength. The method of analysis obviously needs some refining and testing to confirm its validity but it would appear to be the most promising method of approach to analysing ferro-cement sections so far proposed.

The yield strength of the mesh steel commonly used to date is lower than the stress which could be developed in it by the mortar at maximum compressive strain. The question arises as to whether very high yield strength steel mesh is of any value. The author considers that there is some reason to believe that the confinement placed on the mortar by the steel mesh might well enable the mortar and steel in the compressive zone to develop stresses higher than that which the mortar could sustain alone. By using meshes having a yield strength of the order of 1000 to 1500 MPa it may be possible to greatly improve the general properties of ferro-cement sections.

A testing programme to investigate this possibility is at present under way in New Zealand. At this stage there would appear to be an almost certain advantage in using steel which remains elastic until the maximum strain capable of being applied to the mortar has been achieved. If this is assumed to be 0.03, then a yield strength of 680 MPa is indicated.

Although the use of higher strength meshes is very desirable, the result will be the provision of a higher safety factor rather than a higher working load, as the maximum stresses under working load are governed by other considerations (see below, "Design Stresses"). The other major advantage gained is that when overload does occur (and it always will) then the cracks caused by the overload are more likely to close up again when the load is reduced.

Desirable features of a ferro-cement section

Both theory and experimentation demonstrate that maximum bending strength is obtained by placing as much reinforcement as possible adjacent to both faces of the section. Also the requirement that the strength be similar in the perpendicular direction indicates that this reinforcement should consist as much as is possible of mesh rather than bars. If the mesh is to be efficient as tension reinforcement then it should consist of straight wires and have a high yield strength. Bending strength also increases as the thickness of the section is increased. However, as this causes weight problems a good compromise is to use a light-weight material as a sandwich layer between the two outer skins of reinforcement.

One further desirable quality is that the light-weight material be able to contribute to the punching or shear strength of the ferro-cement section. There is, therefore, an ideal ferro-cement construction consisting of two skins of structural mesh reinforcement set in high strength mortar, separated by a layer of light-weight material incorporating chopped fibre of some description.

Although there is at least one manufacturer working in this direction it is unlikely that the great majority of boats will be built in any other way than that already in general use—at least for some time. Boats built by conventional methods should, however, be designed so that there is adequate strength in both directions. This means in practice that where longitudinal steel rods only are used, the mesh should be manufactured so that a greater proportion of the steel in the mesh can be placed in the transverse direction. Where rods are placed in both the longitudinal and transverse directions, then the layers of mesh should have a majority of steel orientated perpendicular to the direction of the immediately adjacent rods: i.e. perpendicular rods should be covered with mesh having a majority of its steel orientated horizontally and *vice-versa*. Chicken mesh is one type of mesh possessing this property. The transverse strength of this type of mesh varies from 40 per cent to 70 per cent of its longitudinal strength and it should therefore be laid up perpendicular to the immediately underlying steel rods. Although the 0.71 mm gauge often used is too light for sound construction, the 1.02 mm gauge which is also readily available is quite satisfactory. Another mesh that can be manufactured with a higher longitudinal strength than transverse strength is the mesh recently developed in New Zealand and this has the added advantage that it is much more efficient structurally, consisting of straight wires and high yield steel.

Design stresses

The common practice of approximating ferro-cement to a homogeneous perfectly elastic material, assuming high values for the apparent modulus of rupture and then taking a proportion of this value as being an acceptable working stress for bending or direct tension is dangerous. Not only is the designer assuming that the modulus of rupture is not greatly affected by steel distribution, but also some of the modulus of rupture values claimed obviously are derived from the bending moment at which yield has occurred in the tension steel rather than the moment causing cracking of the mortar.

In the author's opinion the only acceptable method of determining safe working stresses is to relate these to acceptable crack widths. This is the philosophy that operates in both reinforced and pre-stressed concrete design and it is fully applicable to ferro-cement construction. The determination of what is an acceptable crack width for ferro-cement in a marine environment and a simple method of relating this to design still has to be determined. However, the equivalent steel girder method of analysis does allow the stress in the layer of mesh adjacent to the tension face to be determined and it is probable that sufficient control on crack width could be made by limiting this stress to a value dependent only on the mesh wire diameter and the mesh type. The bending moment producing this stress should then be checked against ultimate capacity to ensure that there is an adequate safety factor. There has already been some valuable work done by S. P. Shah which relates to this problem.

DESIGNING FOR DURABILITY

Durability is the final aspect to consider in design but is, of course, no less important than manufacture or strength requirements. The durability of a hull is affected by at least seven factors.

Mortar mix: The requirements of a durable mortar have already been discussed. They can be summarized as being low water : cement ratio, thorough mixing and curing, constituents free of deleterious chemicals.

Mortar penetration: It is essential that adequate vibration be applied while plastering, or air bubbles will result, leaving room for moisture to cause eventual rusting of the reinforcement.

Cover: Rusting will occur on the wire adjacent to the surface unless adequate cover is provided. Unfortunately, plasterers have only the mesh to guide them and some patches of inadequate cover are unavoidable. The outer layer of wire should therefore be either galvanized or be of stainless steel. Caution should be taken in using unprotected steel.

Where galvanizing is used, chromium trioxide should also be mixed with the mortar to avoid a reaction which produces poor bond and many gas bubbles in the final matrix.

Applied coatings: The use of a suitable protective priming paint is almost essential in practice to give adequate protection to the steel and provide a base for anti-fouling or finishing coats.

Electrolysis: This is the main cause of apparent rusting occurring in hulls. It is caused by faulty earthing of engines and equipment or by stray electrical currents under the water. Contact between fittings bolted to the hull and the hull reinforcement must be avoided.

Diesel oil: Diesel oil has disastrous effects on ferro-cement. Ferro-cement tanks, whether coated or not, should not be used to hold diesel oil, and the area around the engine should be protectively coated so that diesel spillage is not soaked up by the ferro-cement.

Fire: Ferro-cement is very fire resistant. Tests made by the Auckland University have shown, however, that oxidization of the galvanizing does create spalling of the mortar. Again, the use of chromium trioxide does reduce this effect. Adequate cover over the steel is also beneficial.

FUTURE DEVELOPMENTS

Serious work needs to be done, in particular on improving punching strength. This could appear to necessitate the combination of ferro-cement with other materials.

Two possibilities are: (a) the use of fibres in the mortar or (b) the application of outer skins of fibre glass.

Other areas where work is needed have already been pinpointed in the paper, e.g. crack width control and sandwich construction.

CONCLUSIONS

The principles of ferro-cement design and construction are now sufficiently understood and tested in practice for the designer to have full confidence in the material and to be able to design hulls that will perform well in service. However, there is tremendous scope for improvement both in the understanding of the behaviour of ferro-cement and also in the material itself. Research programmes having these aims should also be linked with an investigation into the strength requirements of hulls in service conditions. Although there is room for sophisticated work to determine impact loading and hull stresses of boats at sea, a major problem is that of damage caused by impact with sharp objects. This would appear to be a problem of statistics as there is no way for a designer to predict the magnitude of this type of loading or to ensure that the hull is sufficiently strong to cope with it if it were known. A programme to collect data on impact damage of hulls in service and relate this to hull strengths, with the object of being able to place statistical estimates on the probability that a certain hull operated under certain conditions would suffer damage, would assist in designing to an acceptable risk level.

References

HOFSOY, A and GUKILD, I Bond studies on hot dip galvanized
1969   reinforcement in concrete. *ACI Journal*, Proc. V66 (17), March, 174–184.
POWERS, T C The mechanisms of shrinkage and reversible
1965   creep of hardened cement paste. *International Conference on the Structure of Concrete.*
SCRIVENER, J C and CARR, A J An analysis of ferro-cement
1971   boat hulls. *IASS Pacific Symposium on Hydro-mechanically Loaded Shells—Part 1.* Honolulu, Hawaii, USA, October 10–15, Paper No. 3–7, 15 pp.

Discussion on the Material Properties of Ferro-Cement

Pama (Rapporteur) said that most authors treated ferro-cement as a composite material with its properties varying at different stages of loading.

Several authors had analysed ferro-cement as a composite material with cement mortar as the matrix and wire mesh as the fibres. Shah and Srinivasan, Lee, Raisinghani and Pama, and Bigg all advocated the use of the law of mixture of composite material in analysing the behaviour of ferro-cement at various stages of loading.

In these papers, the material, with non-linear load deflection curve, was idealized as a tri-linear material. The non-linear load deflection curve was replaced by three straight lines for convenience in the analysis. In the uncracked range, the strength and modulus of elasticity of the composite were determined from the properties of the constituent materials and their respective volume fractions by the laws of mixture. The same was done in the cracked range, except that the contribution of the mortar was neglected as it was assumed to have cracked. It was in the determination of the ultimate strength of ferro-cement in bending (crack widening range or yield range) that the authors had differed. Shah and Srinivasan quoted a formula for the ultimate bending moment of the material (due to Trancrete and Hayes) as:

$$M_{ult} = \frac{\text{(Tensile strength of mesh) (Moment of inertia of wire mesh)}}{\text{Half the depth of the beam}}.$$

This formula was derived from the assumption of a classical homogeneous elastic beam.

The second method was to use the equivalent steel-girder approach as advocated by Moar. The concrete and the steel in the compression side were considered as the compression flange of the equivalent girder and the wire mesh in the tension side as the tension steel. The method apparently gave fairly accurate results.

The third approach, that of Lee, Raisinghani and Pama, was based on equilibrium and stress-strain law of the material. This assumes that the concrete carries the compressive stresses and the steel carries all the tensile stresses, the two creating forces which are in equilibrium. The couple formed is termed the ultimate moment of resistance of the section. For behaviour in axial compression, flexure, shear and tension, the composite material approach appears adequate. However, in practice, the vessel acts as a shell structure and the state of stress of an element is far more complex. Obviously there is a need to know more about the Poisson's ratio of ferro-cement but nobody seems to have discussed this particular mechanical property at length.

The other property of ferro-cement, not adequately covered in the papers was that due to impact. Pedersen had described an interesting investigation on the impact strength of ferro-cement compared with glassfibre-reinforced polyester and plywood. He had some interesting curves which compared these different panels on the basis of cost, strength and weight. More work, both experimental and theoretical, needed to be done on this.

The intensity and distribution of cracking in bending was described by **Buchner**. He concluded that the most effective control of cracking was obtained where a multitude of fine cracks spread uniformly over the surface rather than where a limited number of large cracks developed at irregular spacing, exposing the reinforcement to possible corrosion under working conditions.

Kowalski and **Walkus** dealt with concrete technology in the quality control of ferro-cement vessels. They questioned the validity of using the conventional standard control test specimens since ferro-cement is a very thin material. They suggested that perhaps smaller and different standard specimens should also be used for evaluating the properties of mortar and ferro-cement.

The determination of the material properties to meet the requirements of marine usage was summarized by Moar from the viewpoint of manufacturer, designer and user. He concluded there was still a lot to be learned about such properties, perhaps in combination with other materials.

Ellen dealt with the practical design of ferro-cement as a reinforced or as a post-tensioned section, with formulae for determining the ultimate strength by treating it as a reinforced concrete member. He had extended his method to cover post-tensioned ferro-cement sections. Two basic methods of applying the post-tension were described. It was claimed that, at working load, strength is greater and weight reduced by some 40 per cent as compared with an equivalent section conventionally reinforced.

It appeared that there was no established definition of ferro-cement on which all design data, construction methods, and evaluations of material properties could be based. **Bigg** argued that it is not adequate to define ferro-cement in terms of mortar and steel only. A definition must include the other constituent materials in the mortar and the physical and chemical properties of the steel. This lack of a standard definition was confusing and standard terms must be adopted, preferably with a specification of the design, analysis and construction of ferro-cement bodies.

TESTING OF FERRO-CEMENT AS A MEANS OF ANALYSING BEHAVIOUR

Pama (Thailand) said that in the Asian Institute of Technology ferro-cement was tested as a panel supported at three corners and depressed at the other to get the torsional properties of the two-dimensional element. Relevant to this testing were the standard specimens used in evaluating the properties of the mortar, and he asked whether these should be the same size as the specimens used for testing concrete.

Moar (New Zealand) stated that his company used a 50×50 mm (2×2 in) cube because with a 150×150 mm (6×6 in) or 300×150 mm (12×6 in) cylinder there is a danger of internal cracking of the specimen, due to shrinkage in curing, producing incorrect test results. Even the 50×50 mm (2×2 in) cube is not entirely satisfactory, and something in between, such as a 150×75 mm (6×3 in) cylinder might be more suitable.

Pama (Thailand) remarked that in Eastern European countries a small beam specimen $160 \times 40 \times 40$ mm ($6.3 \times 1.6 \times 1.6$ in) is used both for tension and compression tests.

Bigg (Canada) and **Buchner** (Australia) proposed the American Society for Testing and Materials (ASTM) standard on mortar testing as the most suitable. One of the tests also involved the use of a small beam specimen which was first used to give a measure of the tensile strength of the material. The ends were then cut and used to determine the compressive strength.

Bigg (Canada) remarked that a number of different tensile tests for mortar could be used, all of them giving different results in terms of the actual tensile strength. A standard test for all researchers was needed so that results could be compared, one mortar against another. He also considered that although many authors found that they could predict the ultimate strength of ferro-cement accurately with reinforced concrete results, what should be determined was the service failure—that is in durability, corrosion and the ability of the material to recoup initial damage. For example, an impact load in a vessel might cause initial cracking but the boat could reach home port with the leaks handled adequately by the bilge pumps. In such a case by how much had the life of the vessel been reduced because of subsequent corrosion by sea water? While several papers discussed cracks and cracking control, none seemed to consider crack width. How much water should to be allowed to get to the reinforcement before a crack must be repaired? The British Columbia Research Council was undertaking a preliminary investigation along these lines in Canada. The proposal was to consider cracks of known widths, expose them to a corrosive environment and mechanically test them at a later date to see if, compared to control specimens, there had been a loss of strength. Ferro-cement was probably completely anisotropic, which meant it could not be defined in terms of one elastic constant. The problem was the conflict between the researcher and the builder. The builder wanted to build his vessel with a minimum of testing, the researcher wanted to understand the material. Perhaps something could be learned from testing of glass-reinforced plastics, steel and wooden construction. Was two-dimensional testing carried out on these materials and was it necessary to do so with ferro-cement?

MORTAR COVER, CRACKING AND CRACK WIDTH

The question of cover reinforcement and its relation to corrosion and cracking was raised by **Buchner** (Australia), who suggested that a clear distinction should be made between reinforced concrete and ferro-cement, a crack in reinforced concrete being considered as a different problem from a crack in ferro-cement, particularly in vessels with thin sections subjected to marine environments.

Moar (New Zealand) considered that ferro-cement was still concrete even though a special form, and should be considered as an extreme case of reinforced concrete with reinforcement of a small diameter very close to the surface. Cracking in this case related to the size of the reinforcement as well as to its distance from the surface, crack control resulting from small wires close to the surface. It was also pointed out that microscopic hairline cracks were still present and often followed the pattern of the outside layers of mesh, sometimes being revealed when the hull is dampened. Bezukladov *et al.* had shown that stress and strain at first crack increased with increasing specific surface.

Several participants observed that increased crack width was apparent when cement cover was thick and without the necessary reinforcement close to the surface.

Bigg (Canada) made the point that two problems were intermixed in the discussion: one, the question of permeability of the mortar, i.e. how much cover was needed to protect the reinforcement, and two, how wide a crack could be tolerated. He suggested the permissible crack width should be related to width of crack at the reinforcement and not at the surface.

Some discussion took place concerning paint films and whether they could be considered sufficiently extendable to keep flexural cracks covered.

Hunt (New Zealand) pointed out that an average paint film was only 0.04 mm ($1\frac{1}{2}$ thousandths of an inch) thick, so that even with up to six coats of paint, if a fine crack opened to twice its original width, the paint film would need to expand 100 per cent to keep the crack covered. Kowalski and Walkus in their paper suggested that cracking, when an adequately protective hull paint had been used, should not exceed 50 microns (0.05 mm).

Gulbrandsen (FAO) asked whether this could be considered as a definitive standard to be adhered to and, if not, could research be conducted into corrosion of reinforcement at different crack widths so that a safe standard definition could be arrived at.

CEMENT QUALITY AND ITS TESTING

A request was made as to how one could define a good cement suitable for ferro-cement construction.

Moar (New Zealand) indicated that world standards had been set up by both ASTM and British Standards (BSS), and laboratories throughout the world could test these standards. Two participants cited experience of cement in certain countries where the test results quoted were either incorrect or did not indicate the true nature of the cement, and in one case the ingredients did not conform to standard specifications for Portland cement.

Bigg (Canada) suggested that cement quality could be established by monitoring the compressive strength of a standard mortar sample over 3, 7, 14 and 28 days. From these results many characteristics of the chemical components as well as predictions as to durability and a number of other mechanical properties could be inferred.

Hall (New Zealand) referred to the New Zealand Portland Cement Association and similar associations in other parts of the world whose objectives were to improve and extend the use of cement and concrete, and suggested that such associations could be asked to do research and/or correlate some of the research going on in the world.

Carkeek (New Zealand) mentioned two companies in New Zealand making prepackaged standard mortar suitable for ferro-cement construction. The mixes had suitable additives included and assured accurate batching throughout the plastering stage.

A number of countries were now preparing such prepackaged mortars, and it would be well worth making inquiries for suitable suppliers before begining construction. Reference was also made to various light-weight mortars which appeared to be polymers of some form, and mortars with additions of chopped glass fibre. Various advantages are claimed for these types of mortars and when suitable test data are available they should prove to be useful tools for ferro-cement designers and builders.

CEMENT IN REACTION WITH GALVANIZED MESH AND BLACK-STEEL REINFORCING BARS

Buchner (Australia) observed that most commercially available meshes are galvanized and under certain circumstances some cements will react with the galvanizing to form hydrogen bubbles on the surface of the mesh.

Bowen (New Zealand) commented that weathered (i.e. oxidized) mesh seemed to prevent or cut down hydrogen bubble formation.

Hall (New Zealand) stated that the reaction between cement pastes and zinc or zinc-coated products had long been known and the by-product of this reaction, calcium zincate, did not appear to affect the strength of concrete or plaster.

Hunt (New Zealand), considering the phenomena from a chemist's point of view, thought that the alkaline condition in the cement caused the reaction and the formation of hydrogen bubbles, while with the oxidized (weathered) mesh the result would be the formation of water as a by-product, instead of hydrogen.

Christensen and Williamson (1970) considered that the reaction was an electro-chemical one due to action between two dissimilar metals (the zinc of the galvanized mesh and the iron in the ungalvanized steel reinforcement) in the presence of an electrolyte in the form of the Portland cement mortar. Electron current flowed from the zinc anode to the iron cathode with the electrolyte completing the circuit. Although the galvanic cell action is present in cured mortar, it was not thought to cause so much of a problem in this case because very low electron currents are present. When the mortar is fresh, however, a large electron current is thought to flow from the zinc anode to the iron cathode where hydrogen ions acquire electrons and form hydrogen atoms which are liberated as hydrogen gas. This creates gas-filled voids along the surface of the steel bars. Test samples had been cut open to expose the reinforcing and the surface of the mortar in contact with the bars was seen to be highly pitted. The result could be poor mortar-to-bar bond strength (both chemical and mechanical), high corrosion caused by the continuous void along the bars and possible hydrogen embrittlement of the steel. The reaction could be prevented by eliminating or insulating the dissimilar metals or by chemically inhibiting the galvanic cell action. Chromium ions in solution had been used as a means of inhibiting zinc and reducing the galvanic cell action. Chromium trioxide (CrO_3) added in diluted concentrations of 100–300 ppm by weight to the mix water proved effective. Void-free bonds were found in test specimens treated with CrO_3 and both the apparent modulus and the ultimate strength were increased. It should be noted that chromium trioxide is highly corrosive and care should be taken to protect skin and eyes.

SAND AND SAND GRADING

MacDonald (New Zealand) remarked that the grading curve given in Buchner's paper was much finer in sand range than the one he was using, but both agreed that the spreading of the grading was beneficial for mortar strength. In response to a question on whether only sharp or peddle structure sand could be used, he felt that the mineral content of the sand was as important as the grading. Crushed basalt and crushed granite were being used successfully in some countries and he had similar results with a blend of sharp and relatively rounded sand.

Hall (New Zealand) considered that in ordinary concrete work with a smooth type of pebble structure, as compared with crushed material, the equivalent strength could be obtained with 5 per cent less cement. A sand graded to NZ Standard Specification 2129 when used with a 4:1 mix gave a strength equal to that obtained with 3:1 mix of river sand, which clearly showed the advantage of using a graded material.

Mounsey (Australia) asked whether, in view of the availability in many developing countries of beach or coral sand, it was practicable to wash such sand to remove salt and use it without detrimental effect.

Richardson (New Zealand) had built ferro-cement barges in Tonga using imported silica sand but had also made some field tests which suggested that the coral sand might have less strength.

Perry (Australia) mentioned tests carried out in England by the Cement and Concrete Association on aggregates containing shell. Results showed that quite high percentages of shell could be used without detrimental effect on the strength characteristics of the concrete.

Wells (New Guinea) pointed out that tropical beach sand would be mainly crushed coral which is softer than shell and results obtained with shell might not be applicable to crushed coral.

It appeared to be generally agreed that a graded sand mix conforming to a standard specification of one of the testing societies, BSS, ASTM, etc., would give better strength than an ungraded river sand. However, provided the ungraded sand was free from dirt and clay with all particles passing a 4.75 mm ($\frac{3}{16}$ in) standard sieve with not more than 5–10 per cent passing BS sieve No. 100, 0.15 mm (0.006in) square opening, with an even distribution of intermediate sizes, the grading should be satisfactory for ferro-cement construction. The mineral content of the sand was also important, hard silica, or rock particles being most suitable. Care should be taken in the selection of soft sands, such as coral, as they could be affected by abrasion and chemical reaction.

ADDITIVES USED IN THE MORTAR MIX

Hall (New Zealand), in a discussion of mortar properties, remarked that the free lime generated in any concrete product was a normal part of the hardening process, the amount of free lime in the mix being determined largely by the water:cement ratio, requiring only a 0.22 ratio for complete hydration of the cement. When excess water drained off, channels were formed and as this water flowed through the plaster it brought out the free lime, giving access to any damaging chemicals which could enter by way of the channels. To reduce these, a low water:cement ratio was necessary and this would also reduce the amount of free lime. He considered the addition of pozzolan, which combined with the free lime to form a cementitious product, essential to eliminate free lime which could be acted on by chemicals such as are found in sea water.

Moar (New Zealand) agreed that the water:cement ratio was an important factor, but questioned the figure of 0.22 that was given, and considered that something nearer 0.40 was required for complete hydration.

Buchner (Australia) quoted Neville, A. M. *Properties of Concrete* as giving a figure of 0.38 as the ratio for complete hydration.

Walker (Australia) used a diatomite pozzolan and noted that in the original recommendations from 10 to 30 per cent of pozzolan had been proposed, but now 10 to 12 per cent was recommended in the literature.

MacDonald (New Zealand) also used a pozzolanic additive at 10 per cent of cement weight and considered it necessary to combat attack by salt water.

Janes (Australia) asked if there was a danger that too much of an additive could be used and if optimum amounts should be specified.

Eyres (New Zealand) quoted J R Benford (1970) as stating that, beyond a certain percentage, the addition of pozzolan led to a reduction in strength.

Donovan (New Zealand) asked for comment on the use and suitability of fly ash as a pozzolanic additive to mortars.

Fyson (FAO) remarked that fly ash, as residue from the combustion of coal in power plants, could vary quite widely in composition and noted that tests in Thailand, carried out on panels using a locally available fly ash as a pozzolanic additive, had shown a considerable reduction in strength due to the high sulphur content of the fly ash used.

Kanakasabathy (India) had obtained better test results with a pozzolanic additive made from a local clay material called suki than from fly ash, and **MacDonald** (New Zealand) said that fly ash was more used in New Zealand for reducing the heat of hydration in large construction works than in the finer mortars for ferro-cement.

Perry (Australia) stated that the suitability of fly ash for use in concrete varied with the type of coal used in the furnace. ASTM had published a specification for the quality of fly ash suitable for use in conjunction with cement. The fineness of the ash also had an appreciable bearing on its suitability for use in concrete.

Fyson (FAO) noted that a number of authorities considered that, provided the water:cement ratio was kept low enough to ensure a dense impermeable mix, the use of a pozzolan was not necessary, and therefore perhaps it would be of more interest to look at other additives which could permit low water:cement ratio without loss of workability and still ensure penetration of the mesh. Two such proprietary water-reducing additives had been tested in Thailand. The one chosen for best strength results was based on a sodium salt of lignosulphonic acid used as a cement-dispersing agent which was added in the mix water. Test panels using wetting and dispersing additives of this type gave consistently better results than panels of plain mortar, largely because the water content in the latter had to be higher to achieve satisfactory penetration. In countries with high ambient temperatures it could also be advantageous to use a retarding agent to give more time for the placing and finishing of the mortar before the initial set. The makers of a proprietary retarding agent he had used recommended an increase in the proportion of retarder for every 5°C (10°F) over 21°C (70°F) ambient temperature.

Bowen (New Zealand) mentioned an American company which had been using a polymer additive to the mix water for which they claimed superior weathering properties with high resistance to corrosion.

Behnke (USA) confirmed that he had found that panels that were made with such additives provided significantly improved test results. He is currently using polymer additives in his ferro-cement hulls. Behnke also cited a paper (RC–43, Nov. 1967) by Rohn & Hass Company of Philadelphia, Pennsylvania, USA, that showed the improved abrasion resistance and superior tensile, compressive, flexural and impact strengths of cement samples that resulted from using polymer additives.

Bigg (Canada) commented that, when using polymers, a certain amount of porosity within the mortar matrix was desirable so that the polymer could find its way into the material, hence a higher water:cement ratio could be used than would normally be acceptable for ferro-cement and still obtain higher strength and durability.

Hall (New Zealand) mentioned that he had experience with the use of a polyvinyl acetate (PVA) additive in hard-wearing concrete floors in industry and considered its use most advantageous for this purpose.

Hunt (New Zealand) considered that additives contained chemicals which could be deleterious in too large amounts and conceivably uncontrolled use of an additive could change the nature of the mortar quite critically. PVA, for example, was such a general term. Chemicals that had been added to stabilize the PVA could be quite a critical factor in the final curing and properties of the mortar.

REINFORCEMENT

Several participants requested opinions on the relative merits of woven, hexagonal and square welded mesh.

Walker (Australia) stated that both hexagonal mesh (chicken wire) and square welded mesh were used by his company. On small light-weight hulls, 6 to 9 mm ($\frac{1}{4}$ to $\frac{3}{8}$ in) thick, the wire was stretch-formed over a male mould, and for this, heavy gauge hexagonal mesh was used. In larger boats with skeletal steel made up of rods, 1.4 mm (17–gauge) square welded mesh was found to give a more rigid armature.

Moar (New Zealand) described the punching tests performed by his company in which by pressing a solid steel cylinder through a slab of ferro-cement they achieved results which seemed to coincide closely with those of an impact test, the type of mesh making very little difference to the punching strength. Of more importance was the quantity of mesh in the slab, particularly on the opposite face. Other factors of importance were the thickness of the panel and the compression strength of the mortar.

Donovan (New Zealand) considered that the amount of steel in the mesh reinforcement had a greater relationship to the impact resistance than the type of mesh used. The thicker and heavier the mesh, the greater its resistance to punching.

Moar (New Zealand) described a sample of a mesh specially fabricated for ferro-cement construction. This mesh consisted of a transverse layer of 1·6 mm (16–gauge) wire at 13 mm ($\frac{1}{2}$ in) centres with 1.2 mm (18–gauge) longitudinal wires at 6 mm ($\frac{1}{4}$ in) centres on either side of it. The wires were not woven or welded in any way but held together by a series of zig-zag 0.9 mm (20–gauge) wires running transversely at 13 mm ($\frac{1}{2}$ in) centres located between the 1.6 mm (16–gauge) wires. The distribution of steel was equal in both directions, no account being taken of the zig-zag wires in the strength calculation as this wire tended to straighten out under heavy loads. This was one of the problems with hexagonal and woven mesh, as they also tended to straighten out under heavy loads and cause spalling of the mortar.

The advantages of this mesh were first of all that it had straight wire equally distributed in both directions; secondly it could be moulded around a compound curve whereas welded mesh cannot be bent in a two-dimensional curve. It could be galvanized or left bare as there were no working or welding problems which dictated either. The straight wires could also be of high-tensile steel if required. In the sample shown, the zig-zag 0.9 mm (20–gauge) wires were galvanized as they were near the surface; the inner heavier gauge wires were left bare as there should always be a proper mortar cover over them. Due to the weight of steel in the fabric, one layer was equivalent to 8 layers of light-gauge hexagonal mesh or about 2½ layers of 1·2 mm (18–gauge) square welded mesh. With a frame work of skeletal steel, one layer on each side was considered sufficient. Because all the steel put into the boat was compressed into this thickness, which is roughly 6 mm (¼ in) all the steel could be close to the surface of the ferro-cement skin giving greater bending efficiency.

Reid (New Zealand) gave further information on the commercial uses of this mesh in which he estimated the cost of mesh for a 12.20 m (40 ft) boat as NZ $640 for 1.2 mm (18–gauge) square welded mesh, 4 layers on the outside and 3 layers inside. The cost of each layer of the new mesh would be approximately NZ $150. In the first commercially constructed boat being built by his company, two layers of this mesh plus some light hexagonal mesh and some very finely woven mesh were being used with an overall saving in material and a considerable saving in labour. A machine had been developed to make the mesh in 0.90 m (3 ft) strips to any required length.

Buchner (Australia) asked about possible problems of lapping three widths of this mesh to transfer the tensile stresses and also whether it was possible to form the mesh around sharp corners or tight bends.

Moar (New Zealand) commented on the jointing of the mesh, noting that the transverse 1.6 mm (16–gauge) wires in the sheet were looped at each end, the loops being 20 mm (3/4 in) protrusions from the mesh. By butt jointing the first longitudinal wires of each sheet, there was a 3.75 cm (1½ in) lap of these transverse loops, which gave the full strength of the transverse wires. Tension tests with strips of ferro-cement containing this mesh and incorporating a joint of this type had given the same tensile test strength as a strip without joint.

Reid (New Zealand) noted that formation of full-strength butt joints was easy in test panels but in practice on a curved hull this became more difficult and there was a problem in handling the laps and keeping the thickness down. The ideal would be when a sheet of mesh could be woven wide enough to completely cover the side of a boat and this was apparently a feasible possibility.

Wheeler (New Zealand) said that there had been problems in bending this mesh around the stem and stern area because of its rigidity, but because of its nature it proved possible to hammer the mesh around the stem and force it in the desired direction to run fore and aft finishing at the sheer line. The result was better forming than with welded mesh.

Several questions about this mesh were asked concerning specific surface of reinfrocement and impact resistance in comparison to other meshes.

Moar and **Reid** in replying agreed that specific surface was reduced due to the heavier gauge wire used, but pointed out that the mesh could be varied to suit any particular requirement, and there was no limitation on materials, gauge sizes or wire spacings. With regard to impact, punching tests are mostly affected by the thickness and strength of the mortar; the steel on the tension face did assist punching strength in the same way as tension steel in a beam is of some assistance to the shear strength, but this was not the primary advantage. They had hoped that the zig-zag steel wires would produce some shear steel reinforcing for ferro-cement but tests showed only a small improvement of some 10 to 20 per cent over welded or woven mesh.

Hagenbach (UK) referred to the use of randomly orientated wires in the mortar mix, known under the trade name of Wirerand. This consisted of very small metal fibres which could be produced in any dimension and gauge required.

These wires could be introduced into the mix in various ways, mechanically or even through the nozzle in the gunite process. His company had been experimenting with its use in flat-sided panels for storage boxes and tanks.

Bowen (New Zealand) mentioned a recent US patent dealing with the use of loops instead of randomly oriented wires in the mix and possible advantages due to interlocking between loops.

Romualdi (USA) emphasized that in his original paper on the subject of wire fibre additives for crack arrest, he had been concerned with first crack strength and not the ultimate of the composite. Historically, there had been attempts to put loops of various types into mortar but problems could arise with handling. Straight wires do not interlock and do not therefore tend to knot together in the mixing process. If the wire was not straight it tended to straighten out and not develop the punching forces necessary to arrest the cracks.

DEFINITION OF FERRO-CEMENT

It was suggested that, due to the lack of a standard definition for ferro-cement, considerable confusion existed, particularly in the reporting of information. It was proposed that an attempt be made to isolate parameters controlling the behaviour of the material.

Janes (Australia) suggested that account be taken of one feature unique to ferro-cement: that the reinforcement averages about 385 kg/m³ (24 1b/ft³) of material.

Bigg (Canada) proposed that a clear distinction be made between the characteristics of mesh and rod reinforcement, the surface area in contact with the mortar and the actual volume or weight of steel in the configuration. From the literature and research it was clear that cracking behaviour was controlled largely by the surface in contact with the mortar and the ultimate strength of the material was a function of the number of kilogrammes (pounds) of reinforcement per cubic metre (cubic foot). Any definition concerning a ferro-cement lay up should go considerably further than just a statement of volume percentage. It should also include wire spacing and the geometry and surface area of reinforcement in contact with the mortar. It was felt that a qualitative definition was appropriate because, with so many different constructional combinations possible, a quantitative definition covering them all would be difficult if not impossible to achieve. All types of ferro-cement construction, e.g. skeletal steel, sandwich method and others, should receive a reasonable hearing and the suggestion was made that the material which is called ferro-cement is characterized by mesh and mesh alone.

There was considerable discussion on how to present the basic parameters; the specific surface area of reinforcement, volume fraction of reinforcement, surface cover, etc. Definitions were proposed for parameters that are not as yet standardized within the industry; specific surface area, for example, to mean the surface area of mesh divided by the volume of the mesh rather than the more common volume of the composite, thus avoiding the problem of including the surface area of sandwich materials or the volume contained by skeletal steel or sandwich materials. The volume fraction was defined to be the ratio of the volume of wire mesh to the volume of the composite and a direction was specified because of the usefulness of the volume fraction in estimating ultimate loads in which it was necessary to specify the direction of the load. The definition, as finally agreed, was as follows:

Introduction

With the many configurations of steel reinforcement and mortar possible in ferro-cement structure, it is difficult to define properly the material to suit the classifier, researcher, builder and user. To define the material too quantitatively is restrictive. On the other hand, to define the material too qualitatively is uninformative. Accordingly, it was decided that an essentially qualitative definition was appropriate, with minimum values assigned to basic parameters.

Ferro-cement

Ferro-cement is a composite material which consists of a matrix from hydraulic cement mortar with layers of continuous steel-mesh reinforcement distributed through the matrix. The basic parameters which characterize ferro-cement are: the specific surface area of reinforcement, the volume fraction of reinforcement, the surface cover of mortar over the reinforcement and the relatively high quality of the mortar.

Mortar

Mortar shall mean a mixture of hydraulic cement, sand and water, with or without appropriate admixtures. The components are to be proportioned and of a quality consistent with standard practice for the production of a high quality mortar and the sand is to be of a uniform grading with the maximum particle size consistent with the placement of the mortar throughout the steel armature.

Steel mesh reinforcement

Steel mesh reinforcement shall mean a mesh that is woven, welded, or otherwise fabricated so that the maximum clear spacing between any parallel adjacent element shall not exceed 20 mm ($\frac{3}{4}$ in).

Specific surface area

Specific surface area shall mean the surface of the mesh reinforcement divided by the volume of the reinforcement. It is to be noted that, if a skeletal steel framework is sandwiched between ferro-cement layers, as is common practice, the skeletal steel is not to be included in the determination of specific surface area. The minimum specific surface area shall be 1.2. cm^2/cm^3 (3 in^2/in^3).

Volume fraction

Volume fraction of the wire mesh shall mean the volume of wire mesh reinforcement oriented in a specified direction, expressed per unit volume of composite. The volume fraction of the mesh in any direction shall not be less than $1\frac{1}{2}$ per cent.

Volume fraction of the skeletal steel shall mean the volume of skeletal steel reinforcement oriented in a specified direction, expressed per unit volume of composite.

Armature

The armature shall mean the steel framework of the structure, complete with steel mesh reinforcement.

Skeletal steel

This shall mean any steel-rod or pipe reinforcement located within the ferro-cement. Such additional reinforcement is frequently added for assembly purposes or for added ultimate strength. However, it is emphasized that that portion of the total thickness of material occupied by the skeletal steel framework is not properly classified ferro-cement. The definitions presented herein apply only to that portion of the structure reinforced with the multitude of layers of mesh reinforcement as defined above.

Surface cover

Surface cover refers to the thickness of the matrix over the outermost layer of mesh. This thickness should not generally exceed 3 mm (0.125 in).

Pama (Rapporteur) summarized as follows:

It would appear that the mechanical properties of ferro-cement under static loading could be predicted quite accurately from the laws of mixture of composite material. The strength and modulus of elasticity of ferro-cement had been shown to be a function of the basic properties of the constituent materials, mortar and wire mesh and their respective volume fractions.

Impact resistance is one important mechanical property of ferro-cement on which little is known. The criterion chosen to define the impact resistance varied from author to author. It was suggested that the leakage rate of damaged material should perhaps be used as the criterion.

On the problem of cracking, it would appear that the important parameter involved in crack progation is the specific surface of the material. It was also apparent from tests by Buchner that the most important factor controlling the intensity of cracking is the outermost layer of wire mesh.

Development of ferro-cement as a combination material for marine applications was still in its early stages and co-operation and collaboration between research workers, engineers, chemists, designers, builders and users was required to arrive at satisfactory basic standards.

Part II—SCANTLINGS AND REGULATIONS

Ferro-Cement Boat Hulls Analysed by the Finite Element Method   J C Scrivener and A J Carr

In 1970 the authors were approached by the New Zealand Marine Department, who over the previous two years had become increasingly involved in approval and survey of commercial ferro-cement boats. The Department wished to produce requirements for construction and needed to know the quantity and distribution of reinforcing steel to accommodate the probable loadings. The simplest solution seemed to be in the application of concrete thin shell theory to the problem. As ferro-cement boat hulls are neither of a simply expressible mathematical shape, nor are the boundary conditions amenable to exact mathematical definition, a numerical analysis by the finite element method was chosen.

The initial problem was to determine whether the transverse (athwartship) stresses in typical 35-ft (10.7-m) and 65-ft (19.8-m) hulls were small enough to be carried by mesh-reinforced mortar alone. A static loading consisting of a hydrostatic water load, together with an equivalent inverted hydrostatic load due to wave effects was to be applied to the complete hull from deck to keel. Freely supported and fixed conditions at the deck were to be investigated. The results (Scrivener and Carr, 1971) indicated that the 35-ft (10.7-m) hull was sufficiently reinforced transversely by mesh alone but that the 65-ft (19.8-m) hull needed significant additional transverse reinforcing.

The second phase of the investigation, reported in this paper, was to determine the critical hull length at which transverse reinforcing is just necessary. Suitable hulls were obtained by appropriate scaling of the 35-ft (10.7-m) and 65-ft (19.8-m) hulls.

The third phase was to find the effects of hull shape on maximum stresses. A hull of different shape was found to have a similar critical hull length. In addition, investigations were conducted to find the effect of local thickening of the hull and the effect of hull depth on the stress values.

Membrane and bending stress resultants are plotted in contour diagrams and the maximum transverse bending moments (producing the only critical stresses) are recorded for all the hulls analysed.

DATA AND ANALYSIS

Hull loading

The hulls were loaded as if the trawlers were immersed in sea water up to deck level. Accordingly, a hydrostatic pressure distribution from zero at deck level to maximum at keel was applied together with a loading produced by dynamic wave effects, equivalent to one quarter of the above static loading with an inverted hydrostatic distribution. With a deck load of 3 ft (0.915 m) of sea

water, this loading is that used in a revision of rules for the construction of wooden vessels in Norway and reported by Saethre (1968) (see Fig. 1).

The dead loading produced by fittings, machinery, bulkheads, etc., was taken to be uniformly distributed and added to the density of hull material raising this from approximately 160 lb/ft³ (2.56 kg/m³) to 240 lb/ft³ (3.84 kg/m³). Even this load was insufficient to balance

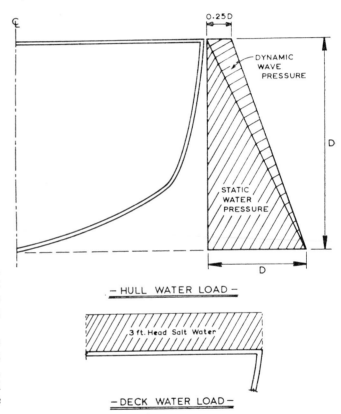

Fig. 1   Static water loads

the upward component of water pressure and overall vertical force equilibrium was obtained by applying further gravity load in two alternative ways:

(a) Deck loading of 3 ft (0.915 m) sea water, deck weight and fittings all applied as a large edge loading on the hull from the deck. The balance of load was made up with a small internal uniformly distributed vertical load on the hull.

(b) Deck loading of water pressure at one-quarter of hull depth, deck weight and fittings all applied as a small edge loading on the hull and the balance as a large internal uniformly distributed load on the hull.

Load case (b) was adopted throughout the later analyses as some early test runs showed that the stress results using load cases (a) and (b) differed very little.

The alternative method for maintaining vertical load equilibrium by applying large line loads at the points of support on the inner bulkheads (which in the analysis were fixed in space) would produce unrealistically large stress reactions from the hull.

To verify that moment equilibrium was satisfied, without the need for large equal and opposite reactive forces at the supports, further analyses were performed with the forward support point shifted from the inner bulkhead to the foremost bulkhead. As no significant change in stresses was found, it was concluded that the loading on the hull was self-equibrating.

Finite element analysis

The doubly curved shell structures of the hulls were analysed using a finite element method and computer programme due to Carr (1967). The element is a plane compatible three-nodal point triangular element which combines a quadratic-strain plane stress element with a fully compatible plate bending element. The resulting element has nine degrees of freedom at each nodal point and has been shown by Cantin and Clough (1968) to give good results in shell structures where membrane action is important.

The smoothly curved hulls were idealized as an assemblage of flat triangular elements and the facetted surface approximation can be seen in Fig. 2, giving a perspective view of the hull idealization. The lines of the 35-ft (10.7-m) and the 65-ft (19.8-m) hulls of Figs. 3 and 4 are as plotted by the computer and show the straight lines joining node points. As nearly 100 nodal points and more than 150 finite elements were used to

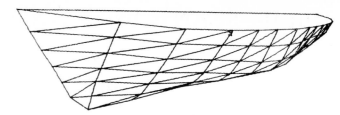

Fig. 2 Finite element mesh—perspective view

cover a half hull, which is quite gently curved, the geometrical approximation is most unlikely to make much change in the behaviour from that of the true shape. The programme computes membrane and bending stress resultants and displacements at the nodal points and at the mid-sides of the elements giving a total of nearly 350 points. Contours of membrane and bending stress were then plotted by the computer.

Because of symmetry of loading and structure about the hull centre-line, only the starboard half of the hull was analysed. Nodal points along the keel were considered to be fixed in rotation about the keel axis. It was necessary to fix some points in space and these were chosen as the two inner bulkheads. Initially two cases of deck support were considered—hull pinned and hull fixed at the deck. Although the two cases gave quite different local stress values near the deck, at small distances from the deck stresses were substantially the same probably due to the thinness of the hull. (For the longer hulls the stresses tended to show greater differences.) Certainly maximum stresses at points away from the deck were not markedly altered. Accordingly, only the case of hull pinned at the deck was computed in later analyses and reported in this paper.

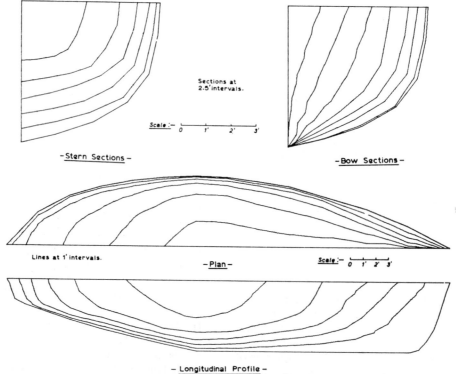

Sections at 2.5′ intervals.

Scale :— 0 1′ 2′ 3′

– Stern Sections –

– Bow Sections –

Lines at 1′ intervals.

– Plan –

Scale :— 0 1′ 2′ 3′

– Longitudinal Profile –

Fig. 3   35-ft hull lines (computer idealized)

The bulkhead support conditions were: zero transverse stress, zero displacement in the bulkhead plane and zero rotation about a longitudinal axis.

Hull details

The hulls of three trawlers were investigated. Lines of a typical 35-ft (10.7-m) hull and of a typical 65-ft (19.8-m) hull were supplied by the New Zealand Marine Department. The third hull was the 44-ft (13.4-m) shape as reported by Samson (1968), without the stiffeners and of

different thickness to that given. The lines are shown in Figs. 3, 4 and 5, the two former being the computer idealizations. The 35-ft (10.7-m) and 65-ft (19.8-m) trawlers had four bulkheads separating the hull into forepeak, engine room, fish hold, oil fuel tanks and storage. The 44-ft (13.4-m) trawler had two full and one part bulkhead.

Part of the investigation was to determine hull lengths at which transverse reinforcing additional to the mesh is necessary. Earlier analyses by Scrivener and Carr

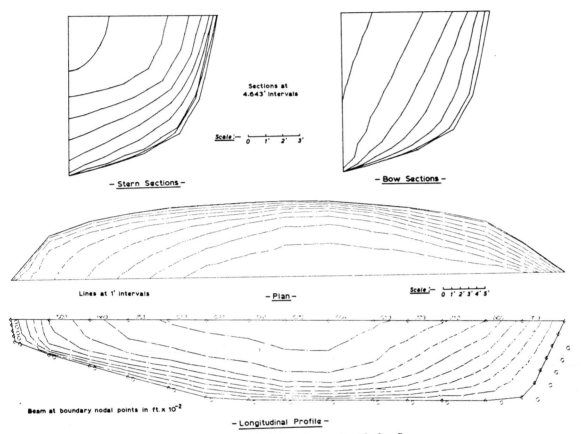

Fig. 4   65-ft hull lines (computer idealized)

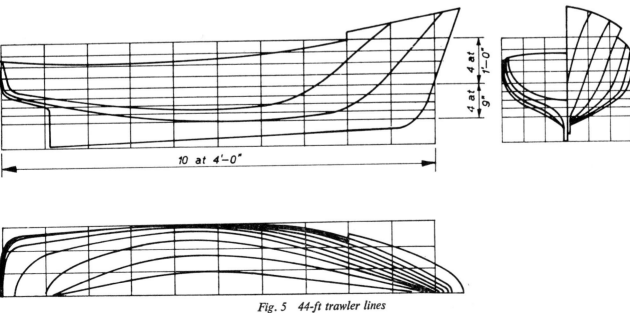

Fig. 5   44-ft trawler lines

83

(1971) had indicated that the 35-ft (10.7-m) hull had sufficient transverse reinforcing within the mesh, whereas the 65-ft (19.8-m) hull required additional transverse reinforcing. Hulls of lengths 40, 45, 50 and 55 ft (12.2, 13.7, 15.3 and 16.8 m) were obtained from both the 35-ft (10.7-m) and the 65-ft (19.8-m) hulls by suitable scaling of the beam, length and depth dimensions. The scaling functions adopted were linear and were those required to convert the 35-ft (10.7-m) hull into a hull of beam, length and depth of the 65-ft (19.8-m) hull and vice-versa.

The hull thicknesses considered were the minimum finished mortar thicknesses for fishing boats and other work boats in accordance with the New Zealand Marine Department provisional requirements (1970) namely:

for 35- and 40-ft (10.7- and 12.2-m) hulls:
1 in (25.4 mm) thickness
for 45-ft (13.7-m) hull: $1\frac{1}{8}$ in (28.5 mm) thickness
for 50-ft (15.3-m) hull: $1\frac{1}{4}$ in (31.7 mm) thickness
for 55-ft (16.8-m) hull: $1\frac{3}{8}$ in (34.9 mm) thickness
for 65-ft (19.8-m) hull: $1\frac{5}{8}$ in (41.2 mm) thickness

The thicknesses were increased arbitrarily in the keel and bow regions to between two and four times the thickness of the remainder of the hull.

FERRO-CEMENT PROPERTIES

The New Zealand Marine Department (1970) requires a minimum steel content equivalent to 24 lb/ft³ (384 kg/m³) of mortar, which is $2\frac{1}{2}$ to 3 per cent by volume in each direction. The derived tensile stresses are to be less than one-half the tensile stress causing cracking of the ferro-cement section.

Modulus of rupture

Collins and Claman (1969) graph the modulus of rupture against volume percentage steel content for various types of reinforcing. With $2\frac{1}{2}$ to 3 per cent by volume of 22-g hexagonal netting, the mesh reinforcing most often used in New Zealand, the ferro-cement modulus of rupture was found to be 1300 lb/in² (8.96 MN/m²).

A range of modulus of rupture test values from 700 to 2200 lb/in² (4.8 to 15.2 MN/m²) for eight layers of $\frac{1}{2}$ in (12.7 mm) hexagonal galvanized wire mesh in a nominal thickness of $\frac{3}{4}$ in (19 mm) are given by Kelly and Mouat (1968). The lower value applies to a specimen "cut lengthwise of panel" and the value is quite uncharacteristic of the test values from other specimens.

On the basis of these two test series, the modulus of rupture for a ferro-cement section with $2\frac{1}{2}$ to 3 per cent reinforcing is approximately 1200 lb/in² (8.28 MN/m²). Using a factor of safety of two, an allowable tensile stress in bending of 600 lb/in² (4.14 MN/m²) was assumed.

(Recent information from some unpublished experiments in New Zealand have given the onset of cracking on a $\frac{3}{4}$ in (19 mm) thick ferro-cement section as 100 lb/ft (445 Nm/m) which converts to a modulus of rupture of 1070 lb/in² (7.37 MN/m²).)

The moment per foot to produce the allowable tensile stress is a function of the thickness of the section. The values based on modulus of rupture of 600 lb/in²

(4.14 MN/m²) and assuming elastic behaviour of the ferro-cement are:

for 1 in (25.4 mm) section,
allowable moment 100 lb ft/ft (445 Nm/m)
for $1\frac{1}{8}$ in (28.5 mm) section,
allowable moment 127 lb ft/ft (564 Nm/m)
for $1\frac{1}{4}$ in (31.7 mm) section,
allowable moment 156 lb ft/ft (692 Nm/m)
for $1\frac{3}{8}$ in (34.9 mm) section,
allowable moment 190 lb ft/ft (844 Nm/m)
for $1\frac{5}{8}$ in (41.2 mm) section,
allowable moment 265 lb ft/ft (1180 Nm/m)

Direct tensile strength

The stress at first crack in ferro-cement specimens tested in direct tension with $2\frac{1}{2}$ to 3 per cent reinforcing by volume with various types of reinforcement are given as:

450–625 lb/in² (3.1–4.3 MN/m²)
by Kelly and Mouat (1968)
500–600 lb/in² (3.4–4.1 MN/m²)
by Collins and Claman (1969)
600–950 lb/in² (4.1–6.5 MN/m²)
by Naaman and Shah (1971)

Taking a conservative figure of 500 lb/in² (3.4 MN/m²) and halving for a safety factor of two, gives an allowable tensile stress at first crack of 250 lb/in² (1.7 MN/m²). This gives an allowable tensile action per foot of:

3000 lb/ft (43.7 kN/m) for a 1 in (25.4 mm) section
3750 lb/ft (54.6 kN/m) for a $1\frac{1}{8}$ in (28.5 mm) section
4870 lb/ft (71.0 kN/m) for a $1\frac{5}{8}$ in (41.2 mm) section

COMPUTED HULL STRESSES

Results from earlier analysis

Scrivener and Carr (1971) showed that for a 35-ft (10.7-m) hull of 1 in (25.4 mm) thickness no additional transverse reinforcing was required as at only two points away from the thickened area of the keel were transverse moments M_{XX} greater than 80 lb ft/ft (355 Nm/m) and in no case did they attain the allowable moment of 100 lb ft/ft (445 Nm/m). The maximum tensile transverse membrane stress N_X obtained was 63 lb/in² (435 kN/m²) well within the maximum. Further, most transverse membrane stresses were compressive and would have the desirable effect of raising the modulus of rupture of the section. The maximum membrane compressive stress was 352 lb/in² (2.43 MN/m²) easily carried by ferro-cement with compressive strength at least 3000 lb/in² (20.7 MN/m²). The twisting moment, away from the keel, did not exceed 50 lb ft/ft (345 Nm/m) and the in-plane shear stress was not greater than 123 lb/in² (848 kN/m²). Although these stresses affect the direction of principal stresses they are too small to raise the stresses to critical values. The longitudinal moment M_{yy} was of the same order as the transverse moment M_{XX} and could easily be accommodated by the extensive longitudinal reinforcing present, as could the longitudinal membrane stresses N_y.

On the other hand, in several areas the transverse moments M_{XX} of the 65-ft (19.8-m) hull of thickness $1\frac{5}{8}$ in (41.2 mm) were up to 550 lb ft/ft (2.45 kNm/m) greatly exceeding the allowable 265 lb ft/ft (1.18 kNm/m) thus requiring additional transverse reinforcing. Relatively high direct tensile stresses N_{XX} of 3000 lb/ft (43.8 kN/m) were also found but these could be accommodated by the section without additional reinforcing as the highest moments and highest direct stresses did not occur in the same areas.

General points of present analysis

Contours of the three membrane stresses and the three bending stresses for one hull are plotted in Figs. 6 and 7. Some apparent anomalies may be seen in these results. For instance, although the hull may be pinned at the deck some moments may occur at the deck nodal points due to the displacement of other nodes of the element. This is due to the displacement function approximation of the finite element method and occurs because it is not possible to satisfy stress and displacement boundary conditions simultaneously.

The maximum transverse bending moments M_{XX} and their location on the hull as obtained from the analyses of the various hull shapes, lengths and thicknesses are recorded in Table 1. The other stresses are not reported as they are easily carried by the sections reinforced with mesh alone.

Hull critical length

The New Zealand Marine Department wished to know at what critical hull length transverse reinforcing additional to that of the mesh was required. To this end the 65-ft (19.8-m) hull was scaled down linearly to the same length, beam and depth as the 35-ft (10.7-m) hull and analyses were conducted on hulls of length 40, 45, 50 and 55 ft (12.2, 13.7, 15.2 and 16.8 m) hulls. In addition, the 35-ft (10.7-m) hull was scaled up to the same length, beam and depth as the 65-ft (19.8-m) hull. A comparison was then made between the stresses in the two shapes of 35-ft (10.7-m) hulls. Although the distribution of stresses was quite different, the maximum transverse bending moments were found to be of very similar magnitude. This was felt to provide a sufficient justification for the validity of the scaling process adopted.

From the analyses of the scaled down 65-ft (19.8-m) hulls it was found that the 40-ft (12.2-m) behaved within allowable bending stresses, but that the 45-ft (13.7-m) hull had small areas where the allowable bending stress was just exceeded. Contours for the three membrane stresses and for the three bending stresses for the 45-(ex-65)-ft hull are presented in Figs. 6 and 7. Hulls longer than 45 ft (13.7 m) were definitely too highly stressed. As a further confirmation of a critical length of 45 ft (13.7 m), the 45-(ex-35)-ft hull was found to give just critical transverse bending stresses (see Table 1 and part of Fig. 8).

It was of extreme interest for the authors to find that this critical length of 45 ft (13.7 m) confirmed the findings of the Marine Department and of construction firms. Their decision had been reached on quite different premises, practical and not theoretical or analytical, as used in this investigation. The correspondence is, of course, quite fortuitous but nevertheless gives the practical and the theoretical parties much more confidence in the decisions of the other!

TABLE 1. MAXIMUM TRANSVERSE BENDING MOMENTS

Hull length (ft)	Position on hull	Actual transverse moment (lb ft/ft)
35	Just below deck, 2.5 ft from bow	80
	Near keel, 2.5 ft from bow	81
35 (Ex 65)	Near deck, aft of forward bulkhead	100
40 (Ex 35)	Just below deck, 2.9 ft from bow	105
	Near keel, 2.9 ft from bow	100
40 (Ex 65)	¼ hull depth, midway between forward bulkheads	112
	Just below deck, midway between centre bulkheads	106
45 (Ex 35)	Just below deck, 3.2 ft from bow	145
	Near keel, 3.2 ft from bow	138
45 (Ex 65)	Just below deck, aft of forward bulkhead	132
	¼ hull depth, midway between forward bulkheads	157
	⅓ hull depth, further aft	139
	Just below deck, midway between between centre bulkheads	147
44 Samson D = 4.167	Just below deck, 9 ft from bow	104
	¼ hull depth, 9 ft from bow	119
	Just above keel, just aft of centre bulkhead	97
44 Samson D = 6.67	Just below deck, 9 ft from bow	168
	¼ hull depth, 9 ft from bow	193
	⅓ hull depth, 9 ft from bow	138
	Just above keel, just aft of centre bulkhead	151
	Just aft of above	132
44 Samson D = 8.092	Just below deck, 9 ft from bow	202
	¼ hull depth, 9 ft from bow	232
	⅓ hull depth, 9 ft from bow	168
	Just above keel, just aft of centre bulkhead	177
	Just aft of above	155
50 (Ex 35)	Just below deck, 3.6 ft from bow	197
	Near keel, 3.6 ft from bow	185
55 (Ex 65)	Near deck, just aft of forward bulkhead	344
	Just below deck, just aft of above	228
	¼ hull depth, midway between forward bulkheads	279
	⅓ hull depth, just aft of above	243
	Just below deck, midway between centre bulkheads	256
	½ hull depth, midway between centre bulkheads	194
65	Allowable moment exceeded in many areas	} From 300 to 500
	Just below deck, just aft of forward bulkhead	
	Top third of hull, midway between forward bulkheads	
	Top third of hull, between centre bulkheads	

Effect of Hull shape and depth

The analyses to determine a hull critical length involved only two shapes, the original 35-ft (10.7-m) and 65-ft (19.8-m) hulls. A further hull shape was also investigated, the lines being due to Samson (1968) who detailed a

85

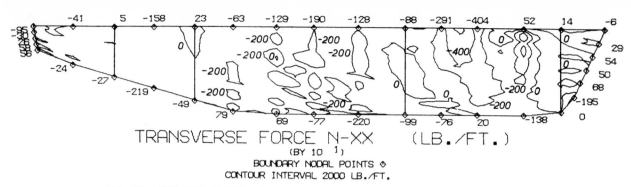

TRANSVERSE FORCE N-XX (LB./FT.)
(BY 10¹)
BOUNDARY NODAL POINTS ◊
CONTOUR INTERVAL 2000 LB./FT.

45 FOOT (EX65) FERROCEMENT TRAWLER HULL

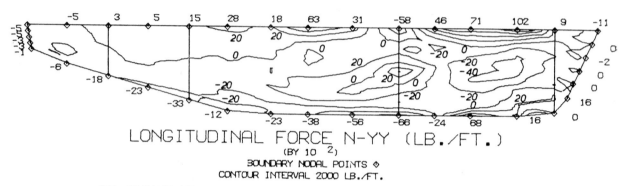

LONGITUDINAL FORCE N-YY (LB./FT.)
(BY 10²)
BOUNDARY NODAL POINTS ◊
CONTOUR INTERVAL 2000 LB./FT.

45 FOOT (EX65) FERROCEMENT TRAWLER HULL

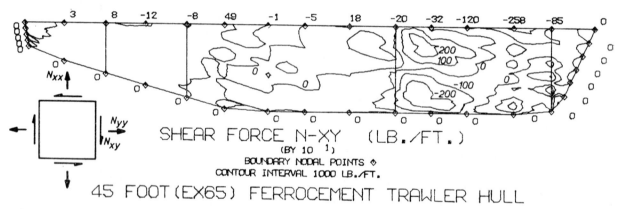

SHEAR FORCE N-XY (LB./FT.)
(BY 10¹)
BOUNDARY NODAL POINTS ◊
CONTOUR INTERVAL 1000 LB./FT.

45 FOOT (EX65) FERROCEMENT TRAWLER HULL

Fig. 6 Membrane stress resultants 45-ft (Ex. 65) hull

44-ft (13.4-m) trawler of thickness $\frac{3}{4}$ in (19 mm) with stiffeners at 4 ft (1.2 m) intervals. However, the hull analysed was of 44 ft (13.4 m) length and of $1\frac{1}{8}$ in (28.5 mm) uniform thickness (except at bow and near the keel where the hull was arbitrarily thickened) in order to give a direct comparison with the 45-ft (13.7-m) critical length hulls. The lines of the Samson trawler are plotted in Fig. 5.

A problem immediately became apparent as the depth D from deck to keel, which governs the magnitude of hydrostatic pressure loading, was greater for the Samson 44-ft (13.4-m) trawler than for the 45-ft (13.7-m) trawlers. Hence for a fair comparison with the two 45-ft (13.7-m) trawlers the loading for the Samson trawler was distributed from deck to keel as in Fig. 1, but with the value

of D used for calculating the maximum hydrostatic pressure as 6.67 ft (2.03 m) which is the depth of the 45-ft (13.7-m) trawlers. The transverse bending moments in the three hulls are plotted in Fig. 8. In spite of the fact that the Samson trawler has only two-and-a-half bulkheads, compared with four in the 45-ft (13.7-m) trawlers, the Samson maximum stresses were only slightly higher. This would seem to indicate that, given the same loading, the hull length is the critical factor in determining maximum transverse bending stresses and that hull shape has comparatively little effect on the maxima even though it determines the distribution.

The high moments near the keel at mid-ship of the Samson trawler (Fig. 8) are in a thickened area and easily accommodated.

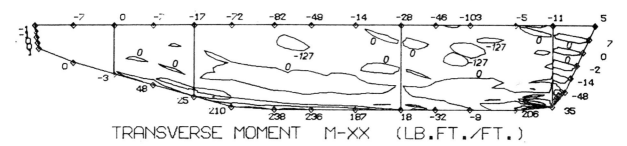

TRANSVERSE MOMENT M-XX (LB.FT./FT.)

BOUNDARY NODAL POINTS ◊
CONTOUR INTERVAL 127 LB.FT./FT.

45 FOOT (EX65) FERROCEMENT TRAWLER HULL

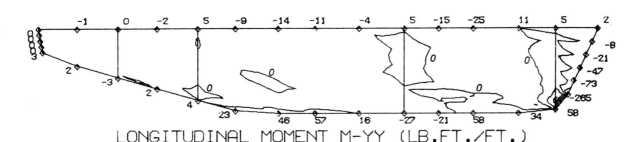

LONGITUDINAL MOMENT M-YY (LB.FT./FT.)

BOUNDARY NODAL POINTS ◊
CONTOUR INTERVAL 127 LB.FT./FT.

45 FOOT (EX65) FERROCEMENT TRAWLER HULL

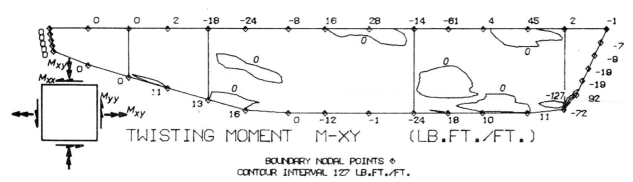

TWISTING MOMENT M-XY (LB.FT./FT.)

BOUNDARY NODAL POINTS ◊
CONTOUR INTERVAL 127 LB.FT./FT.

45 FOOT (EX65) FERROCEMENT TRAWLER HULL

Fig. 7 Bending stress resultants 45-ft (Ex. 65) hull

The further problem of the hydrostatic loading was then investigated. The Samson trawler was analysed for three values of D:

$D = 6.67$ ft (2.03 m), the deck to keel depth of the 45-ft (13.7-m) trawlers;

$D = 8.092$ ft (2.46 m), the actual depth of the Samson trawler;

$D = 4.167$ ft (1.27 m), the draft of the Samson trawler.

It was found that the maximum transverse bending moments were approximately proportional to the depth D—a not unexpected result as almost all of the hull loading depends on D.

This raises the question of code requirement for depth of hydrostatic loading. The deep trawler will be penalized in comparison with the shallow-hulled boat if the depth

D, and consequently the maximum hydrostatic pressure, is taken as the hull depth. Also full immersion of the complete hull may well occur with short boats but is unlikely when the hulls become larger. Thus it may be that the loading as used in these analyses is reasonable for the shorter hulls but too severe for the longer hulls, where a depth D less than the actual hull depth might well be used. Further, particularly for longer hulls, the effects of a longitudinal variation of hydrostatic loading may be significant.

Position of Maximum transverse moments

Each of the three hull shapes analysed had their maximum transverse bending moments occurring near the bow in the upper part of the hull. In this area the longitudinal curvature has become small (at the sharp bow it becomes zero) and transverse curvature cannot be

87

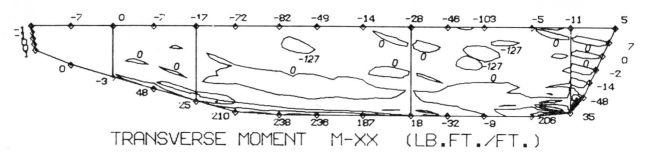

TRANSVERSE MOMENT   M-XX   (LB.FT./FT.)

BOUNDARY NODAL POINTS ◇
CONTOUR INTERVAL 127 LB.FT./FT.

45 FOOT (EX65) FERROCEMENT TRAWLER HULL

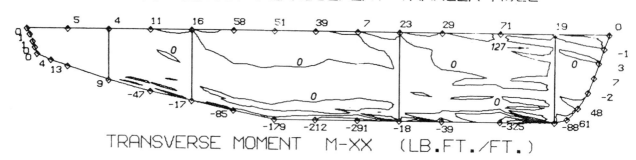

TRANSVERSE MOMENT   M-XX   (LB.FT./FT.)

BOUNDARY NODAL POINTS ◇
CONTOUR INTERVAL 127 LB.FT./FT.

45 FOOT (EX35) FERROCEMENT TRAWLER HULL

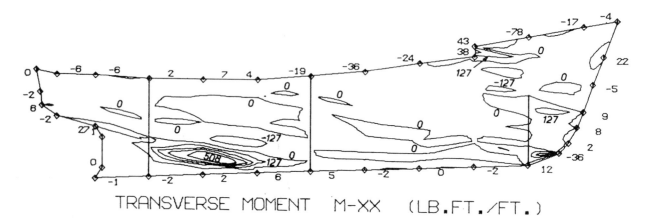

TRANSVERSE MOMENT   M-XX   (LB.FT./FT.)

BOUNDARY NODAL POINTS ◇
CONTOUR INTERVAL 127 LB.FT./FT.

44 FOOT FERROCEMENT TRAWLER HULL

Fig. 8   Transverse bending stresses in three hulls

great as the beam of the hull is necessarily small. This is sometimes the area of change from positive to negative curvature in one direction. In such flat areas, load can only be carried in bending as membrane actions require a curved structure. This flatness is well demonstrated on the 45-(ex-65)-ft hull, where there is an 0.2 ft (61 mm) change of beam over a length of 7 ft (2.14 m) as one travels from the deck near the bow towards the keel amidships. There is a band of high transverse moment along this diagonal line.

The area of high transverse moment near the keel at mid-ship of the 44-ft (13.4-m) Samson trawler again appears to be due to a lack of curvature in that region.

Initially it was hoped to alter curvatures and to find the effect on the moments, but this was abandoned for the reason that any change in curvature involves a change of the complete fairing of the hull lines and of course greatly affects buoyancy, performance and appearance.

Effect of local thickening

Local thickenings in the high moment areas of the 45-(ex-65)-ft hull were made in an attempt to reduce the moments to within allowable limits. The first analysis was with a 25 per cent increase and the second with a 50 per cent increase. The results of the analyses are given in Table 2 and clearly show that local thickening "attracted" more moment to the area requiring more section resistance to withstand the stresses. For three of the four points considered a 50 per cent increase was required in order to ensure that moments came within the allowable. The areas surrounding the increased portions were found to react very little to the increase adjacent to them.

TABLE 2. EFFECT OF LOCAL THICKENING ON TRANSVERSE MOMENTS OF 45 (EX 65) FT HULL

	Original thickness	25% increase	50% increase
Allowable moment (lb ft/ft)	127	199	286
Moments (lb ft/ft) at critical points of hull	132	142	147
	139	203	262
	147	216	285
	157	203	240

CONCLUSIONS

Finite element analyses of ferro-cement hulls loaded hydrostatically from deck level to keel with an additional static load for wave effects indicate that:

1. **The transverse (athwartship) bending moment is the only critical stress.**
2. **The maximum values of transverse bending moment are most likely to occur in flat areas of the hull. Many hulls have flat areas close to the bow near the deck.**
3. **The hull length is most critical in determining the magnitude of the maximum transverse bending moment.**
4. **With an allowable modulus of rupture for a ferro-cement section of 600 lb/in^2 (4.14 MN/m^2) the critical hull length is around 45 ft (13.7 m) with lengths below this not requiring transverse reinforcing additional to that of the mesh.**
5. **Hull shape determines the distribution of transverse bending moments but the maximum values do not depend critically on it.**
6. **Local thickening of areas of a hull "attract" moment so that the benefit of local thickening is not as great as may first be expected.**

References

CANTIN, G and CLOUGH, R W A curved cylindrical shell
1968   finite element. *AIAA Journal*, **6** (6).

CARR, A J *A Refined Finite Element Analysis of Thin Shell*
1967   *Structures Including Dynamic Loadings*. Ph.D. Dissertation, University of California, Berkeley, California, USA.

COLLINS, J F and CLAMAN, J S *Ferro-cement for Marine*
1969   *Applications—an Engineering Evaluation*. Report of Department of Naval Architecture and Marine Engineering, Massachusetts Institute of Technology, Cambridge, Mass., USA.

KELLY, A M and MOUAT, T W Ferro-cement as a fishing
1969   vessel construction material. *Proceedings, Conference on Fishing Vessel Construction Materials, Montreal, 1968*. Ottawa, Canada: Department of Fisheries and Forestry, Fisheries Service, Fisheries Reports No. 12: 135–162.

NAAMAN, A E and SHAH, S P Tensile tests on ferro-cement.
1971   *Proc. ACI*, **68** (9).

NEW ZEALAND MARINE DEPARTMENT *Provisional Require-*
1970   *ments for the Construction of Ferro-cement Boats*, 53/2/3.

SAETHRE, J Some notes on the stress analysis and construc-
1969   tion of fishing vessel structures. *Proceedings, Conference on Fishing Vessel Construction Materials, Montreal, 1968*. Ottawa, Canada: Department of Fisheries and Forestry, Fisheries Service, Fisheries Reports No. 12.

SAMSON, J Ferro-cement boat construction. *Proceedings,*
1969   *Conference on Fishing Vessel Construction Materials, Montreal, 1968*. Ottawa, Canada: Department of Fisheries and Forestry, Fisheries Service, Fisheries Reports No. 12.

SCRIVENER, J C and CARR, A J An analysis of ferro-cement
1971   boat hulls. *Pacific Symposium on Hydromechanically Loaded Shells, Part I*. Honolulu, Hawaii, USA.

Acknowledgements

The authors are grateful to R N Kerr, Secretary for Marine, and D J Eyres, Naval Architect, New Zealand Marine Department who initiated the investigation and to the Department of Civil Engineering and the Computer Centre, University of Canterbury, Christchurch, New Zealand, for their assistance.

Estimation of Design Loads   G L Bowen

Estimation of design loads is an intensively studied topic [the International Ship Structures Congress (1961) listed seventy-seven papers on a response to wave loads alone] in which there is a great gap between research and practice. In the last few years there have been some widely significant developments that indicate a greater opportunity than ever before to reach the objective.

If one knows to some degree of accuracy the stresses a system must withstand, more efficient use can be made of the available resources. An excellent example can be found in light pressurized containers in which fibres are wound in the direction of the principal stresses. Even when pressurized and punctured, they will not burst; hence the name—popless bottles. The ferro-cement equivalent of such an arrangement may well be the use of Wirand as reported by Lankard (1972) but with some direction orientation as required by the stress system.

How strong is strong enough? It will never be known until the loads are known, and the loads will never be known until the vessel's movement in a sea-state is known. This is based on the premise that the greatest loads on scantlings are hydrodynamic loads. This is by no means apparent and I would not say this is the case without field evidence. It may well be satisfactory (and easier!) to assume certain loads as is now done and revise them if service conditions turn out to be worse. Going the other direction is, obviously, more difficult and is the object of this study.

ESTIMATION METHODS DISCUSSED

If one examines the traditional methods of naval architecture it is evident that a ship is treated as a short beam and applied with a static loading. As ships have grown in size and cost a more sophisticated approach based on ship motions has been made. The reasons for a more detailed analysis have been that initial cost has grown justifying a greater analysis expenditure, the short beam has stretched and so have the magnitudes of wave induced bending moments; so there has been a strong desire to minimize motions from the standpoint of safety of the ship and seamen.

This analysis has progressed to a high degree for large vessels; the question is whether or not the same methods can be applied to small craft.

The Frank close-fit ship-motion computer programme

This programme was developed at the US Naval Ship Research and Development Center for computing pitch and heave motions for ships in regular and irregular head waves. From this, it is a simple matter to compute loading since pressures normal to the surface need only be integrated.

The report documenting the programme was written by Frank and Salvesen (1970) and gives the complete programme listing. In the report, the authors compare theoretical output with results from five different hull forms and find the agreement satisfactory. Another fifteen forms had also shown satisfactory agreement but comparisons were not included in the document. Theory, full-scale tests and model results are also compared by Gerritsma and Smith (1967) for Dutch destroyers.

There seems to be little doubt that the Frank programme gives good qualitative and reasonable quantitative information for large vessels. The important questions are: What are the limitations on the theory in general and how are they aggravated by a reduction in size?

(a) The theory is linearized by making the assumption that the ship disturbances are "small" from the equilibrium position and that both the incoming and ship caused waves are "small". Mathematically this means that products of the velocities induced by the ship motions are negligible in their effect upon the ship. Accelerations may be large so amplitudes must be small to yield low velocities. What constitutes "small waves" remains to be seen since the authors have found this a good assumption even for large motions. It is apparent that this restriction applies more to a small craft than a larger one given a fixed sea-state;

(b) The water is assumed to be inviscid. For heave and pitch, damping by the creation of free surface waves would be greater than any expected viscous effect. A roll could expect viscous damping of the same order as wave damping but roll is now allowed. For geometrically similar ships undergoing kinematically similar motions a reduction in size would lead to an increase in Reynolds number effects and an increase in error;

(c) The ship length is assumed to be a great deal larger than the beam and draft, so that each section can be treated as a two-dimensional "strip" with no interaction between sections. The authors state that the assumption would surely be violated for beamy craft. But would it be sufficiently violated as to give poor or misleading results? There is no evidence to confirm or repudiate the results in this case.

The greatest restriction on the motion prediction programme is that it was written mainly to consider longitudinal bending. Only head seas are allowable and only pitch and heave are possible motions. Corrective rudder action would be needed for any coupling between roll and pitch. This would be stronger for a fishing craft with a fine entrance and large midship section than for long vessels of moderate size. Rudder action would require another equation for the craft.

Other programme restrictions are; progress at constant forward velocity and an inability to account for momentum exchange by splash. A separate procedure by Ochi and Motter (1969), however, has been used with the motion prediction programme to calculate impact pressures associated with ship slamming.

These are the unknowns of the Frank programme and may, with restrictions in the derivation, make it totally unsuitable for fishing craft where transverse forces are also of interest. Fortunately, Salvesen, Tuck and Faltinsen (1970) have continued efforts to determine loads on vessels and they have developed a more general method of considerable world-wide interest.

The Salvesen, Tuck, and Faltinsen theory

This theory, in the author's opinion, can predict the heave, pitch, sway, roll and yaw motions as well as the wave-induced vertical and horizontal shear forces, bending moments and torsional moments for a ship advancing at constant speed in regular waves. Many of the previous reservations can be made again but the worst restriction is removed and an examination of transverse forces is now possible under realistic conditions. Figure 1 shows the sign convention and definitions of the various forces and moments. Figures 2–8 show a comparison of theory and experiment for various vessels and these figures are reproduced from N Salvesen et al., SNAME, **78**, 1970, by permission of the Society of Naval Architects and Marine Engineers.

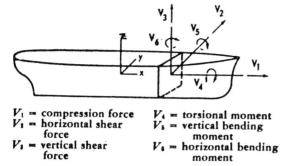

V_1 = compression force
V_2 = horizontal shear force
V_3 = vertical shear force
V_4 = torsional moment
V_5 = vertical bending moment
V_6 = horizontal bending moment

Fig.1　Sign convention for dynamic wave-load components

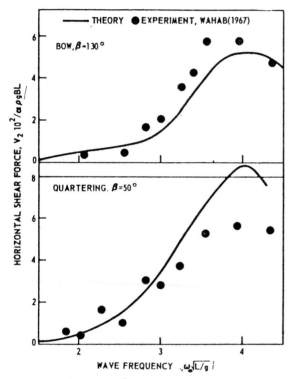

Fig. 2　Horizontal shear-force amplitudes at midship for Series 60, $C_B = 0.80$ in bow and quartering waves

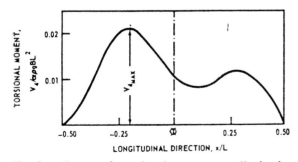

Fig. 3　Computed torsional-moment amplitude for containership in bow waves ($\beta = 120$ deg) with $L/\lambda = 2.0$ and at $F_n = 0.20$

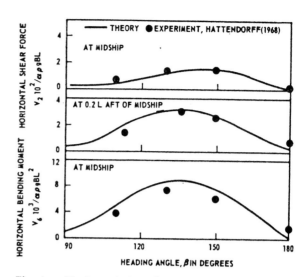

Fig. 4　Horizontal shear-force and bending-moment amplitudes versus heading angle for a containership at zero speed ($L/\lambda = 0.80$)

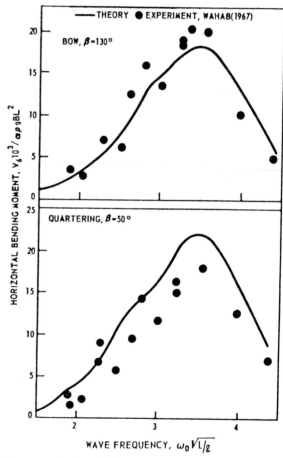

Fig. 5　Horizontal bending-moment amplitudes at midship for Series 60, $C_B = 0.80$ in bow and quartering waves at $F_n = 0.15$

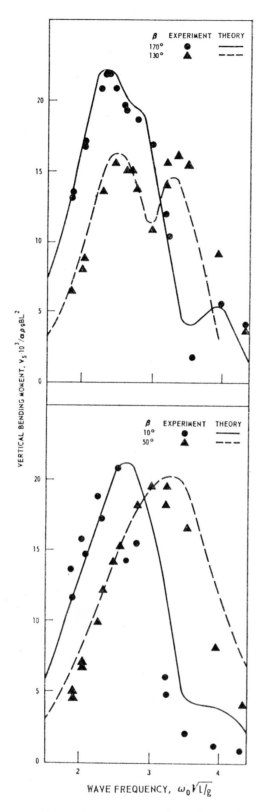

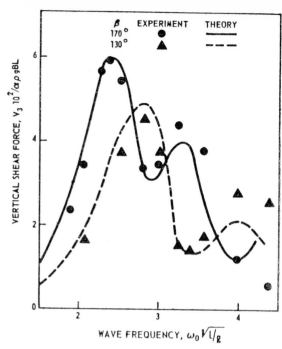

Fig. 7 Vertical shear-force amplitudes at midship for Series 60, $C_B = 0.80$ in head and bow waves at $F_n = 0.15$

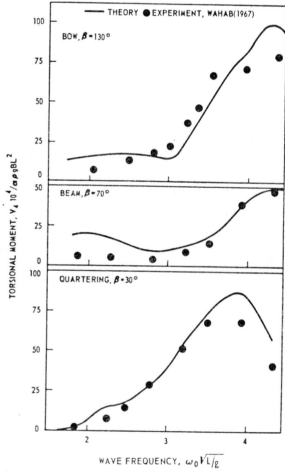

Fig. 6 Vertical bending-moment amplitudes at midship for Series 60, $C_B = 0.80$ in head, bow, quartering, and following waves at $F_n = 0.15$

Fig. 8 Torsional-moment amplitudes at midship for Series 60, $C_B = 0.80$ in bow, beam, and quartering waves at $F_n = 0.15$

(From N. Salvesen, et al., SNAME, 78, 1970, by permission of the Society of Naval Architects and Marine Engineers)

The symbols used in the figures are:

α, incident wave amplitude
β, angle between incident wave and ship heading ($\beta = 180°$ for head seas)
ρ, mass density of water
ω_0, wave frequency
B, ship beam
F_n, Froude number, $U/\sqrt{gL}$
L, ship length between perpendiculars
g, gravitational acceleration
C_B, block coefficient

The Society of Naval Architects and Marine Engineers (SNAME) meeting at which this paper was presented was attended by Lloyd's Register of Shipping, who determined the transverse loading used by Scrivener and Carr (1971). This loading, when applied symmetrically, represents a vessel caught by a beam wave from each side. Static application of the loading must be assumed in the absence of additional information.

The method presented by Salvesen, Tuck and Faltinsen was in the process of review as NSRDC Report 3376 in late 1970. The documentation is still not considered complete.

One use for work such as this is in seakindliness studies. For application to design some scheme needs to be devised so that maximum forces and moments can be found. Fortunately by intensive effort various statistical procedures methods have been devised (see articles reported in the 1961 Ship Structures Congress).

Everything considered, the Salvesen, Tuck and Faltinsen theory is superior in nearly every respect to the Frank programme except that the documentation is not publicly available and the most recent theory has not been generalized to irregular seas.

Slamming

Considerable effort has been directed towards prediction of slamming pressures and estimation of structural response. Szebehely and Ochi (1966) reviewed the literature and listed 113 references dealing with impact and impact estimation procedures. Seven of these references reported results on various vessels. Reports and articles appearing since then have been written by Chuang (1966), Verhagen (1967), Ochi and Motter (1969), Gerlach (1968), Lewison (1970), Johnson (1968), Sellars (1971), Lewison and Maclean (1968) and Hughes (1971).

The most useful result is the one given by Ochi and Motter. It is based upon years of theoretical and experimental study of the slamming problem. They have developed a statistical approach for the calculation of extreme pressures based upon some knowledge of ship motion and geometry in the slamming area. The procedure is as follows:

(a) Considering the type of ship and its operating area, estimate the severest sea state which a ship may encounter once in its lifetime.
(b) Estimate the desired ship speed and navigation time in the sea given in (a).
(c) Compute the relative motion and relative velocity for the locations at which the pressure is desired

in the vicinity of the bow for the speed and sea state in (a) and (b). This can be done experimentally or by using the Frank close-fit ship-motion programme.

(d) Evaluate a constant parameter based upon the section shape at the point where the value of pressure is desired. The value is given for several section shapes in another paper by Ochi (1967). If the shape is more involved an experiment must be performed.

(e) Compute extreme pressures using the equations or computer programme given by Ochi and Motter.

If the computer programme is used, another calculation is made to determine the probabilities of bow emergence and deck wetness. This is an additional benefit which has resulted from the Frank programme.

Although only the occasional drop test has been made with a curved surface, the rough water characteristics of various bow forms are fairly well known. There seems a conflict of opinion, however, regarding the effect of flare. It is usually stated that flare gives a drier vessel and yet wind can bring the spray back on board. There may be better forms to use and still achieve the desired fine-entrance. A strong compound flare appears to be a good form to avoid since the flow may leave the surface as the curvature reverses and cause excessive pressure to be taken over a small area. This form also has the concave sections Sutherland (1972) advised against at his retirement address before the New Zealand Ferro-Cement Association.

Figure 9 shows a slow shock hull developed for a STOL amphibious aircraft by a Japanese firm and reported in *Interavia* (1970). It allowed softer entry with excellent spray suppression.

Loads associated with green water shipping and wave impact

From the hydrodynamic viewpoint there are only a few obvious possibilities where large forces can occur: slamming, green water shipping and wave impact. Whereas slamming causes extreme pressures and has buckled steel plate on larger craft, green water shipping and wave impact are the main cause of worry to fishermen. These are the loadings that reduce stability and can also damage superstructure.

Although articles have been written by Du Cane and Goodrich (1962) and Wahab and Swaan (1964) to illustrate how dangerous situations come about, there is simply no means to accurately estimate the forces involved. If such a method existed, one would expect it to be an order of magnitude more involved than existing ship motion theories. The only recourse is the study of wave forces acting against breakwaters.

In the US, the most widely-used formula for the design of vertical wall structures subject to breaking waves is that of Minikin (1950). For a wave approaching from very deep water the relation assumes the form:

$$p_m = 101 \frac{\gamma d h_w}{\lambda}$$

where p_m is the maximum pressure (at the still water level), d is depth to the toe of the breakwater, h_w is wave

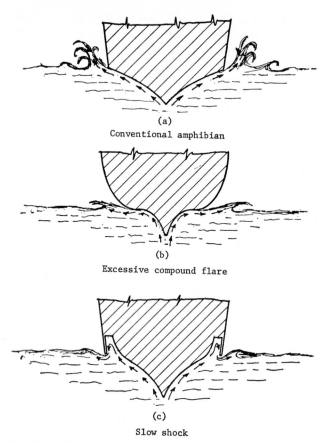

(a)
Conventional amphibian

(b)
Excessive compound flare

(c)
Slow shock

Fig. 9 Hull forms

height and λ is wave length. The equation is dimensionally homogeneous. The maximum shock pressure is assumed to act at the still water level and decreases parabolically to zero at equal distances above and below this level. In a short-crested sea it is easy to estimate shock pressures on the order of 1000 kN/m². Slamming pressures on keels have been measured in full-scale tests at about twice this figure, so the estimate is fairly realistic. More important, there is no reason to believe that a small fishing vessel would suffer smaller impact pressures than a large craft.

Motion of water on board would be even more involved than wave impacts. Fairing would probably be desirable to reduce wake widths. The only literature that would even begin to approach this problem is by Streeter and Wylie (1968) in which they solve an explosion problem for a body suspended in a liquid-filled channel. No knowledge yet exists to link separation and wake conditions.

FULL-SCALE TESTING

Although some work has been done in the investigation of loads imposed by fishing gear: Dickson (1955), Hatfield (1960) and Morgan (1965), there appears to be little guidance as to the hydrodynamic loads imposed on the hull. It has been suggested that full-scale tests might be desirable. For this considerable guidance can be found in the extensive experience accumulated in full-scale testing of larger craft—observations by Mockel (1955, 1960) on fishing craft are also of interest.

General problems

First, what information is desired? Figure 10 from *Theory of Ship Motions* shows the forces acting on a vessel. For loads to be determined accurately, these forces must be measured directly or indirectly—choice must be made on what to measure and the procedure.

One of the worst problems in full-scale testing is relating the seaway and the ship motions. Other problems are: inability to encounter severe weather; difficulty making simultaneous measurements; zero point drift; instrument failure; unreliable electrical supply; and on board the *USCGC Unimak*, faulty strain gauge measurements because a steel plate had exceeded its elastic limit on previous voyages.

If water pressures are sensed, there is the problem of trapping air during craft motion. Pressure transients are also attenuated by tubing.

The non-technical problems would undoubtedly be the over-riding consideration: initial cost (including instrumentation), mooring, maintenance, technical staff, fuel, etc. As important to success would be a supporting facility where data reduction calibration, project organization, etc., could be carried on. In the Advanced Marine Systems Group at the Boeing Company, three experimental craft and two shop facilities were provided, as well as a pilot and co-pilot, supporting surface craft, an instrument group, and a mechanical engineer whose primary function was to see how testing costs could be reduced. The craft were usually in the shops in long preparation for short tests.

Problems peculiar to ferro-cement

What is the relation between stress and strain and how does it vary with time? Smith (1972) formulated an approximate expression based on tests of various forms of standard construction. How would this relation vary with position where thicknesses might differ.

Strain gauging a ferro-cement hull could be most difficult for other reasons. With unsymmetrical reinforcing about the centre-line of the material section, it would be necessary to measure strain on both surfaces. This would expose one gauge to the water and the electrical connexions must pass through the hull or along it where they could be damaged.

There is also a need to separate and to determine both axial and bonding deformation before the stress can be determined. Instrumentation choice for use in thin concrete and interpretation of the results is given by Yu and Waggott (1968).

Recommended instrumentation

Several accounts outline methods of instrumentation. An article by Gover (1955) is now somewhat dated, and a later article by Sauvalle (1961) described equipment developed exclusively for ship testing. Considerable progress can be expected from later information.

There is much to commend the simple measurements of hull pressure as put forth by Hogben (1957) and the statistical approach to hull stress measurements rather than continuous records. Suggested instrumentation so guided would be:

Hull pressure: Diaphragm pressure gauges could be located in a grid pattern with faces flush with the outside of the hull, the gauge being a differential transformer with a zero adjustment. The gauge body can be made of K Monel which has shown good service for this type of application. Gauges would be read simultaneously on a multi-channel recorder and, except for the thrust on the propeller and skin friction, hydrodynamic loading could be calculated by pressure integration.

Hull skin friction: Could be calculated from existing theories or estimated on the basis of through-hull glands and pitot cylinders. One or two of these would be of interest to determine direction of flow and viscous drag at a local point. Full-scale tests have usually not considered this.

Propeller shaft torque and thrust: This has been measured in the past by strain gauges bonded to a special hollow intermediate shaft. The supply and signal is by silver slip rings and silver/graphite brushes. The shaft is calibrated in torsion and compression before installation.

Aerodynamic loading: This could be estimated on the basis of wind tunnel tests and on board instrumentation. Wind speed can be measured by a cup type anemometer and relative wind direction by a vane. Stereo cameras as used in photogrammetry would have to be used to determine sea-state.

Angular acceleration: This can be determined by three angular accelerometers aligned in the various coordinate directions. These instruments have performed satisfactorily in full-scale tests.

Linear acceleration: This can be measured in the three coordinate directions by accelerometers or a 3-axis accelerometer. A number of types may be used.

Roll and pitch angles: Can be measured by a 2-axis gyroscope.

Ship speed: A calibrated log is usually used.

Shaft torque: Measured at the same time as thrust.

Propeller shaft revolutions: This has been measured by magnet and reed switch in previous tests.

Hull stress: May be calculated from measurements or found from strain gauges. The usual type strain gauge probably would not be suitable.

Recording: Instantaneous readings needed to compute forces could be taken on multi-channel recorders. Later these tapes could be processed directly by computer or run through an analog to digital converter and punched on paper tape. A PDP-12 computer is used for this purpose at the University of Auckland.

Statistical recordings should be used for hull stress measurements and the results taken should be analysed statistically to predict probable maximums.

CONCLUSIONS

Loading as encountered by vessels in a sea state have been extensively studied. The method of Salvesen, Tuck and Faltinsen holds promise for the calculation of wave-induced loads and could be useful for seakindliness studies. It can be expected that the theory will not be as good for a small vessel as for a larger one, all other things equal. The Frank programme can be used with a statistical method to estimate impact pressures and these pressures can be expected to be high.

Other high loadings can be expected due to green-water shipping and wave impact. The calculation of these loads appears to have been neglected in the naval architecture literature.

If full-scale testing is desired considerable guidance can be offered from documented past experience. The only apparent problem that appears difficult to solve is the one of strain gauging the concrete.

RECOMMENDATIONS

(a) It needs to be determined whether sea loads or service loads have been the deciding factor in the damage incurred to date with ferro-cement craft.

(b) If results from (a) show reason to believe sea loads can be worse than service loads, the Frank programme should be used and impact pressures estimated. If for no other reason than seakindliness, the Salvesen, Tuck and Faltinsen Method should also be further investigated for application to fishing craft;

(c) Oblique entry of a fine wedge shape into the water could lead to extreme impact loading; loads from beam waves may also be large. An investigation into these effects should be continued;

(d) If a full-scale testing programme is planned; a careful analysis must be made of the costs as compared to what is to be learned.

References

BLAGOVESHCHENSKY, S N *Theory of Ship Motions.* New
1962   York, USA: Dover, 2 vols., 649 pp. (Translated by T and L Sterlkoff from *Kachka Korablia,* 1954.)

CHUANG, S L Experiments on slamming of wedge-shaped
1966   bodies. *J. Ship Res.* **11** (3): 190–198.

DICKSON, W The loads imposed by trawling gear. *Fishing*
1955   *Boats of the World* : 1. London, England: Fishing News, 388–392.

DU CANE, P and GOODRICH, G J The following sea, broaching
1962   and surging. *Trans. RINA* **102** (2): 109–139

FRANK, W and SALVESEN, N The Frank Close-Fit Ship-Motion
1970   Program. Naval Ship Research and Development Center, USA. *NSRDC Report 3289,* 135 pp.

GERLACH, C R Investigation of water impact of blunt rigid
1968   bodies—size scale effects. *SRIP No. 02–2036, TR2.* USA, Southwest Research Institute.

GERRITSMA, J and SMITH, W E Full-scale destroyer motion
1967   measurements. *J. Ship Res.* **11** (1): 1–8.

GOVER, S C Observations on ship motions at sea. *Proceedings*
1955   *of the First Conference on Ships and Waves.* Council on Wave Research and SNAME, USA, 351–364.

HATFIELD, M Measurements on two inshore fishing vessels.
1960   *Fishing Boats of the World* : 2. London, England: Fishing News, 85–97.

HOGBEN, N Ship hull pressure measurements. *Trans. RINA*
1957   **99** : 446–472.

HUGHES, O F Wedge penetration of a free surface. *Pro-*
1971   *ceedings of the Fourth Australian Conference on Hydraulics and Fluid Mechanics.* Melbourne, Australia, 307–320.

JOHNSON, R S The effect of air compressibility in a first
1968   approximation to the ship slamming problem. *J. Ship Res.* **12** (1): 57–68.

LEWISON, G On the reduction of slamming pressures. *Trans.*
1970   *RINA* **112**: 285–306.

LEWISON, G and MACLEAN, W M On the cushioning of
1968   water impact by entrapped air. *J. Ship Res.* **12** (2):
116–130.

MINIKIN, R R *Wind, Waves and Maritime Structures.* Lon-
1950   don, England: Griffin, 216 pp.

MOCKEL, W Behaviour of trawlers at sea. *Fishing Boats of*
1955   *the World* : *1.* London, England: Fishing News,
326–336.

MOCKEL, W Behaviour of trawlers at sea—II. *Fishing Boats*
1960   *of the World* : *2.* London, England: Fishing
News, 404–417.

MORGAN, P G The hydrodynamic design of fishing nets.
1965   *Proceedings of the Second Australian Conference on*
Hydraulics and Fluid Mechanics. Auckland, New
Zealand, 347–362.

OCHI, M K Ship slamming, hydrodynamic impact between
1967   waves and ship bottom forward. *Proceedings of*
Symposium on Fluid–Solid Interaction. Pittsburgh,
Penn., USA: ASME, Applied Mech. Div.

OCHI, M K and MOTTER, L E Prediction of extreme values
1969   of impact pressure associated with ship slamming.
J. Ship Res. **13** (2): 85–91.

SALVESEN, N, TUCK, E O and FALTINSEN, O Ship motions
1970   and sea loads. *Trans. SNAME* (78): 250–287.

SAUVALLE, G Instrumentation for structural seaworthiness
1961   tests. *International Ship Structures Congress.* Report
of the Committee on Response to Wave Loads,
DTMB Report 1537, Ch. 3.

SCOTT, W G *Ferro-cement for Canadian Fishing Vessels.*
1971   Ottawa, Canada: Industrial Development Branch,
Fisheries Service, Department of the Environment,
Project Report No. 42.

SCRIVENER, J C and CARR A J An analysis of ferro-cement
1971   boat hulls. *Proceedings of Pacific Symposium on*
Hydromechanically Loaded Shells. Honolulu, Hawaii,
USA: Int. Assoc. for Shell Structures, 15 pp.

SELLARS, F The influence of structural characteristics on
1971   slamming impact pressures. *J. Ship Res.* **15** (1): 49–58.

SHIN MEIWA STOL amphibian. *Interavia* **25** (11): 1382–1383.
1970

STREETER, V L and WYLIE, E B Two- and three-dimensional
1968   fluid transients. *Proceedings of Symposium on Un-*
steady Flow. Philadelphia, USA: ASME, Fluids
Engr. Div., 9 pp.

SUTHERLAND, W M An address to the New Zealand Ferro-
1972   Cement Marine Association, Auckland, New Zealand. *New Zealand Ferro-Cement Marine Assoc.*
Newsletter, June.

SZEBEHELY, V G and OCHI, M K Hydrodynamic impact and
1966   water entry. *Applied Mechanics Surveys.* Macmillan,
951–957.

VERHAGEN, J H G The impact of a flat plate on a water
1967   surface. *J. Ship Res.* **12** (4): 211–223.

WAHAB, R and SWAAN, W A Coursekeeping and broaching
1964   of ships in following seas. *J. Ship Res.* **9** (2): 1–15.

YU, C W and WAGGOTT, J G Instrumentation in pressure
1967   vessels. *Proceedings of Conference on Prestressed*
Concrete Pressure Vessels. London, England: ICE,
627–634.

Discussion of Scantlings Design and Various Official Regulations

Scrivener (Rapporteur) said that the two papers on scantlings were the theoretical, or analytical, side of the subject. They discussed hydrodynamic loading and possible full-scale testing, and the analysis of hulls of given shape subjected to code loadings. It was significant that only two papers had been offered, but perhaps this was a reflection of the complexity of the problem as it applied to small vessels.

Bowen (New Zealand) reviewed the complex question of the actual hydrodynamic loads and their calculation. He raised the query that perhaps these loads were not those to produce the greatest stresses in the scantlings and pointed out that the analysis of loads on large vessels is reasonably accurate and well documented but questioned the applicability of these analyses to small vessels such as ferro-cement fishing boats.

Scrivener and **Carr** (New Zealand) avoided the question of actual loading and used a code load which was an estimate of the loading applied when a vessel was caught by a beam wave from each side. This may, or may not, be the most severe loading, or even a realistic loading for the scantlings; but it was a simple loading which at least allowed an analysis to be performed. Some typical fishing-boat hulls were analysed, using code hull thicknesses, with assumptions made on hull support and boundary conditions to permit an analysis. To reach conclusions with respect to transverse strength the ferro-cement

strength was estimated from published results. A number of assumptions had to be made in order to produce any answer at all.

ANALYSIS OF HULLS BY THE FINITE ELEMENT METHOD

Scrivener (New Zealand) said that the loading discussed in the paper written jointly with Carr was chosen to give maximum transverse effect. For the 10.65 m (35 ft) hull under chosen loading they obtained similar moments in longitudinal and transverse directions, but some further analyses of wave loadings on vessels had shown very large longitudinal stresses, much larger than those in the transverse direction, but in the results obtained up to this point the deck had not been included. It was hoped to do this at a later date.

Pama (Thailand) found Scrivener's and Carr's results interesting. To simplify calculations they had assumed the side of the hull was supported at the deck edge, first treating it as simply supported and later as fully fixed. He considered that the actual condition would be somewhere in between. The support condition and the loading having been idealized so that the hull became basically a plate structure with the load carried in the short direction instead of the long direction, thus accounting for the high transverse stresses or moments.

96

Gulbrandsen (FAO) referred to an investigation in Norway into the strength of wooden fishing vessels below 30 m (100 ft). Taking the strength of the deck into account it was found that the longitudinal bending moments caused by the hogging or sagging conditions were very small indeed and could be disregarded. The important stresses were caused by transverse bending moments and occurred in the flatter sections of the frames either amidships on the bottom, or forward where Scrivener and Carr had found the biggest stresses.

Perry (Australia) asked if prediction of bending stresses gave a reasonable guide as to whether a second layer of rods was really necessary. He suggested that thickness be increased and more mesh be used close to the surface, as rods were an inefficient way of carrying bending stresses because of their distance from the surface. Increased mesh should be more effective. He also noted that no account appeared to have been taken of shrinkage stresses in the mortar. In his opinion shrinkage contributed largely to the total stress condition of the hull mortar and should be taken into account when determining maximum bending stresses.

Ellen (Australia) considered that a designer could assume for transverse bending that a plate bent from the keel to the deck structure assuming that the deck structure interacted with the hull. If this did not happen then there was considerable difficulty in assessing the longitudinal bending moments near the deck. As curvature increased, the plate became more of an arch spanning from the deck to the keel. In discussions on scantlings from a specification point of view, an arbitrary method of assuming hull thicknesses and material content was required which would enable hulls of a specified size and curvature to span transversely certain distances from keel to deck. The curvature must be related to the problem of span thickness and distance from keel to deck. He considered the longitudinal stresses particularly important and felt that the deck must be included in the calculation for hull design.

Moar (New Zealand) noted that overall bending calculations for small vessels on waves had been checked by staff of his company and they had found very low longitudinal stresses. He added that local bending calculations could be made to determine suitable rod and/or mesh configuration as bending strength is a combination of both mesh and rods. However, the use of skeletal steel and its configuration should not be insisted upon, because his company was building a boat on the sandwich principle, referred to in Sutherland's paper on commercial construction methods, which had a shell thickness of 3.5 cm (1⅜ in) with one layer of special mesh inside and one layer outside. The bending capacity of this lay up in both directions was stronger than their conventional fishing-boat hull with a shell thickness of 2.25 cm (1⅛ in), both longitudinal and transverse rods and three layers of welded mesh on each side. Whatever amount of steel used, its effectiveness was dependent on the configuration.

Behnke (USA) presumed that in their mathematical model Scrivener and Carr had assumed a honogeneous material with two characteristics, the modulus of rupture and the tensile strength of each point, and he asked how points located on rods and bulkheads were handled.

Carr (New Zealand) confirmed that they had assumed that the hull was a homogeneous section and that the rods had been treated as part of the effective modulus of the section. Bulkheads had been considered as having no effect longitudinally and would not deform within their own planes in the transverse direction. In other words all joints on a bulkhead had the same vertical deflexion and the same transverse rotation.

Taking a symmetric loading case, the rotation of any joint on the bulkhead about a longitudinal axis was zero and the strain on the shell in the transverse direction along the bulkhead was again zero. This was because of the rigidity effect of the bulkhead stiffening the shell at these points.

Mowbray (New Zealand) suggested that at least three different design methods were in use, the first being the "rule of thumb" design, based on service experience which had operated very well for centuries in constructing timber vessels. Next was a rational design method and tabulation. This tended to lead to over-heavy design with little chance of easy change from existing to new methods of construction. Ferro-cement is not like steel or other boat-building materials but more like reinforced concrete, and he would not like to see tabulated rigid scantling rules formulated at this stage in the development of the material.

Then there was the Scrivener and Carr approach in which they had broken away from tradition and used a three-dimensional method of finite elements with extensive use of a computer.

This did not necessarily make a better or lighter design, but an analysis of this type might result in a rationalization of the methods used.

Waters (New Zealand) asked whether Carr had considered using moment distribution or other variations of that method on the transverse ring, taking the maximum section and using it as a standard stylized method of assessing the transverse strength.

Carr (New Zealand) said that standard structural analysis based on the idealization of the midship section as a ring could be done but that the finite element method had the advantage of applying the same techniques to the whole vessel at the same time.

Eyres (New Zealand) explained in more detail the background to the Scrivener and Carr paper. The Marine Department had approached the University of Canterbury with the problem of the requirement for transverse steel in smaller ferro-cement craft, since there was in New Zealand at the time very strong feeling on the need for transverse wires in addition to longitudinal wires in boats up to 12 to 14 m (40–45 ft) in length. The Department tended to favour the need for equal amounts of transverse and longitudinal wire in all hulls, but experience had shown that a large number of pleasure and other craft not coming under the Department's jurisdiction and not fitted with transverse wires had been successful in service. The loading adopted in the Scrivener and Carr paper was the loading used by the Det Norske Veritas for determining the scantlings given in their rules for the construction of small wooden boats. It was in fact a loading which had been previously used in studies of the transverse strength of small boats. Waters had mentioned the moment distribution method in this respect and it was suggested that this would be taking a backward step with the finite-element analysis methods now available. It was common practice to apply the finite-element technique to the analysis of the strength problems of large ships today and Carr had been able to apply the technique to a small boat. Boden and Waters had commented on the use of standard-wave bending theory to determine appropriate scantlings for these smaller boats. The application of wave-bending theory to small boats, say, less than 20 m (65 ft) was not a suitable criterion for determining the scantlings. A number of people had submitted designs and undertaken such calculations for smaller vessels. These showed that with the minimum conventional rod mesh configurations the hull had a factor of safety of something like 10+ if longitudinal bending only was taken into account. Further evidence of the unsuitability of longitudinal bending as a criterion for small boat design was that in small steel boat construction the rule of longitudinal continuity of members, so important in large ship construction, was often ignored, without any sign of local failure at discontinuities in the structure.

HYDRODYNAMIC LOADING OF FERRO-CEMENT HULLS

Scrivener (New Zealand) said that Bowen's paper suggested that hydrodynamic loadings should be more closely investigated and asked for Bowen's views on the loading that he and Carr had used to calculate maximum stresses.

Bowen (New Zealand), replying, considered that the loading chosen by Scrivener and Carr, that equivalent to a beam wave from each side at the same time, was a severe one but he had reservations regarding the selection as it did not consider the hydrodynamic parameters he would expect in specifying a loading.

Waters (New Zealand) felt that what was required was a simple method which could be systematically applied by designers and suggested that the factor of safety should be related to the strength at first crack. Bowen had suggested that the next step might be full-scale testing, but he had doubts as to whether a limited series of tests would give the kind of information required. Such tests should not be considered until a maximum amount had been learned from standard model tests in regular waves using a fairly large model of about 5 m (15 ft). Routine model testing possibly associated with a standard drop test of the whole boat would give most of the answers. He suggested that service loads associated with a safety factor relating to the strength at first crack should be the criteria for the type of boat under discussion. With regard to slamming, the rise of floor on the transverse section was the most significant factor. With sufficient rise forward, the slamming effect could be avoided. With regard to flare a recent report described a pronounced flexing of the main hull of a container ship in rough weather which was attributed to excessive flare at the bow. The strains were transmitted through the entire length of the ship. Length was not a factor with the type of fishing vessel being considered but the report did suggest that the force of water pressure on the bow could be transmitted through the ship and this could ultimately be a cause of cracking in a ferro-cement hull.

SCANTLINGS AND CONSTRUCTION RULES OF MARINE BOARDS AND CLASSIFICATION SOCIETIES

Eyres (New Zealand) was concerned to see scantling requirements being published listing specific sizes of wire, rods, etc. He felt that at this stage in the developemnt of the material, such rules, if brought out in any form of legislation, could seriously inhibit progress in the formative stages of ferro-cement. In publishing New Zealand requirements they had been careful not to specify actual sizes of materials, preferring to follow the definition of ferro-cement in specifying rather the minimum steel volume and surface cover.

Watkins (Australia) said that in his experience the average ferro-cement owner builder was not altogether in favour of regulations, but it would be unrealistic to suggest that rules, which are needed for other materials are not needed for ferro-cement. Pama, in summing up the discussion of Part I, had spoken of hull strength as being related to the volume fraction of constituents and this should be the basis for regulations. In

addition, some Australian designers had not made themselves aware of the requirements for important engineering items. The installation of such things as stern tubes, rudder glands, etc., should be regulated.

Janes (Australia) referred to a scantling table from Commonwealth of Australia draft requirements for the construction of ferro-cement vessels prepared by the Ship Structures Safety Branch, Department of Shipping and Transport. This intended to provide basic scantlings for reinforcing mesh, rod sizes and hull thicknesses for vessels having freeboard lengths in the range 9–30 m (30–100 ft). The steel content had been maintained in excess of 480 kg/m^3 (30 lb/ft^3) and the mesh thickness and rod diameters were compatible with predetermined hull sizes. He pointed out that designers and builders had submitted plans on which they as an authority had to make a pronouncement and that was why the table had been produced.

Doleman (USA) said that there were many structures built of what is commonly accepted as ferro-cement which did not meet the requirements as to longitudinal and transverse rods, layers of mesh, thickness, etc., laid down in scantling tables. He considered that if regulations were brought into force without allowance for the development of new materials and methods, bureaucracy being what it is, it would take years to make any changes in such regulations.

Fyson (FAO) queried the method of establishing scantlings purely on theoretical hydrodynamic considerations and felt that the most important consideration for designers was the question of service loads, such as resistance to impact, handling and slipping, etc. Moar's paper, for example, indicated that resistance to local impact improved with increasing hull thickness as well as mortar strength and reinforcement type. Scrivener and Carr had taken a thickness of 2.5 cm (1 in) for a 10.65 m (35 ft) boat but said that on theoretical considerations there was no need for transverse steel. If a thickness of 2·5 cm (1 in) was required for a boat of this size, then transverse steel would be one way to obtain this without increasing mortar cover. Sandwich construction as described by Moar could also be used. Extra thickness to improve impact resistance requires extra rigidity in the hull during the building to support the extra weight of mortar and again transverse steel would be one useful way of obtaining such rigidity. This indicated that sea loads are not the basic criterion for establishing scantlings but rather construction problems and service loads.

Norris (Canada) pointed out that the aim in ferro-cement was to use finely dispersed reinforcement and he would prefer rods kept to a smaller diameter but with more layers of mesh. He also thought that two layers of the rod should be laid diagonally to suppress the tendency to twist, as he had seen hulls in Canada that were so flexible that the propeller shafting was thrown out of alignment.

Walker (Australia) agreed with Norris and mentioned the added advantage of diagonal rods in fairing the hull. Vertical rods pulled round the quicker turn of the bilge could flatten the longitudinal rod between the frames. Running one or two layers of rod diagonally avoided this problem.

Amundsen (Australia) said that there was a need for simple rules and regulations but it should be understood that the more simple the rules, the more difficult the task of defining them. Det Norske Veritas was developing rules for construction of ferro-cement vessels but realized that they had to be framed as principles rather than specific regulations.

Boden (Australia) noted that there appeared to be a feeling, that any attempt to enforce sizes of rod or other restrictions would limit the development of techniques. However, as a designer who had not had a great deal of experience in ferrocement, he wanted some guidance. It appeared that every type of construction made use of some form of wire mesh so that this was one essential. Apparently there was some doubt as to whether rods were absolutely necessary. Therefore, as some things are essential and for others there were alternatives, the guidelines should look something like a tree with a trunk which was basic and from out of it should come branches that would offer alternatives. The sizes, strengths, qualities and other relevant information about these alternatives should be indicated.

Moar (New Zealand) pointed out that his company used timber instead of rods and had a jig that supported the timber, so that stiffness while applying the mortar was not a critical factor. Behnke, and Walker in his smaller boats, did not use rods, nor do many others. In conventional methods the bigger the boat the heavier and thicker the rods needed to support the mortar, but rods should not be specified just because they were needed in one particular manufacturing process. One should rather specify strength characteristics and allow the designer to work out how he was going to achieve them.

Bigg (Canada) considered that scantlings should not be laid down in rigid detail, since, to specify the diameter of a rod, for example, was not sufficient; the kind of steel, how it might be lapped and where it might be placed would all have to be considered. He felt that is was important to isolate those parameters which affected performance and did not believe that a mesh size *per se* or a number of rods were in fact those parameters. It was more fundamental than that and involved the basic quantity of mortar in a number of different aspects, as well as some specific characteristics of the reinforcement and how it was placed.

Betteridge (New Zealand) said that Lloyd's Register of Shipping also considered the publication of a scantlings table to be restrictive and at this time preferred in a developing technology to consider each case on its merits.

Eyres (New Zealand) answering Bowen's question on his paper as to whether strength criteria were to be based on wave-and-sea-load conditions or on service damage, said that the New Zealand Marine Board had over 1000 fishing vessels under survey and would find it difficult to point to a vessel that had failed at sea under normal conditions. Damage or loss of vessels had been due to service loads and he considered that the criterion for the design of ferro-cement boats in the future would be based on service loads and rely on empirical factors as was still done for steel and wooden fishing boats.

PUBLICATIONS OF CLASSIFICATION SOCIETIES

AMERICAN BUREAU OF SHIPPING: Guidelines for the construction of ferro-cement vessels.

1. General Conditions

1.1 *Classification*

Vessels which have been wholly or primarily built of ferrocement, and which have been built under the special supervision of the Surveyors to the Bureau, in accordance with these Guidelines, or their equivalent and other relevant sections of the Rules, will be considered for classification, and where approved by the Committee, distinguished in the Record by the symbols ✠ A1 "Annual Survey". The type of construction "Ferro-Cement" will be noted in the Record.

1.2 *Workmanship*

The Surveyor is to satify himself that all operators employed in the construction of vessels to be considered for classification are properly qualified in the type of work proposed, and that equipment and other facilities are such that acceptable standards can be obtained for the construction of the hull; superstructures and appendages thereto, and for the installation of equipment, machinery, piping and the electrical system.

1.3 *Construction Surveys*

The builder is to maintain a schedule of systematic inspections at regular intervals during the construction of the vessel, and records thereof, made by qualified personnel of the yard, are to be made available for inspection by the Surveyor. The Surveyor is to be present at the completion of all the major stages of construction. Additional visits will depend on the size of the vessel, and requests of the owner or builder.

1.4 *Surveys after Construction*

The hull is to be subject to an Annual Survey on drydock, equivalent to a Special Survey. The hull is to be examined internally and externally, and all framing, appendages, deck houses, bulkheads, etc., are to be examined. These Annual Surveys are to continue, until sufficient experience has been acquired to determine, that surveys at longer intervals are reasonable and proper.

1.5 *Submission of Plans*

Plans showing the particulars, arrangements and details of the principle parts of the hull structure of each vessel, to be built under Special Survey, are to be submitted and approved before the work of construction is commenced. These plans are to indicate clearly the particulars, as well as the details and arrangements of the reinforcements of the hull. A construction schedule, giving details of materials, mixes, reinforcements, mortar application and curing procedures, is also to be submitted. Plans should generally be submitted in triplicate.

1.6 *Calculations*

The designer is to prepare strength calculations to justify the strength of the hull and its components. These calculations are to be based on the values obtained from the testing procedure, as prescribed in Section 4, and are to be submitted with the plans, as required by 1.5.

2. Particulars and Construction

2.1 *Definitions*

The definition of a hull or structure built in Ferro-Cement is as follows: A thin, highly reinforced shell of concrete, in which the steel reinforcement is distributed widely throughout the concrete, so that the material, under stress, acts approximately as homogeneous material. The strength properties of the material are to be determined by testing a significant number of samples of representative panels, according to Section 4. If a similar approval is obtained from a recognized authority, the Bureau may waive these requirements, upon review of the previous tests and such check tests as may be deemed necessary.

2.2 *Reinforcements*

The steel content of the Ferro-Cement should be as high as practicable, and arranged in such a manner as to allow adequate penetration of the mortar, and thereby result in a void-free material. The reinforcing rods, pipes and wire mesh are to be evenly distributed and shaped to form. Transverse frames or bulkheads are to be fitted, to provide adequate transverse strength. The reinforcement network should be securely welded or otherwise fastened together so that it remains in its original position during the application of the mortar.

Structural steel sections may be incorporated into Ferro-Cement structures as longitudinal strength members, floors, etc., but care must be taken to ensure penetration of the mortar, and a proper bonding between the framework and the mesh.

The reinforcements may be tapered towards the ends of the structure, where the hull form becomes "finer", but care is to be taken to avoid discontinuities in the strength of the reinforcements, and ends of members are to be faired into the adjoining structure. The overlaps of the mesh layers at the keel, transom edges, etc., are to be staggered to allow even distribution of reinforcement in those areas, and to ensure satisfactory penetration of the mortar. Butts in reinforcement are to be suitably staggered, to avoid discontinuities.

2.3 *Formwork*

In methods of construction where internal or external forms are employed, satisfactory penetration of the mortar must be ensured, and the reinforcements are to be secured, so that distortion is minimized on application of mortar. The formwork is to have a smooth surface, and is to be thoroughly cleaned before applying the mortar.

2.4 *Concrete*

The methods employed for the mixing, handling, compacting and curing of the concrete are to be consistent and result in high quality material. The mortar should be applied as soon as possible after mixing, and constant agitation of the mix is to be provided during the waiting period. If any separation of water from the mix is observed during the waiting period, the mortar is to be remixed before application. Containers used to transport the mortar are to be clean. Care must be taken during the application of the mortar, so that no void spaces remain adjacent to the reinforcements or in corners. Vibrators, and/or hand rodding, are to be used to compact the mortar at thicker sections. A complete coverage of the reinforcement is to be ensured, although the thickness of coating should be kept at a minimum, and an excessive buildup of cement is to be avoided. Ferro-Cement structures are to be cured in a satisfactory manner. Various methods of curing are acceptable, depending on ambient conditions, but in general, the curing should be done by water spraying, by steam curing under a hood, or by membrane curing. Curing should normally not commence until about three to four hours after the mortar application, or when the mortar has taken its first set. This period may be longer in association with low atmospheric temperatures. The temperature during the curing period is to be kept approximately constant. Where a form is employed, it shall be kept in position for as long as practicable during curing.

3. Materials

3.1 *Cement*

The cement shall ordinary Portland Cement, in accordance with a suitable approved specification, such as ASTM C 535–67T. Other cements will also be considered providing they offer adequate water-tightness and uniform consistency. Cement should be stored under dry conditions, and if the application of the mortar is done in stages, a suitable turnover of cement stock is to be arranged to ensure consistent freshness. Any presence of lumps in the cement renders it questionable for use, and it is to be sieved before mixing.

3.2 *Aggregate*

Aggregates are to have suitable strength and durability and are to be free of foreign materials, including chemical salts. The aggregate is to normally include washed sand of a silicious nature. The aggregate is to comply with a suitable specification such as ASTM C 330–68T.

3.3 *Water*

Water is to be free from foreign materials that may impair the strength and resistance of the mortar. It is to be free of salts.

3.4 *Mixing*

Mixing is to done in such proportions as to consistently give the required strength, as determined by Section 4. The proportions of the mix are to be by weight. The water:cement ratio is to be controlled as low as possible to give the material a consistent quality and workability. Initially this is to be judged by a slump test and practicable workability under the existing conditions. Once this criterion is established, the mortar is to be held to a consistent slump test standard.

3.5 *Reinforcements*

Reinforcements (rods, pipes, expanded metal, wire mesh) are to have sufficient tensile and yield strength and ductility, and other properties essential for good construction. The reinforcements are to comply with a suitable specification, such as ASTM A 615–68, A 185–64 and A 390–66. The reinforcements are to be free from millscale, grease and any other contamination. Light corrosion is not objectionable, but should be brushed to remove free oxide. Black or galvanized reinforcements are acceptable.

4. Testing

4.1 *Mechanical Properties Testing*

The mechanical properties tests, as listed below, are to be performed on representative samples. Prior to commencement of construction, preliminary tests are to be carried out on standard test pieces, as described below, in order to determine that the proportions of the mortar mixes and properties and arrangements of the reinforcements will satisfy the design strength requirements of the vessel. The preliminary test pieces are to be in accordance with a suitable specification such as ASTM C 192–68, although curing may be done at an accelerated rate. Preliminary tests are to be carried out satisfactorily before construction is begun. During construction, test pieces, as described below, are to be made from the same mortar batches used in the actual hull construction, and the following tests are to be carried out.

For each 50 cubic feet or fraction thereof, a minimum of one each if the following tests, direct tensile, compressive, flexural and impact test are to be made. At least three of each of these tests are to be made for each hull or structure. Where larger unit hulls or structures are being built and large identical mixes of mortar are used, one set of tests per batch of 10 cubic yards (7.65 m³) or fraction thereof shall be carried out. A minimum of six sets of tests are to be made for each unit of construction. These tests are to be carried out in a manner that will yield reliable values of the tensile and compressive strength at both cracking and failure, as well as the modulus of rupture and elasticity and impact strength of the reinforced samples. In the construction tests, the curing is to be in accordance with a suitable specification such as ASTM C 31–66.

(a) *Compressive Test*

The compressive test is to be carried out on reinforced samples, which are to measure 4 inches in diameter and 8 inches long. The compressive test is to conform to a suitable specification, such as ASTM C 39–66, and the test report is to conform thereto.

(b) The tensile strength is to be determined by the "split cylinder" test, using similar testing apparatus as in the compressive test above. ASTM C 496–66 specification describes the procedure for this test, and offers the formula to determine the "splitting tensile strength". The test pieces are to be unreinforced and of the same size as those in the compressive test. However, it should be noted that the true tensile strength of the specimen lies between 50 and 70 per cent of the "splitting tensile strength".

(c) *Flexural Test*

The flexural tests are to be carried out on slabs of concrete approximately 4 feet long 12 inches wide and of same thickness as the hull. The tests pieces are to be reinforced and should have the same pattern of reinforcement as the actual hull. The flexural test is to conform to a suitable specification, such as ASTM C 293–68 and ASTM C 78–64, but care must be taken to ensure that the load application and support blocks provide a uniform load across the test piece. Furthermore, readings are to be taken at both cracking and failure.

(d) Impact Test

An impact test is to be performed on representative reinforced panels, The thicknesses and reinforcement of the test panels are to follow the same patterns as those of the actual hull. The panel is to be flat and should measure about 2 feet × 2 feet, and is to have two mutually perpendicular vee notches $\frac{1}{25}$ in (1 mm) wide and $\frac{1}{12}$ in (2 mm) deep across the centroid of test panel. The notches are to be at right angles to the edges, A drop weight type is to be employed. Failure occurs when the test panel develops a leak, and this is to be determined by a water-hose test or equivalent. The test report is to include the following:

(1) Identification number
(2) All dimensions of the specimen
(3) Applied load that causes failure
(4) Curing, history, and moisture condition of specimen at testing
(5) Defects of specimen and age
(6) Ambient conditions

LLOYDS REGISTER OF SHIPPING: Tentative Requirements for the Construction of Yachts and Small Craft in Ferro-Cement

These tentative requirements were published by the Society in 1967 but readers should note that new guidance notes are in course of preparation and will be published in due course—EDITOR.

Part 1. General Requirements

1.1 Survey During Construction

Where ferro-cement is used in yachts and small craft proposed for classification or to be built under supervision, it shall comply with these requirements.

All new boats intended for classification are to be built under the Society's Special Survey and when classed will be entitled to the distinguishing mark ✠ inserted before the character of classification in the Register of Yachts or the Register of Ships, as appropriate. In the case of boats wholly or mainly constructed of this material, the class shall have the notation "Experimental—Ferro-Cement Hull", and shall be subject to annual survey.

1.2 Works

The boat is to be constructed under the survey of a Surveyor to the Society in an establishment where the facilities, equipment, etc., are such that acceptable standards can be obtained both for the construction of the hull and for the installation of any machinery and/or electrical equipment to be fitted.

The boatyard should be staffed by competent tradesmen and supervised by a management familiar with this material, and capable of carrying out the production of high quality work.

1.3 Inspection

The boat is to be built under a rigid inspection system employed by the builder, the inspection being made at regular intervals and stages of construction by a responsible official of the firm. A satisfactory record of these inspections is to be maintained for the Surveyor's inspection.

The construction will normally be inspected by the Surveyor at the following main stages:

(a) When the steel reinforcement is half completed
(b) When the steel reinforcement is completed
(c) During the application and compaction of the mortar
(d) At the stripping of any major formwork
(e) At the end of the curing period

The above visits are intended only as a general guide and the actual number will depend on the size of the construction and the degree to which ferro-cement is being used, and will be arranged between the boatyard and the Surveyor. The boatyards are to keep the Surveyor advised as to the progress of the construction.

Part 2. Materials

2.1 Cement

The cement is to be Ordinary Portland Cement of a type complying with a suitable specification, such as BS 12, and is to have good water tightness properties. Other types of cement will be considered but no mixing of the various types should be carried out.

The cement is to be of the type specified, and is to be fresh and of uniform consistency; material containing lumps and foreign matter is not to be used. The cement is to be held in storage for as short a period as possible, under dry conditions and properly organized as regard turnover of material, etc.

2.2 Aggregates

The aggregates are to be of suitable types with regard to strength, durability and freedom from harmful properties. The material is to be uniform and of a grade which will readily give a satisfactory minimum cover of the reinforcement without risk of segregation and use of excessive water.

2.3 Water

The water used in the mixing is to be fresh and free from harmful materials in solution which will affect the strength and resistance of the mortar. Salt water is not to be used.

2.4 Batching and Mixing of the Concrete Materials

The proportions of cement and aggregates are to be such as to give concrete equivalent to the basis material (see para. 4.2). The quantities of the materials are normally to be determined by weight, although the aggregates may be determined by volume where so desired.

The water : cement ratio is to be controlled as low as possible to give a material consistent in quality and workability.

2.5 Reinforcement

The rods, bars and wires are to be of steel having a satisfactory yield stress, ductility, tensile strength and other essential properties and complying with a suitable specification such as BS 18 or B.S. 785.

The wire mesh is to be formed of a suitable diameter steel wire, laid up in such a manner as to preserve as much of the strength properties of the basic wire as possible. A sample of the mesh is to be submitted along with the material data.

The reinforcement is to be clean and free of millscale, oil, grease, paint or other contamination.

Part 3. Design and Construction

3.1 Scantlings

These requirements envisage the hull and other structures built in ferro-cement, being a form of reinforced concrete in which a high steel content is sub-divided widely throughout the material, so that the structures will act when under stress as though produced from a homogeneous material.

In view of only a limited number of builders at present using this material and also until such times as a common practice is established, the scantlings of the structures will be based on the representative strength figures referred to below, and on an examination of the design and construction methods to be employed. Each case will be examined individually and considered on its merits.

Basic strength properties of representative panels laid up using the same mix and mesh reinforcement as are proposed for the structures, are to be determined as given in part 4. However, where such representative properties have been previously established by an acceptable authority, these may be considered by the Society and the need for these tests may be dispensed with.

3.2 Submission of Plans and Data

Plans, in triplicate, are to be submitted for approval for each design before construction is commenced. These plans shall show the arrangement and detail of the reinforcement of the hull and other structures. Such other plans as may be necessary to define the structural arrangements are to be submitted.

A data sheet is to be submitted giving details of the materials, mixes, curing procedure, etc., of the ferro-cement construction.

3.3 Steel Reinforcement

The steel content of the ferro-cement is to be as high as practicable, and the disposition of the rods and mesh to be consistent with the production of void-free material. The rods and mesh are to be correctly disposed and shaped to form, with sufficient transverse members to maintain the form of the hull, and to be securely wired and welded to avoid movement during the placement of the mortar.

The keel centreline member, longitudinal girders, floors, etc., are to be formed with rods and mesh and may incorporate rolled steel sections, but the build-up of reinforcement should not prevent satisfactory penetration of the mortar. Two or more layers of mesh forming the member are to be worked into the hull form, due regard being paid to the sharpness of curvature to avoid large voids within the base of the member.

Any discontinuities in the strength of the reinforcement are to be avoided and the ends of members are to be properly faired into the adjoining structure. The wires of the mesh layers can be orientated to suit the arrangement of lay-up but should not unduly affect the panel strength and prevent penetration of the mortar. The edges of the mesh layers forming the overlaps along the hull centrelines, transom boundary, etc., are to be staggered-back to permit the reinforcement to be neatly formed and allow satisfactory mortar penetration. Butts in the mesh reinforcement should be correctly arranged and suitably staggered.

The welding of rods and bars is to be carried out by a skilled operator care being taken to avoid the burning-through of the reinforcement on account of excessive heat generation.

3.4 Formwork

The structures are assumed to be normally built up by the application of mortar to one side of the reinforcement and trowelled to a finish on the other, however, production using formwork can be employed provided void-free material can be achieved.

Where formwork is used, it should be dimensionally accurate and have adequate stability and strength to resist the weight of the pour. The panelling should be well fitting and free from joints and cracks liable to leak. Free water and debris are to be removed before a pour commences. The forms may be hosed down prior to pouring to remove any settled dust.

3.5 Concrete

The various practices for the mixing, handling, compaction and curing of the concrete should be consistent and closely supervised to ensure high quality material. The practices should comply with paras 3.6 to 3.8 and the builder should be guided by established Codes of Practice, such as CP 114 (1957) of the BSI.

3.6 Handling

The mortar should normally be placed within 1½ hours of adding the mixing water, and with continual agitation during the waiting period. During handling and placing of the mortar, care is to be taken to avoid segregation of the mix and if this is seen to be occurring, remedial steps are to be taken.

If the mortar is transported in barrows or skips, these are to be clean and smooth inside and free from leaks.

3.7 Compaction

The material must be thoroughly compacted during placing to ensure the absence of voids around reinforcements and in the corners of any forms. Formless ferro-cement shells are to be compacted by applying the mortar from one side of the reinforcement only and hand trowelling the opposite side. Vibrators and hand rodding are to be used in the thicker sections between forms.

Although the minimum amount of mortar coverage over the reinforcement is desirable, this amount is not to be less than that consistent with satisfactory protection for the steel.

3.8 Curing

The various structures are to be properly cured and the set concrete is to be kept wet for a period which will depend on the type of cement being used and the ambient conditions. The method of curing should normally be by water spray but other methods which prevent evaporation of the residual water will be considered.

Where formwork has been used, it should be kept in position for as long as practicable. Due regard is to be paid to the ambient conditions, the type of concrete and the position of the structure before the formwork is stripped.

3.9 Items not Particularly Specified

If the decks, deckhouse, superstructure, bulkheads, etc., are of materials other than ferro-cement, the construction is to be in accordance with the Society's Rules applicable to the particular material being used.

Where special reference is not made herein to specific requirements, the construction is to be efficient for the intended service and is to conform to good practice.

Part 4. Testing

4.1 General Requirements

The following tests, or equivalent tests as agreed by the Surveyor, are to be carried out on sample panels, the mortar mix and the placed concrete structure. Other tests may be required as necessary at the discretion of the Surveyor.

4.2 Sample Representative Panels

Sample panels laid up from the same materials and mix, and reinforced with the same number of layers of wire mesh as are proposed for the hull, are to be prepared and tested to determine the typical mechanical properties of the ferro-cement. The tests are to be carried out by a recognized laboratory and the results submitted to the Society; however, in certain circumstances, test results by the builder may be considered.

The flexural and the impact strengths are to be determined on reinforced panels, but the tensile and the compressive strengths may be obtained from the un-reinforced material.

4.3 Slump Testing of the Concrete Mixes

A selection of mixes are to be tested in the standard slump cone for workability and water content and are to show a minimum slump consistent with reasonable workability.

4.4 Compression Testing of Concrete Samples

A suitable number of standard test cubes or cylinders are to be taken during the course of application of the concrete as representative of the material being used in the construction. The samples are to be selected and filled in the presence of the Surveyor and are to be suitably identified.

The samples are to be cured under standard conditions (such as given in BS 1881) and the compressive strength determined after 7 days and 28 days cure. The tests are to be witnessed by the Surveyor, or if done by a testing laboratory, the certified results are to be submitted to the Surveyor.

4.5 Watertightness of the Structure

The hull and other surfaces which are intended to be watertight, are to be closely inspected for surface faults after completion of trowelling, or when formwork is first stripped when applicable. A smooth, sound appearing surface will normally be presumed watertight until tested by hose, by filling or afloat.

Spot checking by air testing may require to be done at the discretion of the Surveyor.

MARINE BOARD OF QUEENSLAND (AUSTRALIA):
Requirements for the Construction and Survey of Ferro-Cement Fishing Vessels of maximum Length 60 feet.

1. General Requirements

Where ferro-cement is used in fishing vessel construction for the purpose of Certification by the Board, the following Regulations shall apply.

Where alternative arrangements or methods are proposed, due notification should be given to the Marine Board to allow assessment prior to construction.

2. Submission of Plans

2.1 The Navigation (Survey & Equipment of Fishing Vessels) Regulations of 1960 requires that a person to whose order a fishing vessel is to be constructed and the owner of a fishing vessel which is to be materially altered before going into Service, shall submit to the Board, not later than one month before any construction or alteration is commenced, the following plans, information and data;

(i) the general arrangement plans;
(ii) the construction plans, including midship and longitudinal sections;
(iii) the lines plans;
(iv) the scantlings of all members, including deck, shell, and watertight bulkheads, and methods of fastening;
(v) the details of the closing devices;
(vi) the bilge pumping arrangements;
(vii) the details of the oil fuel system, including filling and venting arrangements, piping and valves; fuel tank construction;
(viii) the fire protection arrangements;
(ix) the details of the rudder and stern frames, propeller brackets, engine and thrust seatings, propeller shafting, bearing and couplings, steering gear and alternative method of steering;
(x) the stability information; and
(xi) such further plans; information and data as the Board considers necessary and requests:

(a) Provided that in the case of a vessel which is to be materially altered the Board may determine that, in the circumstances of the case, such of the foregoing plans, information or data, as it considers unnecessary or impracticable, need not be submitted.
(b) The fee payable to the Board for the examination of all or any of the foregoing plans, information and data, shall be a fee equal to one half of the annual survey fee for the class of vessel to which such plans, information or data refer.
(c) A person shall not commence or continue the construction or material alteration of a vessel, or attempt any of these things or cause, suffer, permit or allow any of these things to be done, before the Board has approved the relevant plans, information and data.
(d) When the Board has approved the relevant plans, information and data, the person to whose order a vessel is to be constructed, or the owner of a vessel which is to be materially altered, as the case may be, shall apply within fourteen days to the Board for the survey of the vessel.

Plans in duplicate, in the case of the survey area New South Wales border to Gladstone shall be submitted and in the case of vessels to be constructed north of Gladstone, plans shall be submitted in triplicate to the Senior Engineer Surveyor of the Marine Board for approval.

A specification shall be submitted giving details of materials, mixes and curing procedures to be adopted during construction.

The vessel is to be constructed under the inspection of a Marine Board Engineer Surveyor, and the establishment undertaking the building shall demonstrate the capacity to provide quantity and quality control and also the ability to provide an area for construction that can be sealed to exclude air currents causing rapid dehydration of the concrete or alternative methods of curing acceptable to the Board.

For purpose of Certification, the boat shall be built under rigid inspection, and inspections by the Engineer Surveyor will be carried out at the following stages of hull construction.

(a) During the lay-up of steel reinforcement
(b) At the completion of reinforcement and prior to plastering
(c) During the plastering operation
(d) At the conclusion of the curing period prior to painting
(e) During the period of outfitting and subsequent trials

It is the responsibility of the builder to notify the Marine Board as to the progress of construction. Certification will not be recommended if the inspections nominated above are not carried out.

An initial survey on a slipway shall be conducted after a three months' period of operation following satisfactory final inspection and trials followed by normal certificate currency, if the initial survey proves satisfactory.

3. Materials

3.1 Cement

The cement shall be of an ordinary Portland cement of a type conforming with a recognized specification, for example, AS 2/1963. Other types of cement will be considered but shall be the subject of notification to the Marine Board for approval prior to commencement of construction.

The cement shall be of the type specified and is to be fresh and of regular consistency. The cement shall be held in storage for as short a time as possible and a test certificate shall be obtained from the supplier indicating age and quality of the cement and submitted to the Board. Cement containing lumps and foreign matter is not to be used.

3.2 *Sand*

Almost any type of sand can be used for ferro-cement construction, but a sand with a fairly long grading will assist workability. Sands may contain impurities which have an adverse effect on cement, cause retardation of set, and strength loss, while the presence of chlorides may promote corrosion of reinforcement. Very fine material shall not exceed 4 per cent of the aggregate used, as increased shrinkage and increased water demand may result. A watertight hull cannot be achieved if the water:cement ratio is too high. Recommended mixes by proportions shall not be used without first making tests for workability. See under Batching.

Bulking of sand shall be taken into account when preparing for batching. (If the true amount of sand is not determined it is possible that an error in sand addition to the mix of as much as 63 per cent may result).

Trial mixes shall be made up and carefully recorded against results in a mock panel to assess suitability and resultant reasonable workability. The maximum grain size should pass through a number 7 B.S. sieve.

Water-proofing additives are of doubtful value and shall not be used.

3.3 *Steel*

Steel content will vary with the hull or panel thickness, and should be specified to the Marine Board on the form of weight per square foot. The acceptable minimum shall be 3 lb per square foot. Hull thickness should be included in the specification and is to be of minimum 7/8 of an inch for vessels in the 45 ft to 60 ft range. (Vessels under 45 ft will be the subject of special consideration.)

The use of pipe frames is not recommended due to possible distortion and will be the subject of special consideration. Transverse frame lay-up and spacing should be clearly shown on the drawings submitted. Maximum spacing should not exceed 24 in and of lesser spacing where necessary to maintain hull shape and strength. The depth of frames should be clearly defined.

Adequate hull support shall be provided prior to the commencement of laying-up and plastering, otherwise distortion of the hull from settlement will result.

The entire weight shall be supported on the overhead framework and extra internal props should be fitted to maintain fair lines.

Bulkheads shall be fitted as required by the Model Code of Recommended Practice for the Construction and Survey of Fishing Vessels.

Horizontal and vertical spacers of 4 or 5 imperial wire gauge shall be fitted and tied at $2\frac{1}{2}$ in centres maximum. Welding, apart from stem and stern connexions, should generally be avoided due to the possibility of distortion making correction of fairness necessary. (High tensile or hard drawn wire spacers are superior to mild steel in resistance to local bending qualities.)

Keel reinforcement of minimum diameter 5/8 in should be specified and shown on the drawings submitted showing attachment to other primary members. Centre line members, longitudinal girders, floors, etc. are to be formed with rods and mesh and may incorporate rod steel sections but the lay-up of reinforcement should ensure satisfactory penetration of mortar. Particular care shall be taken to avoid sharpness of curvature so as not to promote voids. Care should also be taken with the bow shape, as a sharp stem presents difficulties in compacting mortar.

3.4 *Steel Mesh*

Light gauge (16 to 22 gauge) welded $\frac{1}{2}$ in mesh shall be applied over the horizontal and vertical spacers and suitably tied.

Hexagonal mesh will not be accepted for certification by the Marine Board.

If galvanized wire is used, bending qualities are to be ensured by allowing the mesh to weather and oxidize prior to plastering.

A minimum of 3 layers of $\frac{1}{2}$ in square mesh each side shall be applied to the primary mesh. These make up the inner and outer layers of the panel, those on the inside being carried over the frames and suitably rounded to form adequate stiffeners.

3.5 *Pozzolans*

Pozzolans are used for producing workability of fresh mortar and take the form of fly ash from boiler smoke stacks or diatomaceous earth. These may be included as a replacement for up to 10 per cent of the cement.

Portland pozzolanic cements shall not be used for the whole mix as the percentage of pozzolan is excessive. Pozzolanic cement in the ratio of 1 to 1 with normal Portland cement will be accepted.

3.6 *Water*

The water used in the mix shall be fresh and free from harmful materials in solution which could affect strength and resistance of the mortar. Salt water shall not be used.

The water to cement ratio should not be greater than 0.5 by weight and for increased strength; a lower figure of 0.45 should be aimed at.

$$\text{Water to cement ratio} = \frac{\text{weight of water used}}{\text{total weight of cement used}}.$$

The water to cement ratio affects permeability (the ability to leak) and at a figure of 0.68 it is impossible to obtain leak-proof ferro-cement.

The use of cold water is very effective in combating increased evaporation in areas with ambient temperatures in excess of 85°F.

In extreme conditions, where facilities exist, it can be considered desirable to use crushed ice with the mixing water.

The use of 50–50 mix of ice and water can achieve a temperature reduction of 20°F per cubic yard of mix. The ice (maximum particle size $1\frac{1}{2}$ in) shall be added during the mixing cycle and should be completely melted before entering the mixer.

3.7 *Possible Galvanic Action*

To resist the possibility of galvanic action between mild steel and galvanized steel, or between galvanized steel and alloy skin fittings, all fittings, to be attached to galvanized mesh (if used) shall be galvanized prior to inclusion and allowed to weather.

All fittings shall be adequately connected to avoid hull strain under load. Similarly, adequate longitudinal reinforcement shall be fitted in the way of such fittings. Anchor plates with reinforcement stirrups can be cast into the hull to carry these fittings.

Timber shall not be cast into the hull as the moisture effect will promote leakage following shrinkage.

3.8 *Batching*

The quantities are to be submitted in the specification and these quantities shall be determined by weight and not by volume. Hand mixing is to be avoided and a motorized mortar mixer of the paddle type should be used.

Sand to cement:pozzolan ratio shall be confined between the limits of 1.8. and 2.1 to 1.

4.1 *Plastering and Compaction*

Plastering should be carried out by experienced plasters, and may be carried out from either inside or outside the hull.

The application of plaster to steel reinforcement shall be certified in writing by a qualified Clerk of Works, Technical Officer or qualified Engineer. The certificate shall include reference to plant, equipment methods, materials and existing trade practices and the Marine Board's Draft Code.

The use of surface vibrators is permitted but such equipment should be handled with great care due to the possibility of disturbing compacted mortar. If a spray application is contemplated approval should first be sought from the Board.

The materials shall be thoroughly compacted during placement to ensure the absence of voids around reinforcements and in the corners of any forms.

Although the minimum amount of mortar coverage over the reinforcement is desirable this amount is not to be less than that consistent with suitable protection for the steel and should average $\frac{1}{16}$ in. Where possible, deck and hull plastering should be completed in one operation.

If the hull only is plastered starters should be carried over for bulkheads, deep frames, decks, etc.

Joints in construction are acceptable only if proper techniques are employed. Details are to be submitted to the Board for consideration.

New mortar should never be added to surfaces showing a shiny finish (laitence). Laitence shall be renewed by scrubbing or water blasting taking care not to damage the mortar. This will produce a surafce suitable for a key to new mortar.

Portland cement grout, as a cream, brushed well into the previously dampened surface shall be used and fresh mortar applied not later than 15 minutes.

If a manufactured jointing product is to be used, the Board shall be advised in the specification.

5.1 *Curing*

The various structures are to be properly cured and the retention of water during a period of 21 days is recommended. The exclusion of air currents is of prime importance to avoid dehydration and resultant shrinkage cracking.

Curing shall commence not earlier than 5 hours or later than 12 hours after completion of plastering.

Methods of ensuring proper curing include water sprays on hessian covering the hull or plastic covers over the hull and water trays located inside the plastic screen to promote moisture.

Curing materials shall not be used.

6.1 *Testing*

A test panel shall be submitted to the Marine Board for testing and shall be of dimensions 2 ft square and of similar lay-up to the method used in hull reinforcement. This panel will be plastered in the presence of a Surveyor, and suitably marked for the purpose of identification.

Similarly, slump tests in accordance with Australian Standard A101/1967 and a minimum of 6 test cylinders in accordance with AS A103/1968 shall be taken at the discretion of the Surveyor. Test cylinders and the panel shall be cured with the hull prior to submission to the Board.

Test cylinders are to be weighed when taken out of moulds and weights recorded in the appendix. These shall be tested by a recognized Authority and results submitted to the Senior Engineer Surveyor of the Marine Board for evaluation. All costs incurred shall be met by the owner.

All hull compartments are to be tested by flooding, in the presence of the Engineer Surveyor at the expiration of 90 days from completion of plastering.

7.1 *Fitting Out of Vessel*

The remainder of construction details including engineering and outfitting shall be submitted to the Marine Board for appraisal prior to the commencement of construction.

8.1 *Painting*

The hull shall not be painted until the final survey has been carried out by the Surveyor. Following curing the hull shall be allowed to dry out followed by a light sanding prior to paint application.

9.1 The importance of quality and quantity control during laying-up of reinforcing and selective tests of material during the plastering and curing operations cannot be over-emphasized. An unskilled approach to ferro-cement construction will ensure a second-class result.

NEW ZEALAND MARINE DEPARTMENT: Requirements for the construction of ferro-cement boats.

Introduction

These requirements are intended to apply to small ferro-cement boats built in New Zealand and which are subject to survey by the Marine Department or the owners of which request plans and/or construction to be approved by the Department.

Section 1—Definitions

In using these rules the following definitions apply:

Length, L—means registered length as defined in the Shipping and Seamen Act, 1952, namely:

"The length of the ship measured from the fore side of the head of the stem to the after side of the head of the stern post, or to the fore side of the head of the rudder stock if no stern post is provided."

Approval—means approved by the Secretary for Marine.

Section 2—General Requirements

2.1 *Submission of plans and specifications*

For each vessel for which Marine Department approval of plans is required, the following plans in duplicate, drawn to a suitable scale, are to be submitted:

General arrangement plan.

Longitudinal section and transverse sections showing adequately the amount and distribution of reinforcement in hull and decks and finished thickness of mortar.

Such additional plans (if any) as are required to show full details of construction and arrangement of:

Watertight bulkheads
Oil fuel tanks
Rudder
Propeller brackets
Propeller shafting and bearings
Machinery seatings
Steering gear details
Deckhouses and superstructure
Diagrammatic bilge pumping and fire main arrangement
Diagrammatic electrical arrangement
Outline specification giving details of anchors and cables, navigational equipment, lifesaving and fire appliances, radio and other equipment
Specification giving details of the mortar mix, method of application and details of curing method proposed.
Reinforcement material and sizes.

2.2 *Building and workmanship*

The boat is to be built strictly in conformity with the approved plans and specification and subject to any conditions specified by the department when granting approval.

The boat is to be constructed at a site where the available facilities, equipment, etc., are considered by a Surveyor of Ships suitable for the maintenance of standards associated with ferro-cement construction and also good boatbuilding practice, including the installation of machinery and electrical equipment, etc.

All workmanship must be of a standard acceptable to a Surveyor of Ships and plastering is to be carried out by persons experienced in this work, and under the supervision of a person who must have satisfied a Surveyor of Ships that he is sufficiently experienced and qualified to exercise such supervision.

2.3 *Inspection and survey*

The boat is to be built under a quality control system employed by the builder and approved by a Surveyor of Ships and a satisfactory record of such control is to be maintained for the Surveyor's approval.

In addition, the boat under construction will be visited periodically by a Surveyor of Ships who will inspect the boat not less than once during the following stages where applicable:

1. During erection of the reinforcement.
2. When reinforcement is complete.
3. During application of the mortar.
4. At the end of the curing period and the removal of any formwork.
5. Following any repair work necessary as a result of previous inspection.
6. During the fitting-out period.
7. Final inspection and tests afloat.

It is the responsibility of the builder to keep the Surveyor informed as to the progress of construction in order that the visits may be made at appropriate times.

Section 3—Materials

3.1 *General*

Materials are to comply with NZSS 1051, 1953 "Concrete Materials and Methods of Test" where applicable.

3.2 *Cement*

The cement is to be ordinary Portland cement complying with NZSS 184 or similar approved standard. Other cements will receive special consideration.

The cement should be fresh and of uniform consistency. Where there is evidence of lumps or any foreign matter in the material, it should not be used. The cement is to be stored under dry conditions and for as short a duration as possible.

3.3 *Admixtures*

Special consideration will be given to the addition of materials to the concrete for special purposes. Approval may be given where the material is added to directly or indirectly reduce the water : cement ratio, and where approved standards are published for the additive.

3.4 *Aggregates*

Should be obtained from a reliable supplier and, where applicable, should comply with NZSS 2129, 1967 or similar approved standard.

The aggregate should be inert with respect to other materials used and of a suitable type having regard to the strength, density, shrinkage, and durability of the mortar made with the aggregate.

Grading of the aggregate is to be such that a mortar of the specified proportions is produced, with a uniform distribution of the aggregate and adequate cover over the reinforcement, which will work readily into position without segregation and without use of a high water content.

3.5 *Water*

Water used in the mixing is to be fresh and free from any organic and harmful solutions which will lead to a deterioration in the properties of the mortar. Salt water is not to be used.

3.6 *Batching and mixing of mortar materials*

The ingredients should be proportioned to give a workable dense mortar which can be thoroughly compacted on the framework provided. The water : cement ratio should be controlled as low as practicable to give compliance with the requirements of Section 5 of these rules and attention should be paid to estimating the moisture content of the aggregate used in this respect.

Quantities of materials are normally to be determined by weight although the aggregates may be determined by volume, due allowance being made for bulking due to moisture.

3.7 *Making of mortar*

Unless otherwise approved by a Surveyor of Ships, mortar should be made at the site and, where applicable, in accordance with NZSS 1900 Chapter 8, 1964 or similar approved standard.

3.8 *Reinforcement*

All reinforcement should be of steel rods, bars or wire conforming to NZSS 197, 1949 or similar approved standard.

The reinforcement should be clean and free from all loose mill scale, dust and loose rust, and coatings such as paint, oil or anything which may reduce bond.

The welding of reinforcement is to be carried out by a skilled operator, care being taken to avoid the burning through of the reinforcement on account of excessive heat generation.

Longitudinal reinforcing rods should not be welded to transverse reinforcing rods except where approved by a Surveyor of Ships.

Application of heat to obtain bends in steel reinforcement, particularly where higher tensile steels are used, will not be permitted except with the approval of a Surveyor of Ships.

Section 4—Design and Construction

4.1 *Design*

Boats submitted for approval in this medium should be displacement craft having well-rounded lines without excessive areas of flat hull. Particular attention should be given to avoiding sharp knuckles and protuberances, especially on fishing vessels and other workboats. Particular attention should be paid to the provision of adequate and well-placed beltings and other rubbing bars. Ferro-cement bulwarks should be avoided on fishing vessels and workboats and, where fitted, should be independent of the main hull.

4.2 *Minimum construction requirements*

Vessels having reinforcement in the form of wire rods covered by any form of mesh are to have a minimum steel content equivalent to 385 kg per cubic metre of mortar (24 lb per cubic foot of mortar). Where the registered length of the vessel is in excess of 13.71 m (45 ft) the wire rods are to provide approved transverse reinforcement in addition to that fore and aft.

Where the reinforcement material is other than wire rods as core with mesh covering, then sufficient evidence of the final materials' structural strength must be demonstrated to the Department's satisfaction by means of structural tests on panels and records of the performance in service of this material.

4.3 *Method of construction*

Construction should be by the suspended hull method, i.e., the erection of reinforcement on framing, either permanent or temporary. Local supports approved by a Surveyor of Ships may be provided to prevent distortion.

Other methods of construction will be specially considered, and details should be submitted.

4.4 *Reinforcement*

Steel rods and/or mesh are to be disposed and shaped to the boat's form such that the production of void-free material may be obtained. Adequate reinforcement is to be placed locally where high loads are experienced. Any discontinuities in the strength of the reinforcement are to be avoided and an adequate overlap is to be provided where reinforcing rods are joined.

Hull and deck reinforcement must be arranged to give an integral structure.

Reinforcement and mesh are to be securely wired to avoid movement during the placing of the mortar.

4.5 *Mortar*

Mixing, handling and compaction of the mortar should be consistent and closely supervised to ensure high quality material. The builder should be guided by established codes of practice such as NZSS 1900 Chapter 9, 1964 or similar approved standard.

The mortar must be thoroughly compacted during placing to ensure the absence of voids around reinforcement and in the corners of any framework.

Under no circumstances should the mortar be compacted simultaneously from both sides of the reinforcement in one operation. Vibrators and hand rodding are to be used in the thicker sections.

The mortar should be placed within a reasonably short period of adding the mixing water and with continual agitation during the waiting period. During handling and placing of the mortar care is to be taken to avoid segregation of the mix.

Where the main hull is plastered in more than one operation and decks are plastered in a separate operation from the hull, care is taken to ensure a sound joint between the hull sections and the hull and deck.

The use of bonding agents where mortar joints are made will be given special consideration. Under no circumstances is any bonding agent which is unstable in water to be used.

Bulkheads should either be built integral with the hull, or bulkhead grounds may be provided which are also to be integral with the hull, and to which the bulkheads are subsequently attached.

Apertures for hull fittings should, where possible, be formed prior to placing mortar or may be cut after completion and curing of the hull. All apertures should have the bare concrete surface adequately sealed before fixing the skin fittings.

4.6 *Curing*

The hull and other concrete structures are to be properly cured once the mortar has taken its first set. The set concrete is to be kept wet for a period dependent on the type of cement used and the ambient conditions. The method of curing should normally be by water spray but other methods which prevent undue evaporation of the residual water will be considered.

Where any framework is used, e.g., at the keel, it should be kept in position for as long as practicable during the curing period.

4.7 *Other structural materials*

Deckhouses or other structures of wood or steel are to comply with Marine Department requirements appropriate to the class of boat concerned. For fishing boats these are "Wooden Fishing Boats, their Machinery, and Equipment" or "Requirements for the Hull Construction, Machinery and Equipment of Steel Fishing Boats".

Where refrigerated fish holds or ice boxes are fitted, special attention should be paid to insulation in order to minimize the temperature gradient through the concrete shell. Details of the insulation are to be approved by a Surveyor of Ships.

Engine seating and shafting, steering gear, electrical installation, pumping and equipment should also comply with Marine Department requirements. Separate fuel tanks are to be fitted, but where approval is requested for ferro-cement fuel tanks cast integral with the hull structure, full details of the tank and structure are to be submitted for approval.

Section 5—Testing

5.1 *General requirements*

The following tests or approved equivalent tests agreed with a Surveyor of Ships are to be carried out on the mortar. The cost of all tests is to be borne by the builder.

5.2 *Slump testing of the mortar*

The mortar should be subject to sufficient slump tests which are in accordance with Part II of NZSS 192, 1962 or similar approved standard. The slump of the mortar should be the lowest possible that will permit thorough compaction and should not exceed 50 mm (2 in).

5.3 *Compression tests*

The plasterer is to be responsible for providing at least six standard test cylinders moulded from random samples of the mix during manufacture and placing of the mortar and these should be suitably identified. The standard test cylinders should be cured under standard conditions and tested at 28 days in accordance with the requirements of NZSS 192, 1952 or similar approved standard. The certified results provided by a testing laboratory should be made available to a Surveyor of Ships. A minimum crushing strength of 28 days' cure of 5000 psi will be accepted.

5.4 *Drilling*

Where the Surveyor of Ships suspects any voids in the hull mortar he may request suitable holes to be drilled to ascertain the homogeneity of finished mortar.

5.5 *Watertightness of the structure*

The hull and other surfaces which are intended to be watertight are to be closely inspected for surface faults after curing, and when any formwork is removed. Where the surface appears free from any visual defects it normally will be presumed watertight unless tested by hose, flooding or afloat.

Section 6—Cleaning down and painting

6.1 *Cleaning down*

The method and time of cleaning down the hull should be approved by a Surveyor of Ships. All loose ends of wire should be cut back and care taken to fill all pinholes with epoxy filler cement or similar approved filler.

6.2 *Painting*

The paint system should be that recommended by a paint manufacturer for application to ferro-cement boats.

Part III—CONSTRUCTION METHODS AND COSTS

Construction, Maintenance and Repair of a 26-Metre Ferro-Cement Stern Trawler P A Leonard

This paper deals primarily with the problems associated with the design, construction, management and operation of four 26-m ferro-cement stern trawlers. The first of these vessels, *Roslyn 1*, has been in operation since January 1972 while the second vessel, *Roslyn 2*, is nearing completion.

DESIGN

In considering the design of a ferro-cement vessel the question "How strong is strong enough?" immediately arises. A clear distinction must be drawn between the design of pleasure craft and commercial vessels such as fishing vessels.

Taken generally the designers of ferro-cement pleasure craft are either amateur designers with a basic working knowledge of the material or professional naval architects with limited or no practical experience with ferro-cement. More emphasis seems to be placed on aesthetic aspects than on strength, and most designers seem hesitant to discuss the strength of their vessels or the basis on which they specify a certain configuration of reinforcing steel and wire mesh or assume any responsibility for them. Most amateur builders appear to be fair-weather sailors and do not subject their vessels to the punishment that a commercial vessel must withstand in normal operation. Added to this is the fact that in many countries pleasure boats are only subjected to the most cursory examination by Government Authorities on registration or licensing and no plans are required to be submitted in advance for approval, nor are the vessels subjected to annual survey by the Licensing Authority. This therefore raises the question of whether some designs are in fact of sufficient strength.

This does not mean that very successful amateur boats have not been built which have withstood the most arduous conditions, but simply demonstrates why ferro-cement pleasure boats cannot generally be compared to ferro-cement commercial vessels.

Commercial vessels are required to work efficiently for at least eleven months a year in all but the most extreme weather conditions and this is particularly important in the South China Sea, which has a typhoon season. For the safety of the vessel and crew, the builders of commercial vessels are required to have their plans approved by the Licensing Authority prior to construction and they must be built under survey as well as surveyed annually.

Prior to the commencement of design of the *Roslyn 1* the Agriculture and Fisheries Department of the Hong Kong Government was consulted to determine the most suitable size and type of fishing vessel for Hong Kong.

It was decided that for the time being the 26-m wooden trawlers designed by the Agriculture and Fisheries Department, with certain modifications to meet Western standards, would be the most suitable model.

A primary decision in the design of a vessel is the engine to be installed.

The characteristics of seventeen different marine engines were examined and as a result a 480 bhp at 425 rpm Danish engine with controllable-pitch propeller was selected. The operation of *Roslyn 1* to date has proved this to have been a wise choice in every respect.

A senior naval architect from the United Kingdom conducted a study of plans and specifications of previous vessels and extensive tests were carried out to determine the strengths and characteristics of ferro-cement. Following this study and after consultation with a firm of civil engineers he returned to the United Kingdom to design the vessels.

The Agriculture and Fisheries Department, with its specialized local knowledge, assisted in designing the layout and non-ferro-cement aspects of the vessel. One problem in design was that there was no suitable ferro-cement precedent to serve as reliable guidelines for the scantlings.

RESEARCH AND TESTING

Because of lack of extensive and reliable data on ferro-cement and its use in vessels the size of *Roslyn 1*, extensive research and testing of ferro-cement was carried out prior to and concurrent with the design. Previous test results obtained in respect of *Pak Tak*, a 16-m fishing vessel, and others were of some assistance in this. These tests were carried out in Hong Kong University with participation and assistance of the Department of Civil Engineering.

The objects of the tests were to: determine what configurations of reinforcing rods and wire mesh forming the matrix produced the strengths and characteristics required; determine which configurations were most suitable in direct relation to the physical application of the matrix and the cost of doing so; verify the theoretical strength of the ferro-cement to be used.

It was decided to adopt the British Standards procedures for testing mortar and concrete. Ferro-cement panels measuring 1143 mm × 304.8 mm were used to determine the flexural strength of the material by supporting the panels over a span of 1 m and applying a transverse line load at midspan. Loading was applied by a hydraulic jack in small increments while recording the deflexion of the panel at midspan corresponding to the load. Deflexions of up to 101 mm were recorded at an ultimate load of 1497 kg on a panel averaging 32 mm in thickness (see Fig. 1).

The punching shear of panels was determined by supporting 356 mm × 356 mm panels on four rollers forming a 305 mm square. The load was applied hydraulically through a 51 mm steel block placed in the centre. Ultimate loads of 2390 kg were recorded on panels with an average thickness of 29.5 mm. For the punching shear tests particular care was taken during construction of the panels to ensure that no steel rods occurred in the area over which the load was applied as otherwise no shear could be obtained with the 2268 kg jack available at the time. The results of the punching shear tests can therefore only be regarded as an indication of actual minimum punching shear of the panels.

Attempts were also made to determine the tensile strength of ferro-cement on the same basis as British Standards tests for mortar, by the use of briguettes. Enlarged ferro-cement briguettes or dumb-bells were made and tested. However, slipping of the specimens in the jaws of the equipment available precluded accurate results and new equipment is being designed for this test.

Prior to any test the length, width and average thickness of each panel was recorded, together with the configuration of the matrix and the unit weights of the reinforcing rods, the mesh and the mortar.

In the interpretation of test results it must be remembered that tests of ferro-cement panels are carried out on flat sections. These sections seldom occur in a vessel and on the principle that ferro-cement is strongest in a curved section it is logical to assume on this consideration alone that the ferro-cement vessel is stronger than the tests indicate. This ensures a built-in extra margin of safety important in a relatively new material.

CONSTRUCTION

The lofting of a ferro-cement vessel is fundamentally the same as the lofting of any other vessel.

The pipe frame method was used for the construction of *Roslyn 1*.

There are indications of recent preferences shown for construction utilizing moulds. This is an advantage when a series production of one standard vessel is envisaged. However, the inherent disadvantage of this method is that when a limited number of vessels are required it is difficult to amortize the cost of the mould without substantially increasing the cost of each vessel, even taking into consideration the lower cost of construction claimed by some for the mould method.

The frames were first constructed by bending pipes to shape on the loft floor and nailing them in position. The individual pipes were then welded in position and additional braces welded on for rigidity.

When the frames were completed they were positioned on keel blocks and aligned. Bracing pipes were then welded to the frames longitudinally and overhead to maintain alignment and spacing between frames.

With *Roslyn 1*, one layer of high tensile steel rod laid longitudinally was tied to the frames, followed by one

Fig. 1 Flexural strength testing

layer of mild steel rod laid vertically and around the vessel, tied to the longitudinal steel rods. This was followed by another layer of high tensile steel rod laid on a long diagonal and tied to the other rods.

The use of high tensile steel rods was primarily to obtain fairness of the hull rather than for its intrinsic strength.

The inside and outside of the hull was then covered in three layers of 13 mm hexagonal wire mesh: each side with one longitudinal layer, one vertical layer and one diagonal layer and securely tied at regular intervals.

Tying the rods and mesh proved to be a monotonous and slow job for the labour, with a resultant loss of efficiency. Mechanical methods of tying were tried, but none proved entirely satisfactory.

Tests were carried out and eventually a suitable welding rod was found and a number of specimen panels were prepared: some with the rods tied with wire and others with the rods welded. Hammer tests were carried out on both types of panels and although the spot welds eventually broke there was no doubt whatsoever that the welded panels were much stronger.

The construction of *Roslyn 2* was carried out with spot welding of the reinforcing rods instead of tying and the entire structure was substantially more rigid and fair as a result.

Plastering of the hull posed a problem. It is considered desirable where possible to plaster the hull in one operation in a single day. The area of the hull imposed a physical limitation to this and therefore the hull was plastered in two stages.

First the outside of the hull was plastered with the morter penetrating to about the middle of the matrix. This was allowed to cure before the inside of the hull was plastered using vibrators in troughs of mortar.

Prior to plastering, consideration was given to several methods of plastering the hull in stages. Two other possibilities were considered: one was to plaster the hull from the keel up to approximately the waterline in one operation and then complete the rest as a separate operation; the other was to plaster from the bows to about midship in one operation and complete the hull as a separate operation.

Both methods were rejected in favour of the method adopted, as test panels made with different coloured mortar showed a good bond of the mortar with a particularly good mechanical key.

In smaller vessels it is still preferable to plaster the hull in one operation when this can reasonably be done, as apart from any other consideration this enables the plastering to be completed faster.

In the past bulkheads were prefabricated in steel and bolted to concrete webs integral with the hull using a suitable jointing compound. This system is far from satisfactory for commercial vessels as apart from being time-consuming it is almost impossible to make them watertight. The only possible merit of this system is that it allows the bulkheads to "work" in conjunction with the vessel in a seaway and alleviates undue stress on the hull in way of the bulkheads.

On *Roslyn 1* it was decided to construct ferro-cement bulkheads and wing tanks. The bulkheads were constructed with horizontal rods welded to the frames at regular intervals with vertical rods welded to the horizontal rods extending from the deck to the keel. A similar configuration of rods was placed approximately 38 mm away and both sides covered with wire mesh and shuttered. The bulkheads were cast by pouring mortar from deck level and the use of pencil vibrators from above and a large number of plate vibrators on both sides of the bulkheads. In order to dissipate any undue stress on the hull in way of the bulkheads with the working of the vessel, additional longitudinal rods were placed in the hull over one frame space on either side.

The *Roslyn 1* has three fuel tanks and one water tank. The two wing tanks for fuel each with a capacity of 8 t, the aft tank with a capacity of 20 t and the forward water tank with a capacity of 22 t were all constructed in a similar manner to the bulkheads. The tanks were coated with an epoxy tank coating compound and have been tested to an 8-ft head of water without trouble.

This method of constructing bulkheads and tanks, although successful, has proved to be time consuming and expensive as well as adding weight to the vessel.

As a result, the bulkheads and tanks of *Roslyn 2* have been constructed in steel. To make them watertight, the bulkheads have been welded direct to the pipe frames with additional reinforcing rod ties at regular intervals extending 15 cm from the sides of the bulkheads into the hull. They have been stiffened in the normal manner for steel bulkheads. To avoid undue stress on the hull additional reinforcing rods were placed in the hull for one frame space on either side of the bulkheads. The tanks were constructed in a similar manner.

This has proved to be by far the most successful and expeditious way of fitting bulkheads and tanks.

The decks were cast by shuttering the underside and pouring the mortar from above. With the use of plate vibrators, this was the simplest part of the entire concrete work.

It had been considered desirable to treat the deck with a bituminous compound mixed with cement to a thickness of about 20 mm to give a good working surface, and to protect the deck against accidental chipping as a result of heavy and sharp objects being dropped. This was done on *Pak Tak* and after a few months, the bituminous compound was found to crack and lift in places with obvious water entrapment. The bituminous compound was removed and the decks left bare, to this date without detrimental effect.

The superstructure of the 26-m ferro-cement stern trawlers is steel and fabricated in the manner normal for steel ships. Attachment to the deck is by way of bolting to ferro-cement webs using a suitable jointing compound.

CURING

Various methods of curing have been tested, including steam, spray-on chemical cure, fresh-water spray and salt-water spray.

By far the most expedient is steam curing which was used on *Pak Tak*. However, the size of the 26-m vessels, the amount of steam required, and the problem of enveloping the vessel has precluded this method of curing, particularly as it is not possible to hire steam boilers of sufficient capacity in Hong Kong.

109

Chemical curing has proved unsatisfactory in that it is supposed to retain 80 per cent of the moisture in the mortar and did not do so effectively. Removing the chemical from the hull on completion of curing was found to be difficult.

Salt-water spray has been found to be quite satisfactory except for the deposits on the hull which create a problem if mesh has been left exposed.

Next to steam, fresh-water spray has been found to be the most satisfactory method providing care is exercised to ensure that the hull is not permitted to dry during the curing cycle.

CONSTRUCTION COST

2926 m of pipe for frames and bracing	US$1001.74
6422 m² of wire mesh	3693.04
8.2 t of 7 mm high tensile steel rod	2132.87
5.3 t of 6.4 mm mild steel rods	778.61
3.5 t of 12.7 mm mild steel rods	583.30
0.52 t of 16 mm mild steel rods	83.13
32 t of cement	801.40
31 m³ of sand	992.36
Timber for form work	1305.74
Additives	74.78
Steel reinforcing beams on deck	1284.00
Epoxy hull sealer and paint	1713.04
Hard wood fendering, including steel rubbing strip, etc.	2086.96
Labour bending and erecting pipe frames, attaching reinforcing steel and wire mesh	26739.13
Plastering charges, application of epoxy sealer and painting	5521.74
Miscellaneous expenses	861.58
	US$49,653.42

TRIALS

On completion of *Roslyn 1* sea trials were held with the surveyors on board. In four runs over the official measured mile, the vessel averaged 10.8 knots, although weather conditions were far from ideal.

As the vessel was originally designed to do 10 knots, this was very satisfactory under operating conditions, the engine producing the actual horse-power advertized by the manufacturers.

Manoeuvring trials produced the following average results:

(a) Hard over to starboard: turning circle 1½ ship length in 56 sec.
(b) Hard over to port: turning circle 1½ ship length in 57 sec.

A bollard pull test was carried out and a static pull of 6.4 t was achieved.

The very satisfactory manoeuvring and bollard pull results are attributed to the nozzle rudder designed to work in conjunction with the controllable pitch propeller supplied as part of the engine (see Fig. 2).

An inclining experiment confirmed earlier calculations that the vessel met IMCO requirements.

Fig. 2   Stern view of 26-m trawler

CLASSIFICATION

To ensure that the *Roslyn 1* and the other 26-m ferro-cement stern trawlers are built to the highest international standards these vessels are built under survey by Lloyd's Register of Shipping.

In view of the advantages of building vessels to Class and the limited detailed information generally available on ferro-cement it would be short-sighted and possibly costly for the builder of commercial vessels not to build to the requirements of a classification society.

Roslyn 1 was built to Lloyd's Rules for steel trawlers adapted to ferro-cement where necessary.

MAINTENANCE AND REPAIR

Pak Tak has been in continuous operation since February 1970 and has repeatedly ventured over 400 mi from Hong Kong on fishing trips. *Pak Tak* has required no maintenance on her ferro-cement work other than painting, despite the fact that being a long liner she is continuously launching and recovering motorized sampans from her deck.

She has been subjected to the usual collisions in a crowded fishing port, as well as occasional collisions with sea walls. In most cases no damage was sustained. In the most serious cases, only slight chipping on the surface in way of impact was observed with no other apparent damage. Such slight damages have been repaired by the crew by application of mortar, which constitutes a perfectly satisfactory permanent repair. It can therefore safely be said that the maintenance and repair of ferro-cement work on *Pak Tak* from commencement of operations in February 1970 to date has been negligible.

When typhoon "Rose" hit Hong Kong in August 1971, the *Roslyn 1* was being fitted out afloat. She was brought to a typhoon shelter and being one of the last vessels to arrive she was nearest the breakwater entrance. This typhoon was one of the most severe to hit Hong Kong in many years, causing widespread damage to property, damage and sinking of many large merchant ships and small craft in the harbour and the loss of many lives. At the height of the typhoon many vessels in the typhoon shelter broke adrift and were blown out of the entrance, striking *Roslyn 1* in passing before being smashed up on an adjacent island.

Following the typhoon a survey was conducted on *Roslyn 1*, and although there was evidence of her having been hit repeatedly, the actual damage to the vessel consisted of:

> ferro-cement bulwarks on port side amidships set in over several metres;
> starboard side of stern ramp chipped on the surface over an area of about 60 cm²;
> port side of hull damaged 50 cm below waterline amidships, allowing a trickle of water to enter the vessel.

The damage to the ferro-cement work was repaired by the application of an epoxy bonding agent and mortar. In order to repair the hull damage below the waterline, the vessel was listed to starboard to expose the damaged area. Examination of this showed that although there was abrasion over an area of about 929 cm² the actual hole was very small and was repaired after chipping away loose concrete over an area of only a few cm². The nature of the damage seemed to indicate that it was caused by the anchor of a large junk striking the vessel head-on amidships.

During the typhoon, considerable equipment was blown or washed off the deck and the main engine was moved out of alignment as it was not yet bolted down.

The damage to the ferro-cement work was repaired at a cost of approximately US$500.00.

On 3 February, 1972, *Roslyn 1* encountered very heavy weather in the South China Sea near Hainan with wind force 7 to 8 on Beaufort Scale and heavy seas breaking on deck. In recovering her nets one of the port divertor chains broke and the divertor was caught under the stern ramp by the warp. It took approximately 2 h to free the divertor, during which time it continuously banged the underside of the stern ramp with the heavy pitching of the vessel and holed the hull completely flooding the steering gear compartment.

On recovery of the starboard divertor with the vessel's derrick, the divertor smashed the after fuel tank steel vent pipe. With the flooding of the steering gear compartment and seas breaking on deck the after fuel tank was flooded with sea water through the broken pipe.

The vessel returned to port with her after deck awash to within 2 ft of the fish hold hatch.

Approximately 20 t of emulsified fuel and water were pumped out of the after fuel tank and 12 t of water out of the steering gear compartment, while the fore peak and forward tanks were flooded to expose the damaged stern.

Examination of the damage showed considerable surface abrasion and a small hole on the port side of the steering gear compartment obviously caused by the nose cone of the divertor.

The actual hole was oval and approximately 50 mm maximum diameter. The ferro-cement around the hole was spalled over an area of approximately 190 cm².

Repair consisted of chipping away loose concrete in the damaged area, fairing the reinforcing steel, applying an epoxy bonding agent and mortar.

The total cost of damage repairs to the vessel amounted to approximately US$6000.00, of which direct repairs to the ferro-cement work amounted to approximately US$180.00.

Instead of otter doors, the *Roslyn 1* was using diverting depressors which can be likened to a torpedo with a sharp pointed steel nose cone and sharp fins.

In repairs to *Roslyn 1*, one potential disadvantage of ferro-cement to the commercial operator was manifested. In hull repairs, particularly in the way of tanks where both sides of the hull are coated with epoxy compounds, sufficient time lapse must be allowed for the mortar to cure. This does not assume much importance in small repairs where as a matter of expediency an epoxy mortar, as opposed to a cement mortar, can be used. However, when extensive repairs are involved, the additional cost of curing an epoxy mortar must be related to time loss.

The relatively minor extent of damage to *Pak Tak* and *Roslyn 1* described above cannot be attributed to ferro-cement alone as the hulls of both vessels are protected by substantial wooden fenders capped with flat steel bars extending around the vessels. It is reasonable to assume that in the larger proportion of collisions, the brunt of the impact has been taken by the fenders which has distributed the load over the vessel.

CONCLUSION

Ferro-cement enjoys considerable popularity among pleasure boat owners but the use of this material for commercial or fishing vessels is still very limited.

This may be attributed to the lack of technical data readily available on the material itself and on construction methods. Researchers of ferro-cement, particularly when they are involved in commercial building themselves, are reluctant to reveal full technical information without recompense. This is reasonable enough as in many cases the cost of research into ferro-cement has not been repaid by production, and commercial organizations cannot be expected to carry out research for the benefit of others. As a result, much of the technical information disclosed is out of context and can be misleading.

Unlike GRP, where large chemical manufacturers carry out intensive research into the material and its applications with the technical information being made readily available to prospective manufacturers, ferro-cement has no such support.

It is therefore obvious that where ferro-cement has great potential, especially in developing countries where labour is relatively cheap and materials available, it will not become established as a boat-building material without an intensive research programme into the material itself, and the most economic methods of production, with the information being disseminated internationally.

Such a programme, to be effective would have to be financed by an international organization which would be able and prepared to disseminate the information. To be successful, such a programme should be conducted by a firm of established naval architects working in collaboration with researchers into ferro-cement, and an established ferro-cement boat builder to ensure that technical research and specifications are directly related to the practicalities of production and costs, with tests carried out by an independent third party such as a university, and certified.

The objects of the programme should be:

to determine the relative strengths of mortar in relation to the different types of sand, and cement and the sand : cement ratios and cement : water ratios;

to determine the relative strengths and characteristics of ferro-cement in relation to different types, sizes, quantities and distribution of wire mesh and reinforcing steel;

to produce tables of strengths of ferro-cement directly related to scantling tables for steel ships to facilitate the design of ferro-cement vessels;

to investigate and determine the most satisfactory and economical method of each aspect of ferro-cement construction;

to produce a range of standard designs of fishing vessels from, say, 10.5 m to 30.5 m.

Due to the number of empirical elements in the design of vessels it is only in this way that the question "How strong is strong enough?" can readily be answered, and people throughout the world will be able to produce safe, efficient and economical ferro-cement vessels.

Ferro-Cement Vessels on the Pacific Coast of North America P Noble and W Cleaver

The first ferro-cement boats built on the Pacific Coast of North America were pleasure craft constructed during the mid-1960s. From that time to the present, a number of ferro-cement boats have been built in the area, including several fishing vessels, tugs and barges.

This paper describes the types of vessel, the construction methods and materials for boats which have been built and a breakdown of the material and labour costs for these craft. It will deal with construction methods and materials which have proved to be satisfactory in service and give information on material costs and man-hour requirements for estimating purposes.

TYPES OF VESSELS

Pleasure boats

By far the most ferro-cement boats at present under construction or in service on the Pacific coast of North America are pleasure boats. For the most part they are heavy displacement sailing yachts from 9 to 15 m (30 to 50 ft) in length.

The majority are being built by amateur builders, most of whom have little or no previous boat-building experience. Figures 1 and 2 show typical boats of this class.

A number of companies and individual yacht designers are producing designs for the amateur builder, and this has been largely responsible for the proliferation of backyard projects. Many of these boats have been started by their owner-builders, encouraged by the reportedly low material costs and ease of construction, and have reached the stage where work has ceased due to limited funds or lack of skill required to produce a finished boat from a bare hull.

Some motor and sailing yachts have been produced commercially in California, Washington and British Columbia, but at the time of writing the number so produced has not been significant and as no great saving in purchase price has been offered the buyer, there seems little likelihood that there will be a large increase in the number of commercially-built pleasure boats in the near future.

Fig. 1   11-m (37-ft) sailing yacht, Vancouver, BC, Canada

Fig. 2   14-m (46-ft) sailing yacht, Victoria, BC, Canada

Fishing vessels

Salmon fishing is the most important fishery along the coast from Alaska to California and it is carried on mainly from small boats of 9 to 18 m (30 to 60 ft) in length. It is as part of this fleet that most of the ferro-cement fishing boats built in the area operate. Salmon are caught by using gillnets, trolling gear and purse seines. The gillnet boats are usually less than 11 mm (36 ft) in length and work the inshore waters and river estuaries. Both high-speed planing boats and normal displacement vessels are used. Due to its high weight factor, ferro-cement is not suited to the former type and only displacement gillnetters have been built to date. Most high-speed vessels are built of fibreglass or aluminium. Trollers are usually one or two-man boats of 9 to 16 m (30 to 52 ft), which catch salmon by trolling lures. These boats operate further offshore than gillnetters and usually stay at sea for a longer period. A typical troller which was one of the first ferro-cement boats built in British Columbia and which now fishes on the West coast of Vancouver Island, is shown in Fig. 3. Trollers tend to be heavy-displacement boats and thus are well suited to construction in ferro-cement. Figures 4 and 5 show the *Queen Esther*, a 15-m (50-ft) ferro-cement troller built in 1968 in Tacoma, Washington, and has since been operating in S.E. Alaskan waters. She should not be regarded as typical, having relatively shallow draught, twin screws, a 15-kn cruising speed and rather more accommodation than normal.

Salmon are also caught by purse seines. Both drum and power-block seines are used. In British Columbia no seiners have been built in ferro-cement but in Washington several small power-block seiners have been built. Figure 6 shows the *Perry*, a 14 × 4.4-m (45.5 × 14.5-ft) seiner built in Washington to fish out of Cordova, Alaska.

There are a few boats that have been built in ferro-cement for crab and other types of fishing but there are probably fewer than ten such vessels on the whole coast.

Recent changes in regulation in Canada have required all fishing boats to meet certain standards of cleanliness in fishholds. Ferro-cement is being used extensively, over urethane foam insulation, in lining fishholds in steel, wood and fibreglass boats, to provide an easily cleanable non-porous surface.

Fig. 3   13-m (43-ft) troller, Port Alberni, BC, Canada

Fig. 4   15-m (50-ft) troller, Tacoma, Washington, USA

One special marine application of steel reinforced mortar in British Columbia is in refrigerated-brine packer barges used to transport salmon from catching areas to canneries. This can be a trip of several hundred miles and the salmon are held in refrigerated circulating brine, usually at about −1°C. The barges have refrigeration machinery but no propulsion machinery and are towed. Some five or six of these barges have been built in Vancouver, ranging from an 18-m (60-ft) barge which can carry 110 t of fish to a 36 × 11 × 2.7-m

Fig. 5   15-m (50-ft) troller, Tacoma, Washington, USA

Fig. 6   14-m (46-ft) seiner, Tacoma, Washington, USA

(120 × 36 × 9-ft) barge which has a dead-weight capacity of around 300 t. The natural insulation qualities of the mortar, together with the smooth, easily cleaned, hygienic interior of the fish tanks, make these brine packer barges successful in operation.

Miscellaneous vessels

A small number of ferro-cement vessels have been built as tenders, tugs and general-purpose boats.

In Alaska, B.C., Washington and Oregon, small tugs are used extensively in the logging industry and a few have been constructed in ferro-cement. However, their work demands constant high impact loading from collision with logs and ferro-cement has not generally been satisfactory under such continuous high stressing. Wood and fibreglass have also been unsatisfactory and steel is the only material which has, to date, proved able to stand up to the rugged service conditions.

One 12 × 4-m (40 × 13-ft) tug was built in Vancouver in 1967 in ferro-cement and it had the unusual feature of a ferro-cement propulsion nozzle. The nozzle was 0.92 m (3 ft) in diameter, was steerable and proved

satisfactory in service, although the tug suffered considerable damage from impact with logs.

Several other applications of floating ferro-cement structures have been completed on the Pacific coast in the past few years including floating gasoline stations, marina floats and breakwaters, and seaplane docks.

CONSTRUCTION METHODS AND TECHNIQUES

Pipe or rod frame method

The pipe or rod-frame method used on the Pacific coast is basically the same as that used in Australia and New Zealand. Frames are bent from pipe or rod, to shapes defined on the loft floor and are welded and braced to maintain their shape. The frames are then hung on 600 to 1000 mm centres to give the shape of the vessel. Additional pipe or rod is used to give the stem and keel profile and the transom frame, if any. Rods running fore and aft are then attached to the outside of the frames by tying or welding. A further layer of transverse rods is sometimes added on the inside of the longitudinal rods. The network so formed is then sandwiched by three or four layers of mesh on both the outside and inside and the whole layup is tied, laced or hog-ringed together.

Typical scantlings for a 12-m (40-ft) fishing boat built using the pipe-frame method are given below in Table 1.

TABLE 1. SCANTLINGS TYPICAL FOR A 12-M FISHING BOAT

Member	Scantling
Frames	18-mm galvanized pipe on 800-mm spacing
Longitudinal rods	6-mm on 50-mm spacing, mild steel
Transverse rods	6-mm on 100-mm spacing, mild steel
Mesh	8 layers 12 × 0.65-mm hexagonal woven mesh, galvanized

A few boats using the pipe-frame method have been built upside-down, but the majority are suspended from overhead, and supported along the keel.

Wooden plug method

A large number of boats, mostly pleasure craft, have been built using the wooden plug method. Basically this method involves building a plug in the shape of the vessel from rough lumber and then attaching, by nailing or stapling, the mesh and rod layup.

Figure 7 shows a 17-m (56-ft) professionally constructed yacht built over a plug, awaiting application of the outer layers of mesh.

Figure 8 shows a 10-m (33-ft) gillnetter hull built over a wooden plug. The photograph was taken as the placing of mortar was commencing. This method has a number of drawbacks, the biggest being the difficulty in obtaining satisfactory penetration when applying the mortar. Figure 9 shows an example of poor penetration on a boat plastered over a wooden plug.

The method does have some advantages, including the ability of the wooden plug to support the mortar weight, as well as allowing plasterers and workmen to

Fig. 7   17-m (56-ft) yacht on wood plug, Lulu Island, BC, Canada

Fig. 8   10-m (33-ft) gillnetter hull on wood plug, Tacoma, Washington, USA

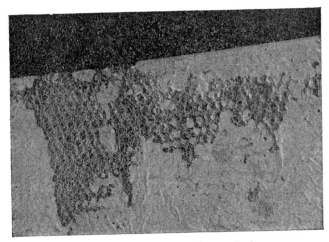

Fig. 9   Poor penetration with wood plug method

walk on the hull while working. The rough lumber planking of the plug also tends to fair out minor irregularities that may be caused by inaccurate lofting by amateurs.

All the vessels known to the authors on the Pacific coast, built using this method, have used an inverted male plug, and in many cases the work has been carried out in the open as no extensive support framework is required to suspend the frames.

Typical scantlings for a 15-m (50-ft) fishing boat built using the wooden plug method are given in Table 2.

TABLE 2. TYPICAL SCANTLINGS FOR 15-M FISHING BOAT

Member	Scantling
Frames	none (wooden bulkheads and floors fibreglassed in place)
Longitudinal rods	6-mm on 40-mm spacing, high tensile steel
Transverse rods	6-mm on 75-mm spacing, high tensile steel
Mesh	8 layers 12 × 0.65-mm hexagonal woven mesh

Ribband and mould method

The ribband and mould method involves using the same technique as is used in building wooden boats. Wooden station moulds are built on the loft floor and are then erected either right-side-up or inverted. A series of ribbands or battens is then attached to the moulds to give a "space frame" to which the mesh and rods of the hull layup may be tied, stapled or nailed. The ribbands may be left in place during plastering, but are often removed by cutting between the moulds, after the hull layup has been tightly laced.

Figure 10 shows the ribband and mould method as used to build a 17-m (56-ft) motor sailer in North Vancouver, B.C. and Table 3 gives typical scantlings for such a vessel.

TABLE 3. TYPICAL SCANTLINGS FOR 17-M MOTOR SAILER

Member	Scantling
Frames	none (structural wooden bulkheads and floors fibreglassed in place)
Longitudinal rods	6-mm at 50-mm spacing, mild steel,
Mesh	7 layers (3 in—4 out) 12 × 0.9-mm squared, welded mesh, galvanized

Occasionally, with this method the ribbands are omitted and the station moulds are placed close together. When this is done, it is usual to employ high-tensile longitudinal rods to obtain a fair hull.

Other methods

Various forms of cavity moulds have been experimented with on the Pacific coast, most with a view to mass production, but as yet there is much development work to be done in this particular area before a satisfactory solution will be obtained.

Fig. 10   Ribband and mould method, North Vancouver, BC, Canada

One interesting method was used in Vancouver, B.C. to construct a 36-m (120-ft) barge. A hollow was prepared in a river bank the required shape of the barge, and after the reinforcing was arranged, the mortar was placed and allowed to cure. To launch the barge the river bank was breached and the earth cavity flooded, so that the barge floated out.

There are a number of variations on the main method and each builder tends to use the techniques which best suit his equipment and experience; yards used to constructing wooden boats and now building in ferro-cement tend to use either the ribband and mould method or the wooden-plug method, and yards accustomed to building steel vessels normally use the pipe-frame method.

A method called the web-frame method, where station moulds fabricated from rods and mesh form part of the finished vessel, was experimented with but never found much popularity in the area. When web frames are required for structural reasons in one of the other building methods, they are built in separately.

MORTAR PREPARATION AND APPLICATION

The mortar used in ferro-cement boat construction on the Pacific coast is a rich cement-sand mixture with a water : cement : sand ratio of approximately 1 : 2 : 4 by weight. Certainly no more than one part of water is used and often much less if sufficient workability of the mortar can be obtained.

Various additives have been used but at the present time only pozzolan is common to most builders. Air entraining agents, plasticising agents, epoxies, etc., have been tried, but their use is by no means generally accepted.

The cement used is usually a sulphate-resistant Portland type V, but a number of commercial builders use a high-early cement with a fast setting time. The cement is normally in bags, which makes for easy manhandling and weight batching.

The sand used is always sharp and when delivered in bulk, is usually sieved. Some builders prefer to use sandblasting sand, which is supplied in bags and which does not require sieving. It again has the advantages of easy batching and manhandling, while under normal circumstances remaining completely dry.

Fresh water is always used to mix the mortar, and in colder weather, hot water has been found to be an advantage in assisting the mortar to set up sufficiently to allow the plasterers to perform the finishing work in a reasonable time.

Mixing

The mortar is almost always mixed in a plaster mixer; i.e. a mixer with paddles rotating on a horizontal axis, although rotating drum mixers have been used quite successfully on a number of projects.

When preparing the mortar the water is placed in the mixer first, followed by any additives to be used, and then the cement. The aggregate is always added last, although some of the water may be held back and added with the aggregate to ensure proper workability.

Transportation and application

When thoroughly mixed, the mortar is dumped on to a holding tray from which it is normally shovelled into buckets and carried to the plasterers at work on the boat.

In some commercial operations a mortar pump is used. After mixing, the mortar is dumped into the pump hopper and pumped up to where the plasterers are working. This is very convenient, but the rate of delivery of the pump is usually much higher than the rate at which the plasterers can work the mortar. The result is that the pump is only run for short periods. The problem of the mortar in the supply pipe setting up between the short pumping spells is a big difficulty with this type of equipment when used on ferro-cement boat-building projects.

Guniting techniques have been used, generally unsuccessfully, on ferro-cement boats in the area. With guniting, the sand and cement are mixed dry and blown by compressed air to a spray nozzle, where water is added to make the mortar. One problem is the difficulty in controlling the water content when mixing is carried out at the nozzle and the mortar is then immediately placed on the hull. Another big difficulty with the guniting process is that of segregation of the mix. The cement and sand particles are of greatly different sizes and the fine distribution of the reinforcing mesh causes there to be a screening effect in which some areas of the shell have high cement and low sand content and in other areas, the reverse is true.

The mortar on most cement boats built on the Pacific coast is placed by hand and is pushed through the hull layup from one side and finished on the other. A finish skim coat 2 to 3 mm thick is applied on the exterior.

With the wooden plug method of construction it is only possible to work the mortar from one side, and to date very few boats thus plastered have had good penetration. It is nearly always necessary to replaster the interior of a boat built using this method.

The finish is usually produced by sponging the mortar after it has begun to set up, and then steel floating to get a smooth surface. Some builders prefer to leave the sponged finish, which gives a good keying surface if there is to be any extensive surface filling carried out.

Curing

Nine boats out of ten on the Pacific coast are cured under a water spray or sprinkler system for 21–28 days. Steam curing, sprayed membrane curing and even complete-submersion curing have all been used successfully, but the water spray is simple, effective and cheap; thus it is likely to remain the dominant method. Newly-cemented hulls are often covered with burlap or newsprint prior to water spraying to give good spread to the water and to give some protection should the hull be exposed to sunlight or wind, which might otherwise cause local drying out of the surface.

MAINTENANCE AND SERVICE EXPERIENCE

Although some early ferro-cement boats were left bare, it is now usual practice to provide surface protection in the form of a paint coating.

When the ferro-cement has been fully cured and no moisture remains which could blister the paint film, the hull is etched with a 30 per cent acid solution. Muriatic acid is normally used, but some builders prefer phosphoric acid. After etching, the hull is washed down thoroughly and the alkalinity is checked with indicator paper. If it is in excess of ph 8, the acid etching and washdown is repeated until this level is attained.

The hull surface is then ground, either by hand with a carborundum brick or using an abrasive wheel. This is followed by a thorough washdown and the hull is then dried out completely. Next, the hull is primed with a sealer on all surfaces and this is allowed to cure fully. After this, the surface can be filled with an epoxy resin filler to eliminate indentations and imperfections. It is most important that the hull surface is sealed before being filled. The filled surfaces are then sanded and faired as required. After removing all dust, a second coat is applied to the hull surfaces. Figure 11 shows a 17-m (56-ft) yacht hull sealed and filled.

Painting

Painting systems in the area usually follow one of the three schemes detailed in Table 4. All these systems have proved effective in providing surface protection to ferro-cement hulls.

All under-water metal parts such as rudders, shoe plates, etc., are prepared and coated in normal fashion.

Repairs

Hull-repair work in general has been minor in nature and provided a good bond has been obtained between the new and existing mortar no difficulties have been encountered. It is usual to make extensive use of an epoxy bonding agent when making hull repairs.

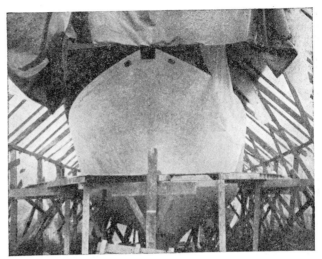

Fig. 11   17-m (56-ft) yacht sealed and filled, North Vancouver, BC, Canada

TABLE 4. PAINTING SYSTEMS

Coating	System 1	System 2	System 3
Underwater:			
Sealer	1 coat thin Chloro-rubber paint	1 coat thin Chloro-rubber paint	1 coat clear epoxy
Finish	2 coat vinyl resin anti-fouling	2 coat vinyl resin anti-fouling	2 coat vinyl resin anti-fouling
Topsides:			
Sealer	1 coat thin Chloro-rubber	1 coat thin Chloro-rubber	1 coat clear epoxy
Finish	2-coat Chloro-rubber paint	1 coat under-coat 2 coat poly-urethane finish	2-coat epoxy finish

General service experience

As stated previously, ferro-cement boats in several instances have suffered extensive impact damage while operating in the debris-strewn waters of the Pacific N.W. It is not easy to say that this definitely points to a weakness in ferro-cement as every year many wooden, fibreglass and even steel boats suffer similar damage from striking logs and other floating objects.

It has been found, however, that in areas which are subject to impact in ordinary service, such as bulwarks, hatch coamings, etc., ferro-cement is something less than ideal and most new fishing vessels are now being built with steel decks, bulwarks and hatch coamings.

On boats which have been in service for some time, some corrosion is apparent and is usually caused by rusting of the mesh exposed in hairline cracks. On examination, this has proved to be only surface corrosion as the cracks seldom extend more than 2 to 3 mm below the surface.

In all cases where repair work has necessitated exposing the rod frame work, the rods have been found to be in good condition with no rusting apparent. In a few cases

117

where voids have been left when plastering, corrosion of the rods locally has taken place.

When using the pipe-frame method it is normal practice to fill the pipes with hot pitch or other similar substance to eliminate the risk of pipes rusting out from inside.

CONSTRUCTION COSTS

Basic material costs

The mortar cost is an average value and does not include the cost of any special additives that may be used.

The mesh is usually supplied in 45-m (50-yd) rolls of either 450 mm (18 in) or 900 mm (36 in) width.

TABLE 5. COST OF BASIC COMPONENT MATERIALS FOR FERRO-CEMENT CONSTRUCTION

Material	Cost, US $
Welded mesh 12 × 0.9-mm square	1.02½ m²
Woven mesh 12 × 0.65-mm hex.	0.64½ m²
6-mm rod	0.10 m (straightened)
4.5-mm rod	0.05½ m (in coils)
Mortar	0.17 m² 10 mm thick

Typical hull layup and costs

The shell layup for a number of boats is given in Table 6. All these boats have been in use for sometime and to date there has been no serious structural failure with any of them.

The scantlings given are not intended as a standard, but rather are included to show that there is a large variation in what has proved practical in service.

Labour requirements

Man-hour requirements for vessels have varied greatly, depending on how adaptable the builder has been in working in the new material.

Figure 12 gives the man-hour requirements to build the hull for boats of varying lengths. The curve is based on actual man-hours recorded by builders who have had previous experiences in ferro-cement construction.

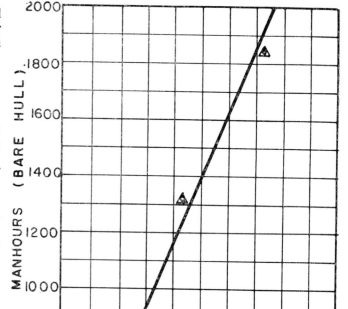

Fig. 12   Hull labour vs. length

The work done includes all lofting, mould-making, rod and mesh work and plastering of the hull, excluding the decks and bulkheads. It does not include grinding, sealing, filling or finishing of the hull.

Figure 13 shows the man-hours required to plaster a boat of varying length. Again it does not include plastering of the deck or bulkheads. To estimate the number of men required, the work should be divided up into shifts of not more than 10 hours. Thus to plaster a boat that will require a total of 120 man-hours, 12 men should work one 10-h shift, or 6 men should work two 10-h shifts.

TABLE 6. HULL LAYUP COSTS

Item	1	2	3	4	5
Vessel	9-m yacht	10-m fishing boat	10-m yacht	16-m fishing boat	14-m fishing boat
Mesh	6 × weld	6 × weld	8 × woven	8 × weld	8 × woven
Long. rods	6 to 50 mm	6 to 50 mm	6 to 50 mm	6 to 50 mm	6 to 50 mm
Trans. rods	none	4 to 100 mm	none	6 to 100 mm	6 to 50 mm
Shell thickness	17.3 mm	20.4 mm	19.8 mm	26.2 mm	26.2 mm
Weight (kg/m²)	56.3	66.4	64.5	85.2	85.2
Cost/m²	US $8.44½	US $9.59½	US $7.48½	US $12.64½	US $9.59½
Cost/kg	US $0.15	US $0.14½	US $0.10	US $0.15	US $0.10

Weld = 12 × 0.9 mm square weld mesh
Woven = 12 × 0.65 hexagonal woven mesh (chicken wire)

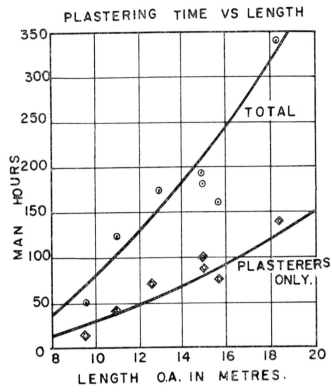

Fig. 13 Plastering time vs. length

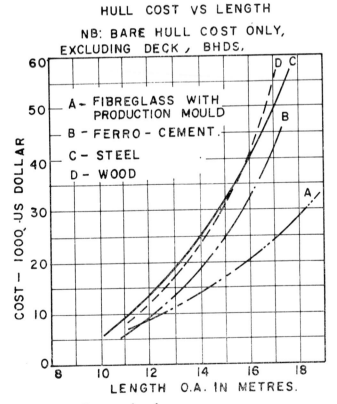

Fig. 14 Hull cost vs. length

Cost comparison

The cost of Canadian Pacific coast fishing boats built of various materials is given in Fig. 14.

Fibreglass shows up as being the best buy, but these are stock production boats built in a cavity mould, while the steel, wood and ferro-cement boats are custom-built, one-off, vessels. The costs are for bare hulls with no decks or internal structures.

TABLE 7. APPROXIMATE COST FOR A 15-M (50-FT) VESSEL READY TO FISH (US $)

Material	Hull cost	Cost to finish	Total cost	Percent of maximum cost
Fibreglass	19,000	80,000	99,000	91
Ferro-cement	28,000	80,000	108,000	99
Steel	34,000	75,000	109,000	100
Wood	34,000	75,000	109,000	100

Cost to finish steel and wood boats is less in local yards as they find it easier to instal decks and internal structure in these vessels.

FUTURE

Ferro-cement seems to be well established as a building material on the Pacific coast of North America. It will undoubtedly continue to be used extensively by the backyard amateur builder and its use by builders of commercial craft will also tend to increase.

Ferro-cement will also be used in the future for such specialized duties as fishhold linings and refrigerated brine barges, as mentioned in the text.

A fishing vessel recently designed by the authors, probably indicates the direction of development of ferro-cement boats in the future. This boats is 20 m (66 ft) long, and has a ferro-cement hull. The decks, bulwarks and bulkheads are of steel, while the housework is aluminium. The fishholds are insulated by 100-mm urethane foam which is then covered by a 12-mm layer of ferro-cement. The hull thickness will be approximately 32-mm. Fuel and fresh water tanks are of steel and installed separately. The vessel is equipped to fish either as a drum seiner or stern trawler.

Ferro-cement has, in less than ten years, gained acceptance as a boat-building material on the Pacific coast. Whilst its use is still limited, the authors feel sure that as more builders become proficient in the construction, and as more operators come to appreciate its in-service advantages, one will see a growing number of ferro-cement vessels operating from ports on the Pacific coast.

Construction of a 32-Metre Ferro-Cement Barge and Other Applications of Ferro-Cement   D Nontanakorn

To promote wider usage of cement as a general construction material in Thailand, ferro-cement has been introduced. This material has many advantages from both marine structural and architectural engineering points of view, as it is rust-proof, and more resilient and lighter than ordinary reinforced concrete. Ferro-cement is likely to be particularly well-suited to South-East Asian countries since it requires a minimum of skilled labour, and all the materials can be found locally. By employing this technique in boat-building, the country can save scarce natural resources—in this case, timber which is becoming rarer and increasingly more expensive; it can replace steel also—not only at a cheaper price but with savings in much-needed foreign exchange.

PROPERTIES OF FERRO-CEMENT

Experimental

A series of tests were conducted to find a suitable mix proportion and to ascertain the general properties of the material. The conclusion was that the ratio of sand : cement should be 1.75 : 1.00 by weight, with water : cement ratio of 0.35 plus chemical additive to improve the workability of the mix. Table 1 shows the results of the strength test of cement mortar at various curing ages (test results obtained from Daranandana et al., 1969).

The panels employed for impact test were prepared by using steel rod of 6 mm diameter to form a screen with rectangular grid 10 × 12.5 cm, four layers of wire mesh were then tied on each side and cement mortar was applied by hand from one side to the other with an average thickness of 2.5 cm. The specimens were cured for a period of 21 days. Table 2 shows the results of impact testing of the ferro-cement slabs (test results obtained from Daranandana et al., 1969).

The results in Table 2 indicate that the difference in impact energy of the two impact loads was considerable; even when cracks occurred, the material still resisted the passage of water, an important characteristic for boat hulls which require a high degree of flexibility and water-proofing qualities.

Design

Due to the conditions of the river and other requirements, a barge could only draw a maximum of 2.5 m of water when fully loaded and the size was also limited. The barge should therefore have a flat bottom and the most economical size was determined to be 32 m long, 6.6 m wide and 3.0 m deep with loading capacity of approximately 320 t with a deadweight of 85 t and drawing 55 cm of water when unloaded and 2.15 m when fully loaded.

The pipe-frame method was chosen for construction because it did not require any heavy equipment or skilled labour. The pipe itself does not give any strength to the hull but merely delineates the shape of the barge.

The barge has a double bottom with the bulkheads placed at intervals of 1 m to stiffen the bottom and the sides. It was also designed to take any torsion moment which might occur during the journey and to prevent water entering the hull and damaging the goods. The profile and cross-section are shown in Fig. 1.

The interior was divided into four compartments for loading purposes with sliding hatches on deck. No engine was provided because it was to be towed.

FERRO-CEMENT BARGE CONSTRUCTION

In the construction, the frame of iron pipes of 19 mm diameter were placed 1 m apart, along the longitudinal plane to form a hull; these pipes were hung from the roof of the construction shed. The frame was connected

TABLE 1. FLEXURAL AND COMPRESSIVE STRENGTHS

Specimen 4 × 4 × 14 cm	Strength kg/cm²					
	Flexural (days)			Compressive (days)		
	3	7	21	3	7	21
Mortar without admixture	63	72	77	340	442	509
Mortar with admixture	65	79	78	438	564	678

TABLE 2. IMPACT TESTS

Specimen	Weight of slab (kg)	At initiation of crack			At steel deformation		
		Impact load (kg)	Dropping height (m)	Impact energy (kgm)	Impact load (kg)	Dropping height (m)	Impact energy (kgm)
Size 1.0 × 1.0 m	54	40	1.75	70	50	2.75	137.5

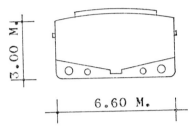

32.00 M.

3.00 M.

6.60 M.

Fig. 1   Profile and cross-section of the barge

by the same diameter of pipe to stiffen the hull shape. Steel rods of 6 mm diameter forming a screen of 10 × 12.5 cm were tied to a pipe frame. Five and four layers of hexagonal chicken wire were placed and tied up firmly to the outer and inner side of the frame respectively. Plastering was done by careful application of cement mortar through the reinforcement by hand from the inner to the outer side of the barge. The surface was finished by trowel and sponge. The barge hull was kept continually wet for 21 days by means of a sprinkler system. Figures 2 and 3 show the barge during the construction period.

After the hull was finished, the same procedure of tying the reinforcement and plastering was applied to the second bottom and the deck. When the whole process was completed, the necessary equipment, such as rudders, rudder arms and steering gear, etc., were installed. Finally, an epoxy paint was applied to seal in any stray ends of the mesh frame work.

The finished barge was launched in the middle of October 1970. The accommodation, deck house, sliding hatches, wood fender, etc., were then fitted. The barge was ready for its maiden voyage at the end of December.

Fig. 3   Plastering from the inner to outer side

Cost

This was an experimental barge and it was constructed to demonstrate the possibility of using ferro-cement techniques in barge building. The total construction time of one year was longer than it should have been; the actual time could probably be reduced to one-third so that labour cost could be cut down considerably.

Cost breakdowns are estimated as follows:

(a) labour cost	US$11,000
(b) materials	US$ 9,500
(c) miscellaneous (including hatches, steering gear, etc.)	US$ 5,000
Total	US$25,500

The above figures show that the cost can be calculated at US$80 per cargo ton.

The hull cost per unit area of ferro-cement was equivalent to US$14 per m^2.

Fig. 2   Reinforcement mesh in place ready for plastering

121

Maiden voyage

At the end of December 1970, this 320-t barge, the largest ferro-cement riverine structure ever built in South-East Asia, went on its maiden voyage of about 120 km, with a half capacity load of 150 t of bagged cement. Everything went well during the journey. There was minor damage to the hull on arrival due to a slight collision with a steel barge's fender while manoeuvring to berth. Repairs were not as complicated as they would have been for a steel or wooden barge. The damaged area was cleaned, then replastered with an epoxy bonding agent applied to the edges. To prevent future damage, large-size used tyres were hung around the barge as shown in Fig. 4.

Fig. 4   The barge during the journey

Accidental damage and repair

Five accidents have occurred to the barge since the first trip but none was serious and were repaired as described above.

The latest and most serious accident happened at the end of 1971 when the barge grounded at low tide carrying a full load. The bottom was badly damaged by the hard clay of the river bed. Fortunately, the barge has a double hull which prevented water from damaging the cement in the holds. After the cement was unloaded, epoxy (under-water type) was applied to the bottom surface. The damaged area inside the hull was repaired by the method mentioned above. Repairs took seven days.

Usage

The barge is now in good condition and is still used to carry cement from the factory. Sometimes it carries steel billets on the return trip from Bangkok to supply a steel plant located near the cement works.

122

The average number of trips undertaken is four to five a month but a full load is only carried for a period of 4 months; the rest of the time, the barge can only be loaded three-quarters full because of low water level in the river.

OTHER USES OF FERRO-CEMENT

Rice bins

The loss of rice valued at approximately US$100 million per year due to mice, insects, birds and other pests represents considerable wastage for the developing economy of Thailand. A conical-shaped ferro-cement rice-bin, shown in Fig. 5, was therefore designed as an airtight container to prevent the incursion and growth of insects and also allow its thin shape to sustain the distribution force acting against the shell.

The total cost is approximately US$120, 30 per cent of which is labour. The latter item could be eliminated if farmers themselves did the work.

Water tank

Ferro-cement water tanks can replace the galvanized iron tanks. They are more economical and durable and easy to transport if prefabricated.

Experiments have been carried out on the construction of 1800 to 6500 l ferro-cement tanks in rectangular, cylindrical and spherical shapes as shown in Fig. 6.

Fig. 5   Ferro-cement bins for storing rice

Fig. 6   Ferro-cement water tanks

These tanks have a thickness of 1.5 cm with a total weight of 250 kg. The cost is about 25 per cent less than for the equivalent galvanized steel tank but the weight is double. However, experiments using a pre-fabricated form are now being conducted in order to solve the problems of transportation and reduce cost of production.

CONCLUSIONS

Transportation of primary produce, especially grains, by river in Thailand has proved most practical and economic. As agricultural output increases more barges will need to be built and ferro-cement techniques seem to be ideal. The potential as regards fishing vessels is also very large and ferro-cement vessels should become popular, once the early inertia of tradition, suspicion and prejudice on the fishermen's part has been overcome. There are also possibilities of ferro-cement applications in pre-fabricating and building materials. More information regarding research and the study of its properties are still needed, particularly in boat-building.

References

DARANANDANA, N, SUKAPADDHANADHI, N and DISATHIEN, P
1969   *Ferro-cement for Construction of Fishing Vessels.* Bangkok, Thailand: Applied Scientific Research Corporation of Thialand, Research Project No. 21/14.
SAMSON, J and WELLEM, G *How to Build a Ferro-cement Boat,*
1968   2nd Ed. Vancouver, Canada, 120 pp.
SMITH, R B L, *et al. Hermetic Storage of Rice for Thai*
1970   *Farmers.* Bangkok, Thailand: Applied Scientific Research Corporation of Thailand.

Ferro-Cement Boats—Commercial Production Methods in New Zealand   W M Sutherland

The development of production methods for ferro-cement boat-building in New Zealand is described both for commercial and amateur requirements. Actual production man-hours and material costs are quoted for established methods as well as standardized construction methods (simple and sophisticated), with discussion on their respective advantages and disadvantages.

FRAME CONSTRUCTION

Background

The initial construction of ferro-cement boats in New Zealand was undertaken by amateurs using simple materials which were readily available and required minimum skills to use. Thus was born in 1959, the well-known pipe-frame and chicken-netting method.

The incentive, certainly originated from Dr. Nervi, whose early works had been made known through the publications of the Cement and Concrete Association in England. Though somewhat vague, sufficient information was available to enable early enthusiasts to at least make up simple examples using approximately equivalent steel contents and mortar strengths. These original and sometimes crude experiments by amateur boat-builders produced simple, relatively small hulls of adequate structural capacity for very low material costs of approximately US$12 per m² of surface area. Labour was supplied at no charge.

Local publicity soon made it known that amateur builders could obtain a boat for what appeared to be a very low cost and by 1964 some dozens of enthusiasts were under way with projects. The author was one such builder and it soon became evident that the hull is perhaps only 20 per cent of the cost of a boat, so savings in hull cost were greatly watered down. It emerged, however, that a ferro-cement hull could, depending on the cost of labour charged, be built for some 20 per cent less than the equivalent costs of timber or steel construction.

The first construction methods utilized pipe frames bent and welded from 2-cm diameter water pipe with 6-mm longitudinal rods bent around the frames to provide the shape. Similar transverse rods were tied in place and then four layers of hexagonal (chicken) netting placed on either side of the reinforcement. This netting consisted of 22-gauge wire twisted into hexagonal holes approximately 1.2 cm in diameter.

The author's own amateur effort *Marire* and her early appearance in 1964, together with several similar boats, provided a basis for further development. The *Awahnee,* constructed in Auckland in 1965 was the first ferro-cement yacht to undertake round-the-world voyages and her epic passages have been fully described in many journals. In 1966, the first commercial company, Ferro-Cement Limited, commenced simple production using similar techniques.

Due to the very small market potential and lack of any standardization, the pipe-frame method was continued but naturally various efficiencies and improvements to the technique were introduced. The inability to obtain in New Zealand more suitable meshes necessitated the continued use of hexagonal mesh.

Longitudinal and transverse steel was readily available in the form of prestressing wire and this, although double the cost of mild steel rods, provided continuous lengths of 7-mm and 5-mm high tensile straight steel. This greatly assisted in the "fairing" process and reduced labour.

Many pleasure craft and some smaller commercial craft were produced using this technique and their service performance appeared in most cases adequate (Sutherland, 1972).

Regulations

Unfortunately the complete absence of regulations and specifications or standards of performance caused some underestimating of structural requirements in the early years which restricted development.

Experience, with various types of boats did result in preliminary regulations being introduced from 1967 onwards.

Enthusiasm for the new method tended to prevent full publication of any disadvantages and weaknesses of the material.

Construction details

Using the pipe- or truss-frame method of construction, it is difficult to envisage ways which will substantially reduce the overall labour content.

The process of frame construction and assembly leaves opportunities for errors in each construction.

The fastening of both longitudinal and transverse steel is a labour intensive operation and care must be exercised to prevent distortion of the shape when placing transverse rods. All tying is usually a hand operation.

The application of mesh can be both difficult and wasteful of material if inexperienced labour is used.

The tying of the mesh is a slow and labour intensive operation. The final skin thickness is solely dependent on the quality of this tying.

Plastering can be undertaken in either one operation, working from the outside or using a two-stage process in which the outer skin is first plastered and then the inner surface vibrated into place.

In either case the frames can be left in or removed as required.

When using the two-stage plastering technique, the use of steam curing is not possible due to the development of surface laitence effects with steam.

Shrinkage of the hull skin must be considered where very stiff frames are incorporated, as distortion between such points can occur.

The quality of the external surface is entirely dependent on the plasterers.

Advantages

The advantages of this method are:

Overall simplicity of this method allows good average quality products with a minimum of skilled labour.

No tooling up costs if pipe or truss frames are utilized for a single construction. The work force required for construction is relatively small and can be undertaken by one or two men.

When kitset frames are utilized, considerable economy of time and accuracy are possible.

No time schedules are necessary. Work can progress on a stop–start basis utilizing unskilled labour under supervision only.

Varied designs possible—frequently, variations to a specific design are required and these can be readily incorporated. Increased spacing of frames, raised top-side, deepened keel or modified bow or stern are all relatively simple variations which do not cause excessive increase in costs.

Variation of skin thickness or composition is readily accommodated to suit specific load requirements.

Repetitive considerations

By 1968, the commercial company had produced several identical hulls such as the *Matangi* motor sailer, utilizing, " one off" or unit construction.

With continued repetition possible, methods of increasing labour and material efficiency were considered with the result that the pipe frames were removed after plastering and reused for subsequent hulls. This method provided some improvement in labour costs and assisted considerably the problem of mortar penetration which had occurred around previously retained frames.

However, even with increased labour efficiency the savings were being absorbed by higher construction standards required by the company's own development combined with both the customers and Marine Department's growing concern for quality.

The result was that the total labour content remained at approximately 22 man-hours per m^2 of hull surface area, while material costs have risen due to inflation and increased quantities.

Recent developments

Mesh: Service experience combined with a comprehensive research programme indicated the need to obtain improved quality mesh reinforcing and fortunately New Zealand import restrictions were eased to allow quantities of both 19-gauge hexagonal and square welded mesh to be acquired.

The limitations on the quality of ferro-cement and the application of mass production techniques created by existing meshes resulted in a serious investigation into the development of a new and special reinforcement. The new mesh is now being incorporated into production of commercial hulls in New Zealand and details of its characteristics and availability are to be released at the earliest opportunity.

Kitsets: The New Zealand amateur boat builder is still the greatest producer of ferro-cement hulls and the demand for suitable plans and kitset frames to meet the demand has resulted in the development of truss type frames which are readily mass-produced and suitable for such amateur building methods. Their introduction into the commercial production programme has also assisted efficiency still further. Details of this construction are described by Carkeek (1972).

Quantities

The quantities required for hulls constructed by a commercial company during the years 1966 and 1970 are shown in Table 1. Examples are limited to boats constructed to a standard pipe-frame method. The labour content could be achieved by unskilled labour after a reasonable period of training or experience.

The materials represent the total costs in US$ to complete the bare hull ex-factory at the particular time of construction.

TABLE 1. UNIT COST COMPARISON

Description	Surface area (m²)	Labour (h)	Unit labour (h/m²)	Materials (US $)	Unit cost (US $/m²)
Motor sailer 1967 12 × 3.4 × 2 m including decks	76.00	1414	18.7	1165	15.3
Motor sailer 1968 11 × 3.05 × 1.53 m including decks	60.00	1300	21.6	1080	18.0
Yacht 1969 9.8 × 2.8 × 1.8 m no decks	41.2	632	15.4	620	15.00
Launch 1969 10.6 × 3.3 × 0.96 m including decks	73.4	1380	18.8	1340	18.2
Fishing boat 1967 14.7 × 4.6 × 1.56 m including decks, etc.	170.00	3050	17.90	2360	13.8
Yacht 1968 9.2 × 3.0 × 1.84 m no decks	36.0	518	14.4	480	13.0
Motor sailer 1969 16.5 × 4.6 × 1.84 m with decks	150.00	2560	17.0	2650	17.60

In interpreting these figures, allowances must be made for inflation due to time and variation in local labour and material costs.

In some cases slight variations are due to the inclusion of plastering subcontractors under material cost. Also these hulls are all based on specifications prior to 1970, since when material contents have increased somewhat.

SANDWICH CONSTRUCTION

Development

As previously stated, the New Zealand market is unfortunately very limited and does not encourage the utilization of mass production techniques. However, some repetition combined with the results of research and development has led to the adoption of a compromise between the "one off" and mass production methods.

Labour has been reduced to approximately 9 h/m². Material cost remains approximately constant at US$14/m². Also the cost of jigs and equipment must be considered.

The method consists in principle of using a complete steel structure with frames at approximately 60 cm spacings around which timber battens 20 mm square are fastened at 8 cm spacings. With the framework in an upside-down position, the battens are then fastened and the layers of mesh fixed using pneumatic stapling machines. After plastering the outer skin and allowing time for curing, the framework with partially completed hull is rolled over and the framework then removed. The internal mesh is then stapled into position and the final plastering completed. The timber battens remain in place and lightweight mortars are utilized as necessary.

Several special construction techniques ensure good bond between plaster coats, penetration and protection of the timber.

Advantages

The advantages of this technique are:

Reduced overall cost
Higher flexural strength of skin
Increased skin rigidity
Speed of construction
Ability to incorporate internal fittings readily, e.g. engine, beds, bulkhead-grounds, etc.

Disadvantages

The quality of the outer surface is still dependent on the skill of the plasterers
Ultra thin shell hulls are not possible. The minimum thickness would appear to be approximately 3 cm.

Comments

The use of timber as void formers may give rise to questions but for many years concrete has been proved to be an excellent preservative for timber and there have been few, if any, examples of timber fully enclosed in concrete, suffering from deterioration. Should such a case occur it would not have any detrimental effect and would only become apparent if damage was sustained to the hull.

This same technique can be applied to the single-frame system and is virtually an extension of the "cedar mould" method utilized in Canada.

MASS PRODUCTION TECHNIQUES

Male moulding

In this method a complete male mould is constructed of some material such as timber, ferro-cement or fibreglass. Over this, a separating membrane must be placed before stretching or fastening the layers of mesh. Plastering is then carried out in the conventional methods.

Advantages

Where the shape of the hull is such as to enable simple mesh placement, construction time can be greatly reduced. However, such cases are relatively few.

Plastering can be carried out with the hull in an inverted position which greatly simplifies the process.

Disadvantages

On demoulding the interior surface, the hull is left very smooth, which inhibits simple and efficient fastening of interior fittings.

Shrinkage of the mortar against the male mould can cause considerable difficulties in mould removal and unless careful attention is paid to this problem, serious cracking of the hull can occur.

Unless the shape of the hull is particularly suitable, the problem of holding the mesh in place against the mould is extremely difficult.

Variations to hull shape are difficult to achieve and absolute standardization is essential.

The external surface is always a function of the plasterers ability.

Female moulding

This technique offers the greatest advantage for ferro-cement construction when standardization is possible.

Advantages

Absolute minimum labour content of all methods.

Outer surface constant and of high quality regardless of labour skill.

Interior surface available for inclusion of fittings, grounds, or engine beds, etc.

Additional stiffening, bulkhead grounds, etc., are readily placed.

Variation in internal layout simple to achieve.

Demoulding assisted by shrinkage of the mortar, which prevents cracking.

Disadvantages

Complete standardization essential.

Very high cost of moulds.

Expertise required to execute the process.

Fibreglass-ferro-cement combination

The application of a standard fibreglass gel coat and outer skin provides a high quality permanent finish coat to a rigid ferro-cement hull and the future development of this process offers considerable scope.

Injection moulding

In this method, an inner and an outer mould are required, both of which must be produced to a high standard of finish.

The mesh reinforcement can be quickly placed and pressed into position.

High quality mortar or grout can be forced under pressure into the space.

This technique has been utilized for special products such as power poles, pipes, etc., but the sophisticated plant required is extremely expensive and only very large production of boats of standard sizes and shapes could justify such expenditure.

CONCLUSIONS

In this modern age, it is difficult to find any material which has properties equivalent to those of cement mortar:

It can be readily mixed by inexperienced labour.

It is readily available throughout the world.

It can be moulded or cast into many shapes, regardless of size.

The cost of materials is very low.

Combine mortar with suitable fibres and a material is produced which has no equal in the world today.

Its versatility, cost and ability to accommodate extremes in manufacture make it the ideal material for the construction of boats or structures in developing countries.

In countries with sophisticated production capacities, prejudice or lack of interest have retarded the full development and utilization of the material and it may well be the developing countries who lead the way to the full and proper use of ferro-cement.

References

CARKEEK, C Kitset construction. *FAO Seminar on the Design*
1972 *and Construction of Ferro-cement Fishing Vessels,*
9–13 October, 1972. Wellington, New Zealand.

SUTHERLAND, W M Ferro-cement Boats—service experience
1972 in New Zealand. *FAO Seminar on the Design and*
Construction of Ferro-cement Fishing Vessels, 9–13
October, 1972. Wellington, New Zealand.

Use of a Cavity Mould for Constructing 15-Metre Ferro-Cement Fishing Boats R W Behnke and E C Doleman

Ferro-cement possesses many desirable properties as a boat-building material. These are well known and include durability, ease of repair, availability of low-cost raw materials and resistance to fire, marine borers and corrosion. At the present state-of-the-art, ferro-cement is not well suited for light displacement vessels less than 10 m in length. Fibreglass and aluminium currently have better strength and weight characteristics for these type hulls. It also appears that in many other applications, conventional ferro-cement boat-building techniques have limitations that offset the advantages of this material.

Traditional ferro-cement boat-building methods, although well suited for "one-off" construction, have the following limitations:

Cost

Conventional ferro-cement construction, like most other forms of boat-building, is labour intensive. The man-hours required to build the steel armature, apply the mortar and finish the hull have changed little in twenty-five years. Unlike moulded fibreglass hulls, the unit cost of building ten ferro-cement hulls is substantially the same as building one hull. Moreover, the total cost of building a hull in ferro-cement is rarely more than 10 per cent less than the cost of building the hull in wood or steel. One-off ferro-cement construction can only reduce hull costs appreciably when it enjoys the advantage of low-priced labour. In the industrialized countries, this situation exists only among backyard boat-builders, who are willing to discount the value of their spare time.

Quality

It is difficult to force mortar through multiple layers of steel mesh and rods without leaving hidden void areas. This applies to both manual placement and pneumatic methods, such as gunite. Since incomplete penetration reduces the strength of the ferro-cement structure, every effort must be made to locate voids. This is usually done by systematic tapping of the complete hull. Wherever a hollow sound is located, the defective area is repaired. The effectiveness of this procedure is questionable. Fabrication problems with traditional boat-building materials can usually be found by visual examination or they are localized at the seams, consequently, quality control of ferro-cement products built via conventional techniques is slower, less reliable and more costly than products built of other materials.

It is also difficult to control the thickness and, therefore, the weight of ferro-cement hulls precisely. This is not a problem with other boat-building materials.

Appearance

Symmetry is usually assumed by naval architects and boat buyers. In addition to aesthetic considerations, it influences the performance of the vessel. It appears that this quality is more difficult to achieve with ferro-cement than with other materials. Although some extremely smooth and fair ferro-cement hulls have been built, they are the exception rather than the rule. Most cannot compare in appearance to metal, wood or fibreglass hulls. To de-emphasize imperfections in the finish, flat paints are used almost exclusively on ferro-cement hulls. Although appearance is not a major concern in work and commercial fishing boats, it is of great importance for pleasure boats. Grinding, filling and sanding a conventional ferro-cement hull to compete in this market is possible, but economically unattractive.

In 1969, one of the authors decided to replace his 8-m fibreglass cabin cruiser with a larger boat that was better suited for big game fishing in Hawaiian waters. He specified a low-maintenance displacement hull and heavy duty construction. After reviewing the literature, he learned that several small companies in California and Florida were using cavity mould techniques to produce ferro-cement hulls. He visited their facilities, examined their hulls and found they were comparable to fibreglass hulls in quality and appearance and lower in price. Unfortunately, none of these builders had a mould suitable for his needs. The added cost of building a mould to order made the the cost prohibitive. It seemed, however, that a hull of the dimensions he sought should have broad appeal in Hawaii. Depending upon the fitting, it could be used for sport fishing, cruising, marine research or commercial fishing and crabbing. The cavity mould technique was also well suited to building other marine structures such as floats and barges. Additionally, moulded ferro-cement also appeared to hold promise in constructing low-cost housing and was being tested for this purpose by several companies in Florida. In 1970 the rights of a proprietary ferro-cement moulding process were obtained and several experienced boat-builders from Hawaii were trained in the technique. The following sections describe the design and development of a cavity mould and the construction of a moulded ferro-cement hull.

DESIGN

The specifications prepared for the naval architect were relatively simple:

> length over-all was to be approximately 15 m;
> hull material would be moulded ferro-cement 2 cm in thickness with a weight of 50 kg/m^2;
> the hull should be adaptable to both work and pleasure craft;
> as a sport fisherman or a cabin cruiser, it should have a range of 1500 km and a cruising speed of at least 18 km/h;
> maximum use should be made of ferro-cement for bulkheads, decks, house and tanks.

The designer reviewed the specifications and proposed an adaptation of the popular salmon and albacore trollers that are used along the West Coast of North

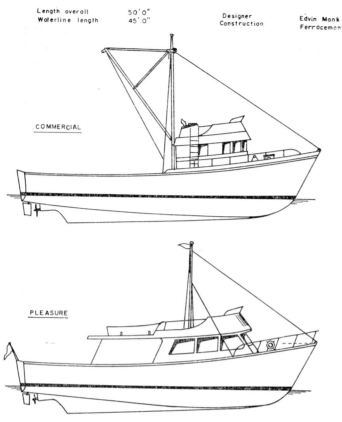

Length overall 50' 0"
Waterline length 45' 0"
Designer Edvin Monk
Construction Ferrocement

COMMERCIAL

PLEASURE

Fig. 1 Profiles

America. Profiles for a pleasure and a commercial configuration are provided in Fig. 1.

Based on past experience with ferro-cement, the designer assumed a weight of 55 kg/m², 10 per cent above the estimate provided in the specifications. He permitted integral ferro-cement tanks but insisted that the decks and cabin be made of a lighter material. At his recommendation, fibreglass-over-plywood was utilized.

MOULD CONSTRUCTION

Two methods of building the reusable ferro-cement mould were evaluated. In the first, a male wood plug is constructed and a mould prepared from it. This is the technique usually employed in the fibreglass industry. In the second, the female mould is built directly. Since the mould can be considered a ferro-cement hull with an exceptionally smooth and fair inner surface, conventional ferro-cement building methods may be used for constructing it. The direct method was selected.

Two unusual features of the mould design were removable transom and keel moulds. The removable curved transom was built of wood covered with formica. With the mould transom removed, the completed hull can be lifted from the mould in a building 5-m in height. With a fixed transom, at least 7-m is required.

The removable keel mould was built in anticipation of problems in separating the hull from the mould. The deep, narrow keel was the most likely trouble spot. In the event of a problem, the removable keel mould and the completed hull could both be lifted from the ferro-cement mould. The fibreglass mould could then be split and separated from the keel.

The process used to build the mould is a variation of the "cedar mould" technique. After the lofting was complete, and allowance made for the thickness of the ferro-cement mould and wood planking, external stations were built of 2.5 cm plywood. These were positioned and held in place by a pipe-frame network that was welded to a base made of steel beams. Inexpensive sheathing (2.5 × 10 cm) was nailed to the plywood stations and planed to achieve fairness. Two layers of plastic sheeting were then applied to the interior surface of the sheathing as a sealer.

Next, five layers of expanded metal lath were gun-stapled to the wood frame. The lath was cut neatly, shaped with a roller and laid with edges meeting. The mortar was then applied in two passes. In the first pass a soft mix was trowelled and vibrated to improve the penetration. The next pass was made with a stiffer mix and was smooth trowelled.

The day after the plastering, the mould was checked with fairing battens. High spots were ground down, low spots were filled and the interior of the mould was painted with a cement wash. This cut-and-fill process was repeated many times to get an extremely smooth and fair surface. After the mould had cured for thirty days, a coat of high-gloss swimming pool paint was applied. The keel mould and transom were then inserted in the mould.

Ten holes were drilled through the mould along the turn of the bilge to provide a method for introducing water between the hull and the mould at release time. These holes were sealed with tape prior to layup.

HULL CONSTRUCTION

Critical parts of the cavity mould process outlined here are proprietary and protected by the US Patent Office (Patent 3,652,755, 1972).

In concept, the cavity mould technique for building ferro-cement hulls is similar to that used in the fibreglass boat-building industry. The mould was first painted with a separating compound to minimize release problems. A thin layer, approximately 3 mm of enriched mortar was then applied to the mould as a space or gel coat. This gel coat becomes the exterior surface of the hull.

A steel rod basket was placed in the keel mould prior to the layup. Although some 2.5 × 2.5 cm welded mesh was used in the flat sections, expanded metal lath was the primary reinforcing material. It is inexpensive and can be worked to follow the compound curves of the mould.

A bonding compound was sprayed on the gel coat, followed by a layer of mortar. The first layer of expanded metal lath was cut and laid in the soft mortar. Additional mortar was then pneumatically applied to the lath. Four additional layers of lath and mortar were added to bring the hull to the desired thickness. To eliminate weak spots, successive layers of the expanded metal lath were shingled to overlap all seams. The interior surface was then trowelled to remove any excess mortar. It should be noted that steel reinforcing rods were used only in the construction of the keel. If required, they can easily be introduced during the layup process.

Steel engine stringers, ferro-cement water tanks and fibreglass-covered-plywood bulkheads were installed while the hull was still inside the mould. Plans to use ferro-cement bulkheads were changed after the first one built proved to be too heavy. Because of reported chemical reactions between diesel fuel and ferro-cement, steel tanks were used for this purpose.

After a thirty-day curing period, small wooden wedges were driven between the hull and the mould. Water was pumped into the gap and through the holes that had previously been drilled in the mould to release the hull. A crane was then attached to several reinforcing rods imbedded in the keel and the hull was lifted approximately 6 in. The transom was removed, the hull lifted out and transferred to another location for outfitting. Figure 2 illustrates the mould with transom removed and Fig. 3 a completed hull.

If high-volume production is required, the hull can be cured more quickly with steam or the transom can be removed after several days and both the hull and mould lowered into water. The partially cured hull, supported uniformly by the water, will float and the transomless mould will sink. The hull can then be floated to another location for additional curing. The mould can be used immediately to construct another hull.

Fig. 2   Releasing hull from cavity mould

Fig. 3   Completed hull

COST

The cost data given below was adjusted to compensate for several extraordinary problems that were encountered during the construction of the first mould and hull. These included storm damage, a shipping strike and several unusual labour problems.

Mould

The major cost factors in building the reuseable cavity mould were:

Materials	US$1950
Plans	600
Miscellaneous	900
	US$3450

Labour to build transom, keel and cradle	420 man-hours
Labour to build mould	840
Labour to finish inner surface	270
	1530 man-hours

The labour rate, including fringe benefits, overhead and general and administrative charges was approximately US$7.50/h. The labour cost was US$11,475; the direct cost of building the mould was US$14,925.

Hull

Estimates of the material and labour used to build the first ferro-cement hull in this mould follow:

Materials

Item	Description	Cost
1	Expanded metal lath (1.6 kg/m^2) 555 m^2	US$427
2	Steel reinforcing rod for keel, 100 kg	35
3	Steel plate and channel for stringers, 140 kg	85
4	Premixed (1 : 1) sand : cement (type 5), 8200 kg	315
5	Mortar additives and bonding compounds, 340 l	230
	Total material cost	US$1092

The materials include a wastage allowance. All material prices quoted are for one hull, f.o.b. San Francisco, California, USA. Five hundred dollars should be added for shipping and handling costs to compute the Honolulu price. (Although this may seem high, the cost of shipping a complete hull of this size from San Francisco to Hawaii is at least US$2000.)

129

Labour

Approximately 550 man-hours were required to mould the first ferro-cement hull. Eighty per cent of this time was devoted to the following tasks:

> prepare engine stringers;
> build cage of reinforcing rod for keel;
> clean mould and spray separating compound;
> apply space (gel) coat;
> layup keel;
> cut and fit expanded metal lath and apply mortar;
> install stringers and floor frames.

A foreman and two skilled workers trained in the cavity mould process, supplemented by unskilled labour completed these steps in approximately 15 working days.

The remaining time was used to release the hull from the mould, transfer the hull to a nearby location and clean the hull, mould, equipment and facility.

Equipment

The following capital equipment was purchased or built and used in constructing the cavity mould and the hull:

1	Compressor (gasoline powered, purchased used)	US$1539.20
2	Paddle mixer (purchased new)	1414.15
3	Mortar pump (built)	2112.15
4	Hose (purchased new)	262.09
5	Nozzles (built)	85.26
	Total	US$5412.85

Costs associated with licensing fees, research and development, staff training, construction of test panels, establishing a technical library and similar items amounted to approximately US$90,000 over a two-year period.

LESSONS LEARNED

Design: Mr W M Sutherland made an excellent point when he stated: "A more conservative approach regarding the statements on the weight of ferro-cement should be adopted and the use of concrete decks and superstructures should only be used in very large vessels or if the designer has fully allowed for their real weight."

Mould: It is estimated that if a male plug had been used substantial savings would have been made on the man-hours expended in the construction of the cavity mould. The convex wood plug can be planed and faired much more easily than a concave ferro-cement shell. This approach would also eliminate filled spots in the mould surface. Some of the areas of the mould that had been filled pulled out during the hull release operation. Consequently, two man-days were required to patch the mould and the gel coat of the hull.

Hull: A Teflon compound was used as a separating agent between the mould and the hull. Attempts to paint the hull without sanding proved unsuccessful because a thin layer of Teflon remained on the surface. Use of a separating agent that can be removed with a liquid solvent will eliminate the need to sand the hull before painting.

Ferro-cement frames were used initially to attach the fibreglass over plywood bulkheads to the hull. Epoxy resin, reinforced with fibreglass proved to be more suitable, in both strength and weight, for bonding in these bulkheads.

MATHEMATICAL MODEL

The model described in this section was developed to provide a quantitative basis for comparing the cavity mould method with conventional ferro-cement building methods.

Notation

C = total cost/hull
M = material cost/hull
L = labour cost (burdened)/hull
E = special equipment cost/hull (cavity mould method only)
F = mould cost/hull (cavity mould method only)
conv = Subscript for conventional method
mould = subscript for cavity mould method
N = number of hulls
I = annual compound interest rate
T = term of loan, years
A = annual payment, principal and interest
K = constant (see assumption 5)

Definitions

X = Ratio of cost of materials to labour using conventional methods. This is primarily a function of geographic location.

$$X = \frac{M_{conv}}{L_{conv}} \qquad (1)$$

Y = Ratio of productivity of cavity mould method to conventional methods. This is a function of hull design, the skill level of workers and any special equipment employed.

$$Y = \frac{L_{mould} + E_{mould}}{L_{conv} + E_{conv}} = \frac{L_{mould} + E_{mould}}{L_{conv}} \qquad (2)$$

S = Savings in building N hulls with the cavity mould method.

$$S = N(C_{conv} - C_{mould}) \qquad (3)$$

where C_{mould} varies with N.

P = Percentage savings in building N hulls with cavity mould method rather than conventional methods.

$$P = \frac{S}{C_{conv}} \qquad (4)$$

Assumptions

1. Workshop rental, employee fringe benefits, standard equipment, training, general and administrative costs are included in an overhead factor applied to wages. This overhead factor is assumed to be the same for the cavity-mould and conventional methods.
2. Material costs are the same for all methods, i.e. $M_{conv} = M_{mould} = M$.
3. Financing terms and maintainability are also independent of method used to construct hulls.
4. Neither special equipment nor moulds are required in conventional ferro-cement building techniques. $E_{conv} = F_{conv} = 0$.

5. The cost of the mould can be expressed as a constant (K) times the cost of a conventional ferro-cement hull (C_{conv}) of the same size. That is, cost of mould = $K(C_{conv})$. The cost of the mould per hull (F) can be computed by dividing the total mould cost by N, the number of hulls to be produced.

$$F = \frac{K}{N}(C_{conv}) \qquad (5)$$

Hull cost via conventional methods

The cost of construction of a hull using conventional techniques, C_{conv}, is the sum of the costs of material and labour (including overhead, general and administrative charges, etc.).

$$C_{conv} = M_{conv} + L_{conv}$$

Substituting from Eq. (1),

$$C_{conv} = M + \frac{M}{X} = M\left(\frac{X+1}{X}\right) \qquad (6)$$

Cost of using mould

This can be derived by combining Eqs. (5) and (6).

$$F = \frac{KM}{N}\left(\frac{X+1}{X}\right) \qquad (7)$$

Hull cost via cavity mould method

The cost of construction of a moulded hull is the sum of the costs of labour and material plus the cost of using the mould and special equipment.

$$C_{mould} = M_{mould} + L_{mould} + E_{mould} + F_{mould}$$

Substituting Eqs. (1), (2) and (7),

$$C_{mould} = M + Y\left(\frac{M}{X}\right) + \frac{KM}{N}\left(\frac{X+1}{X}\right) \qquad (8)$$

Savings

The savings, S, in building N hulls via a cavity mould technique can be found by combining Eqs. (3), (6) and (8). To get average savings per hull, divide S by N.

$$S = N[C_{conv} - C_{mould}]$$

$$S = \frac{NM}{X}\left[1 - Y - \frac{K}{N}(X+1)\right] \qquad (9)$$

The savings (percentage), P, in building N hulls via the cavity mould technique can be found by combining Eqs. (4), (6) and (9):

$$P = \frac{S}{N(C_{conv})}$$

$$P = \frac{(1-Y)}{(1+X)} - \frac{K}{N} \qquad (10)$$

Figure 4 describes the range of savings possible by using the cavity mould method for building a number of hulls in an industrialized country where the cost of materials is 10 per cent of the cost of labour using conventional ferro-cement techniques. Figure 4 also shows the savings in a developing country where material costs and labour costs are equal ($X = 1.0$). Values of $Y = 0.5$, 0.33 and 0.25 are considered for

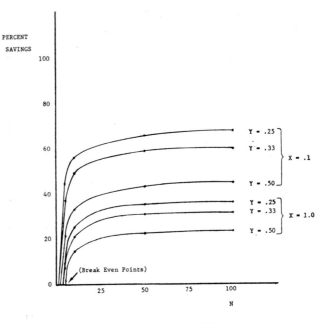

Fig. 4 Cost comparison—Cavity mould vs. conventional ferro-cement techniques ($K = 1.2$)

both cases. These represent two, three and four-fold increases in productivity using the cavity mould method.

Break-even point

The value of N where the P is zero in Fig. 4 or $S = 0$ is called the Break-even point (BEP). It can be computed directly by setting $S = 0$ in Eq. (9) and solving for N.

$$BEP = \frac{K(X+1)}{(1-Y)} \qquad (11)$$

The following table gives B.E.P. for stated values of X and Y, as computed using Eq. (11). Fractional values of N were rounded to the next higher integer. A value of $K = 1.2$ was used.

TABLE 1. NUMBER OF HULLS REQUIRED TO ACHIEVE BREAK-EVEN POINT ($K = 1.2$)

X	Y			
	0	0.25	0.33	0.50
0.1	2	2	2	3
0.3	2	3	3	4
0.5	2	3	3	4
0.7	3	3	4	5
0.9	3	4	4	5
1.1	3	4	4	6

Cost of capital

The equations developed permit a comparison of the initial cost of building a hull with conventional methods or a cavity mould technique. In order to compute the annual cost of using the hull, it is necessary to introduce terms for computing the cost of capital. The following equations were derived from Rutledge and Cairns (1964).

131

Assume that funds to purchase the hulls are borrowed at a compound interest rate, I, and repaid in equal annual installments over a period, T, years. The annual installments, A, can be computed from the following formula.

$$A = \frac{I}{1-(1+I)^{-T}} \tag{12}$$

Table 2 contains the annual payment of principal and interest per US dollar of principal, as computed using Eq. (12).

TABLE 2. ANNUAL PAYMENT PER DOLLAR OF PRINCIPAL

Years (T)	Interest (I)			
	6%	12%	18%	24%
5	0.2374	0.2773	0.3197	0.3642
10	0.1358	0.1769	0.2225	0.2715
15	0.1029	0.1468	0.1963	0.2499
20	0.0871	0.1338	0.1868	0.2433
25	0.0782	0.1275	0.1829	0.2411
30	0.0726	0.1241	0.1812	0.2403

Table 3 shows the total interest payments per dollar of principal. It was derived from Table 2 by multiplying the annual payment by the term of the loan and subtracting 1 from the entry.

TABLE 3. TOTAL INTEREST PAYMENT PER DOLLAR OF PRINCIPAL

Years (T)	Interest (I)			
	6%	12%	18%	24%
5	0.1870	0.3865	0.5985	0.8210
10	0.3580	0.7690	1.2250	1.7150
15	0.5435	1.1570	1.9445	2.7450
20	0.7420	1.6760	2.7360	3.8660
25	0.9550	2.1875	3.5725	5.0275
30	1.1780	2.7230	4.4360	6.2090

Assuming a hull life of 25 years and 6 per cent loan rates, each US$1.00 savings in the initial purchase price of the hull would reduce cumulative interest payments by US$0.95. If the loan rate is 18 per cent, as it is in many developing countries, each US$1.00 reduction in hull-purchase price would save US$3.57 in interest payments during the 25-year period.

EVALUATION

Conventional ferro-cement construction techniques were used to build the cavity mould. By building both the mould and a moulded ferro-cement hull of the same size and shape, a unique opportunity was provided to compare and contrast the cavity mould method and conventional building techniques.

Costs

In conventional construction, the main labour component is devoted to setting up the rod structure and fastening the mesh or wire reinforcing. In the cavity-mould technique, cutting and placing of the mesh require considerably less labour.

For the 15-m boat, the moulded hull required 550 man-hours. The ferro-cement mould, built using conventional techniques, required 1530 man-hours. Because of the additional time spent in building the removable transom and keel and in extra finishing of the mould surface, the man-hours expended are somewhat higher than would be required for a conventional hull. On the other hand, the wood battens were left on the outer surface of the mould and no labour was expended to test for good penetration. These effects seem to cancel out.

Table 4 summarizes the labour and material costs of building the 15-m hull in Honolulu. The cost of the conventional hull was derived by adding the cost of labour required to construct the cavity mould (US$11,475) and the cost of materials used to construct the moulded hull (US$1592).

TABLE 4. LABOUR AND MATERIAL FOR 15-M BOAT AND MOULD

	Labour US $ 7.50/H	Materials US $	Total US $
Mould	11,475	3,450	14,925
Hull (Conv)	11,475	1,592	13,067
Hull (Mould)	4,125	1,592	5,717

Table 5 provides an estimate of the savings possible by using the cavity-mould method to build ten of the 15-m ferro-cement hulls described in Section 7. It was conservatively assumed that the mould and equipment would have no salvage value after the ten hulls were completed.

The same results could have been obtained from the mathematical model by computing the values of X, Y, K (0.1387, 0.4066 and 1.142 respectively) from the data in Table 4.

TABLE 5. COST COMPARISON FOR BUILDING TEN 15-M HULLS

	Conventional US $	Cavity Mould US $
Labour	114,750	41,250
Materials	15,920	15,920
Mould	—	14,925
Equipment	—	5,413
TOTAL	130,670	77,508
SAVINGS	—	53,162
SAVINGS/HULL	—	5,316
% SAVINGS	—	40.7%

Quality

In conventional ferro-cement layup techniques, mortar is applied after the steel armature has been constructed. Since the mortar covers potential void spots from the view of workers and supervisors, it is not always possible to detect potentially weak areas. Examples of incomplete mortar penetration can be found by inspecting conventionally-built ferro-cement moulds. Fortunately, this does not affect hulls produced from the mould. In the cavity-mould process described, the mortar, enriched with chemical additives, was applied first and reinforcing material was forced into the mortar. Complete penetration was achieved using expanded metal lath, one of the most difficult materials to work with using conventional layup methods.

Using the cavity-mould method, the thickness of the hull can be carefully controlled. In addition, extra layers of reinforcing mesh may easily be placed at critical parts of the structure to increase the strength.

There appears to be wide diversity of opinions on the value of expanded metal lath as a reinforcing material in ferro-cement. The major problem appears to be penetration. Results published in Canadian Project Report No. 42 (1971) indicate that ferro-cement constructed with expanded metal lath is less satisfactory than ferro-cement made with most other reinforcing materials. Another paper contained in this same report (Kelly and Mouat, 1968) states that a type of expanded metal lath may increase the cross-bonding and the compressive strength of ferro-cement panels.

There is also a diversity of opinions on the value of mortar additives. Canadian Project Report 42 (1971) suggests that it is better to avoid admixtures because of possible adverse side effects. Collins and Claman (1969), on the other hand, indicate that mortar additives may be extremely useful. They say: "An area of great promise is opened by the fact that cement, unlike steel, aluminium or glass, will accept a variety of additives, with the result that many of its properties can be dramatically changed at will. Additives such as epoxies and other polymers offer the possibility of forming a truly impermeable material, with a dense, hard surface of almost any colour and texture."

Preliminary tests have been conducted to determine the relative strength of panels made with the cavity mould method, using expanded metal lath as the reinforcing material and employing special mortar additives. The results (unpublished) of these tests indicated that the end-product is as good as samples derived from panels that were made with other forms of mesh and mortar. Formal tests will be conducted and results published in the near future.

Five moulded hulls have been completed with this material, and, to date, no structural problems have been reported. As better materials are found, they will be incorporated in the cavity-mould process.

Appearance

The surface of the ferro-cement hull produced by the cavity-mould process is as smooth and fair as a luxury fibreglass yacht. After two coats of high gloss epoxy paint were applied to the hull, it was difficult to convince knowledgeable observers that the hull was made of ferro-cement.

CONCLUSIONS

Although each potential application of the cavity-mould method for building ferro-cement structures must be independently evaluated; several general comments are possible. The cavity-mould method requires less skill and fewer workers than conventional ferro-cement construction techniques. Because of the capital investment required, the method is not designed for the one-of-a-kind ferro-cement boat-builder. This is not to imply the cavity-mould process is limited to high production situations. Savings over conventional ferro-cement construction techniques can often be realized constructing fewer than five hulls. Consequently, the cavity-mould method should be attractive to fishing cooperatives and small regional boat-builders as well as large boat manufacturers.

In industrialized countries, hull savings of 50 per cent or more can be achieved with the production of ten hulls from a mould. Where the design permits use of moulded ferro-cement for decks and superstructure, additional over-all savings can be realized. In the future, the authors expect to see the emergence of companies which produce hulls made of moulded ferro-cement for the fisherman and the amateur boat-builder. These companies, patterned after those in the fibreglass industry, will offer a variety of ferro-cement hulls at low prices for outfitting by the owner or a yard of his choice. The owner will, in effect, add the ferro-cement hull to the engines, electronics equipment and other items he buys rather than makes. His labour, then, can be concentrated on the high pay-off carpentry, electrical and mechanical tasks. He will also be assured of a quality ferro-cement hull built by specialists.

In developing countries, the cavity mould method will make possible quantity production of low maintenance ferro-cement boats, docks, floats and other structures. The cavity-mould process will also reduce supervision and quality control problems. The investment required to set up cavity-mould production is lower in a developing country than in an industrialized country. The cavity-mould, the major item of capital equipment, can be built within the host country using local labour and materials. The cost and skills required are approximately the same as those needed to build a single ferro-cement hull employing conventional techniques. This is not true with many other industries where production equipment must be imported from industrial nations and duties and shipping charges increase the total equipment cost.

When ten or more hulls are produced from a single mould, savings of 25 per cent or more are realized, even in locations with low labour costs. Although these savings are less than in the industrialized countries, they could have a greater impact on the end user. Traung and Gulbrandsen (1971) point out that in Canada, the total yearly expenditure for a hull, including interest, taxes, and insurance, is only 12 per cent of the total yearly expenditure of an average fishing boat. Maintenance of the hull adds another 5 per cent to the yearly total. These figures are typical of industrialized countries since labour, materials and interest charges are comparable. Developing countries, on the other hand, are characterized by lower crew costs, limited maintenance facilities and higher interest rates—18 per cent per annum interest rates on loans are not unusual. Any reduction in the cost of hull construction or maintenance, therefore, have a greater impact on the total yearly expenditure in the developing countries than in industrialized countries (see Tables 2 and 3).

It appears that cavity-mould ferro-cement construction techniques will allow the fabrication of hulls and other structures on a production basis, at economically attractive costs, for high quality products in both industrialized and developing countries.

References

COLLINS, J F and CLAMAN, J S *Ferrocement for Marine Application: An Engineering Evaluation (iii).* New England Section SNAME, General Dynamics, Quincy, Mass., USA: 65 pp.

GARDNER, J *National Fisherman.* December, 7 pp.
1971

GREENIUS, A W and SMITH J D *Ferrocement for Canadian*
1971 *Vessels.* Ottawa, Canada: Industrial Development Branch, Fisheries Service, Department of the Environment, Project Report No. 48(iv).

JACKSON, G W and SUTHERLAND, W M *Concrete Boat*
1969 *Building, Its Techniques and Its Future.* Tuckahoe, New York, USA: John de Graff, 106 pp.

RUTLEDGE, W A and CAIRNS, T W *Mathematics for Business*
1964 *Analysis.* University of Tulsa State, USA: Holt Rinehart and Winston.

SCOTT, W D *Ferrocement for Canadian Fishing Vessels.*
1971 Ottawa, Canada: Industrial Development Branch, Fisheries Service, Department of the Environment, Project Report No. 42.

TRAUNG, J O (ed.) *Fishing Boats of the World*, vol. 3. London,
1967 England: Fishing News (Books) Ltd., 648 pp.

US PATENT 3652755 *Methods of Forming Reinforced Con-*
1972 *crete Structures*, 7 pp.

The Use of Kit-Sets for Amateur Construction / G Carkeek

The development and marketing of kit-sets for amateur construction has been the result of a world-wide increase in the popularity of boating and the fact that because of relatively cheap materials the building of ferro-cement boats has come within the financial scope of a much greater number of people.

To simplify construction even further, the making of frames in kit-set form was a natural progression, and the setting up of an operation of this type was a viable proposition once the potential market and operating costs were established.

In the last few years many types of frames and designs of boats have been available. Designers have become more familiar with the material and are providing a large variety of designs and combined with the availability of kit-sets, a world-wide boom in the building of ferro-cement boats has resulted with no sign of declining. As the demand increases, many operators of fleets are considering using ferro-cement for large-scale replacement of existing boats and the establishment of new fleets.

This has led to a new type of kit-set construction where the whole set of frames are set up as a permanent jig and a production run of boats of the same design may be built quickly and cheaply.

In this paper the different types of frames, with advantages and disadvantages of each, are fully described.

PLANS

It is essential that designs take into consideration advantages of the material and also allowances for the extra weight involved. As ferro-cement opened the field for amateurs, an advantage was to have the frame drawing already lofted full size to eliminate the possibility of errors due to the general inexperience of the builder. Even where kit-set frames are available, it is a great advantage to be able to refer to datum marks to help with setting up the boat. The main problem in using plans for measurement is movement of the paper due to humidity changes from day to day and it is necessary for permanent reference to have the body plan marked out on a steel plate.

LOFTING

The use of kit-sets eliminates one of the most difficult tasks faced by a builder and that is lofting the lines full size from a table of offsets. This is not necessary where the designer already provides a full-size body plan but there are limitations on a choice of design.

A kit-set manufacturer with a trained staff can produce a set of frames for any boat from a table of offsets but the cost is dependent on the number of hulls to be built.

TYPES OF FRAMES

Three basic types of frames are in general use, timber, water pipe and truss. Locality and availability will determine the best method for a given situation. In an area rich in timber and with a limited supply of piping, timber frames would probably be used. The same would apply to any type of material, the main consideration being cost.

Pipe frames

As a cheap and readily available material, water pipe was used from the outset by local amateur and professional builders. For instance, in boats up to 60 ft the frames would be $\frac{1}{2}$ in diameter and the stem and stern of $\frac{3}{4}$ in diameter.

134

Advantages

1. As a standard item in the building industry, pipe is readily available. It is not necessary to stick rigidly to a particular pipe for the frames if the size shown on the plan is not available.
2. Comparatively cheap as quantity used is so small.
3. Will bend to shape with basic equipment. It would be possible to shape a frame with just a hole in a block of wood, but obviously one could not expect a perfect boat.
4. Can be used either galvanized or ungalvanized.
5. Unskilled labour can tie stringers to frames, no welding required.
6. Adequate strength in the pipe when embedded in plaster.

Disadvantages

1. Voids are likely to occur around the pipe area due to incomplete penetration of the mortar.
2. The plastered shape is unsuitable as an attachment point for bulkheads and joinery.
3. Its ease of bending is a disadvantage during construction when the weight of workers inside the boat can distort it out of shape.
4. Damage is likely to occur during transportation. It is possible to pack pipe frames but there is a considerable amount of extra work involved. The slightest bump at any stage is enough to cause distortion.

Wooden frames

A common form of construction and probably the most widely used by amateurs. Has not been used in kit-set construction to any great extent.

Advantages

1. Almost any timber can be utilized.
2. Minimal skill required to shape frames, only hand tools if no power available.
3. Easily made in small sections for reassembly and transporting.
4. Staples may be used to fasten mesh. This is a very quick method.

Disadvantages

1. Frames subject to movement with temperature and humidity changes, therefore making continuous adjustment necessary.
2. During plastering timber may draw moisture from the plaster, causing local weak spots if the face adjacent to plaster is not primed.
3. Some difficulty in freighting because of weight.

Truss frames

Truss frames are the most common type used in kit-sets in New Zealand at present.

Advantages

1. Steel content readily available. A wide range of rod types may be used.
2. Lofting eliminated with subsequent saving in labour and costs.
3. Perfect shape maintained during hull construction. No extra bracing required. The inherent strength of the truss form in a transverse direction is more than adequate to counteract the stresses involved during construction of the hull.
4. A frame can be constructed for any part of the hull to suit a layout. In initial designing it is advantageous to provide for a frame where it is intended to position bulkheads or any other equipment.
5. A centralized manufacturer of kit-sets using strict quality control has the capacity to produce large quantities on long runs.
6. A small trained staff allows greater supervision for quality control.
7. Frames incorporated in the structure impart great strength.
8. Permanent attachment points are provided throughout hull for bulkheads and joinery.
9. Designer's datum marks (DWL, etc.) can be fixed permanently with welded lugs to assist in setting up frames;
10. Relatively unskilled labour can complete construction from the kit-set stage.
11. Engine beds may be integral, thus reducing construction costs.
12. Frames will not distort with weight of workers inside boat during construction.
13. Easy to replace frames of stock designs.
14. Strong enough to be used in a jig as a permanent frame.
15. Transportable in sections if required and easily assembled at site. The possibility of damage during transit is greatly reduced because of the strength of the truss form.

Disadvantages

1. High degree of skill required to fabricate and weld truss without distortion.
2. Specialized equipment required—welders, sheet plates and formers.
3. Heat transference during the welding of webs to the inner and outer rods will cause variations.

PERMANENT JIGS

A recent development in kit-set frame construction has been a permanent jig using a solid base with the frames fixed in position. This is used when a number of the same design boats are required and eliminates setting up each boat individually, so reducing costs and speeding building.

A permanent jig may be made in kit-set form and transported to the building site for reassembly in the same way as frames. This new method of construction has greater potential in the commercial field as costs are prohibitive where one boat only is required.

QUALITY CONTROL

In the manufacture of kit-sets this is one of the most important aspects of production. Absolute accuracy is essential, as any error in the finished product will be a major problem to the amateur builder, who in most cases will be unfamiliar with the setting up of frames and will not know where to start looking for any discrepancies. Many boats are built in areas where professional help is not available and the builder is completely reliant on the manufacturer. Where frames are produced in one central point, strict supervision is easier and mistakes are reduced as far as possible.

MARKETING

To justify the expense of setting up an operation for wholesale manufacture of kit-sets, extensive research into design requirements to cover the greatest demand is very important.

Some designers advertise extensively a full range of boats, and if kit-sets are also available, the advantages are obvious.

TRANSPORTATION

Sets of frames, even for large boats, may be easily broken down into units for transportation. It is essential that adequate protection in the form of a completely enclosed crate be used to eliminate damage during transit.

COSTS

Taking a boat of 40 ft as an example, the cost of a set of frames including stem, stern and keel, is approximately NZ$500. The actual labour content is approximately 90 h.

This would not cover costs completely for jigs, etc., and assumes that a production run spreads the cost over several boats.

Unless the amateur has the necessary specialized equipment and knowledge, it is doubtful whether any saving is possible in manufacturing his own frames because of the greater time involved due to unfamiliarity with the process.

The permanent jig method costs considerably more to establish, but where a number of units are to be constructed, the saving in labour makes the initial cost worthwhile.

Explosive Moulding of Ferro-Cement Armatures R C Pickett and J C Black

Here is presented a report on recent experiments using explosive moulding to form mesh and reinforcing rod into the shape of a hull. It is hoped that this method, when developed, will substantially cut the cost of producing multiple hulls of the same shape. It is a method for competent professionals who can use dangerous explosives safely. It is not a technique for amateurs.

Basically, a reinforced cement female form is constructed in the shape of the hull. The mesh and welded reinforcing wire mesh are laid loosely into the mould. A heavy plastic sheet is laid over the final layer of wire and the plastic is filled with water. Appropriate explosives are placed in the water and detonated. The water transmits the shock waves of the explosion and forces the mesh and reinforcing rod into the shape of the hull. Multiple shots may be necessary to ensure that the mesh is correctly shaped and pressed flat so that tying is unnecessary.

The principal advantages of the system are: a reduction of the time needed to produce an armature ready for plastering from several weeks to a few days, the ability to produce hulls of uniform shape quickly, the elimination of tie wires to keep the mesh tight, and a massive saving of labour.

The problems vary with the shape of the hull. Every hull will require some experience and experimentation to find the best placement of the charge, the best size of charge, and the best pattern in which to lay the mesh.

HISTORY

Explosive forming of metals is not a new science. In 1888 iron plates were engraved by Charles Monroe using explosives. In the 1930s many experiments were made in the United States and Great Britain, but it was not until the 1950s that current industrial uses were developed. Ryan Aircraft and Aero-jet General Corporation of the USA have been making prototype and production parts for aircraft and missiles for several years. Ends for tanks and tank cars, architectural panels, cooking pans, and many other products are currently manufactured by explosive moulding.

SCOPE OF EXPERIMENTS

Investigations were conducted during the summer of 1970. Preliminary work was done in forming several 3-ft diameter domes. The mesh and reinforcing was bolted between two 3-ft inside diameter $\frac{1}{2}$-in thick steel rings. The rings and mesh were supported 2 ft off the ground and a circular cardboard dam 16 in high was placed on top of the mesh. The cardboard was lined with a plastic sheet and filled with water. One-eighth of a stick of 40 per cent gel dynamite with an electrical blasting cap formed a dome 12 in deep with 8 layers of $\frac{1}{2}$-in hexagonal mesh wire galvanized after weaving and 2 layers of No. 8 wire formed in a 6-in welded wire mesh.

The type of mesh and the number of layers was varied. They did not affect the quality of the results, but a larger charge was necessary with more mesh. In all cases the mesh acquired a tight, stretched quality that made wire tying unnecessary. No ripping of mesh or creasing was experienced.

Next a hard chine, pram-shaped boat mould was constructed from reinforced concrete. The mesh was draped into the mould so it roughly conformed to the

136

shape of the mould. An inadequate fastening of the mesh to the top edge of the mould resulted in wrinkles and a springy quality in the armature. Once this problem was corrected a suitable armature was formed easily. It took about 4 h to put the mesh in the mould and prepare the original shot. Three other shots were necessary to force the mesh into the hard chine, develop the corners where the bottom, sides, and bow or stern meet, and to give final shape. The entire armature was completed in a single day.

Final experiments dealt with a double-ended, narrow-beam hull mould. The problem was to get the mesh to stretch into the mould so that it would maintain its shape. This was accomplished by stretching the mesh between a pipe bolted in the bow of the mould and a pipe bolted in the stern of the mould. The two sets of mesh were then spread with the explosives. The pipes were left in for plastering. Using this technique, it was also necessary to tie the top edges of the mesh to the top of the mould.

CONSTRUCTION OF THE MOULD

The experiments indicate that the mould should be constructed of heavily reinforced concrete. It is essential that extra reinforcing be placed at angles such as at the transom, at apexes such as the bow, and at any narrowly confined area such as the keel of a sail boat. A mould release compound must be applied to the mould so that the cemented boat will come out of the mould. Drains must be placed in the mould to drain the water if the plastic membrane ruptures. These drains may also be used to remove the boat from the mould hydraulically.

Adequate facilities must be placed at the top edges of the mould to firmly anchor the mesh and reinforcing rod so that it will not draw down into the mould during the initial sizing shots.

The surface texture of the outside of the boat is determined by the texture of the inside of the mould. It must be smooth and clean.

If the shape is shallow or the mesh is draped in a shallow arc it will be necessary to build a dam on top of the mould. The width of the mould should not exceed $1\frac{1}{2}$ times the depth of the water over the mesh. The dam only needs to be strong enough to hold the water. The fact that the dam is destroyed during the blast does not affect the results.

DESIGN LIMITATIONS

It is difficult to form mesh into right angles or sharp bends with explosive moulding. The best results are obtained with gently curved surfaces where the mesh must be stretched to conform. Unless the mesh is stretched it tends to develop a loose quality and needs tying to stay flat.

Ferro-cement is strongest in curved areas and weakest in flat sheets or sharp curves so explosive moulding is compatible with the limitations of the material.

Where sharp corners are necessary the mesh may be stretched from a pipe bolted into the corner or formed by using primacord (a lineal explosive produced in the form of a rope).

Where flat sheets are required, it may be necessary to weight, brace, or tie the sheets at strategic points during plastering.

The ideal shape for explosive moulding is a variation on a dome or cone. This means a round-bottomed, soft-chined, double-ender or rounded-stern boat is the best shape for an explosively-moulded hull. Other shapes may be accomplished with more difficulty. A great deal can be learned with a 10-ft model mould of a 50-ft boat. Big moulds are expensive and a little experimenting can save a lot of money.

MESH PLACEMENT

In the experiments described, both $\frac{1}{2}$-in hexagonal wire mesh galvanized after weaving and $\frac{1}{2}$-in square weave welded wire mesh were used. The reinforcing rod was 10 SWG wire welded into a 6-in or 3-in mesh and 8 SWG and 6 SWG wire welded into a 6-in mesh. The placement of mesh will depend on the shape of the hull. Mesh placed stem to stern was alternated with mesh placed sheer to sheer. The reinforcing rod mesh should be bought in flat sheets for easier working and should be placed to assure minimum spacing between the reinforcing rods. No particular mesh and rod combination was found to be preferable. The controlling consideration was the placing of the mesh to conform to the shape of the hull. It is desirable to use as few tie wires as possible; they can cause tears and deformities. The mesh must be securely attached to the top of the mould so that the mesh will stretch into the mould and not just pull down into the mould.

Stretching causes the mesh to stay tightly pressed together in the shape of the hull. It also takes up the initial stretch in the mesh. Studies have shown that woven mesh that has been galvanized after weaving and welded wire mesh tend to stretch slightly when tension is applied. Explosive moulding takes up the initial stretch and prepares the mesh to withstand immediate tension with little or no stretch. This is important because ferro-cement relies on the steel to take the tension stresses and the cement to take the compression. Cement has very low tensile strength and cracks if the steel does not handle the tension forces without stretching. Explosive moulding provides a crude form of pre-stressing.

If the boat has a thin keel like a sail boat, the keel might be formed separately and then attached to the explosively-formed hull armature.

No advantage was found in forming the mesh a few layers at a time. Eight layers of mesh and the two to four layers of reinforcing mesh were formed at the same time. Sharp wire ends may rupture the plastic membrane and they should be avoided.

Once the mesh is placed in the mould and secured to the top edges a plastic membrane such as a heavy sheet of polyethylene should be draped inside the mesh and filled with water. Lightweight plastics tend to rip into small pieces which get stuck in the mesh. Heavy plastics tend not to stretch and therefore tear. This is a problem that needs more research, however it takes very little time to pick the pieces of plastic out of a small experimental shape.

Care should be taken to keep water from getting between the mould and the mesh. The idea is to accelerate the wire mesh and it is more difficult to accelerate it through water than through air. If a dam is used to get sufficient water depth, the dam should be constructed so that it will not restrict the passage of air from the area between the mesh and the mould.

EXPLOSIVES

Any commonly available explosive that can be detonated under water in small amounts will work. Here 40 per cent gel dynamite and primacord with electrical blasting caps were used. It is theoretically better to use high velocity explosives because it is easier to shape the shock wave.

The explosives are placed at one of a number of points so that when they are detonated, the resulting shock wave will provide thrust to accomplish the desired results. A point charge produces a spherical wave that is ideal for producing a dome. A lineal charge produces a cylindrical wave. Combinations of lineal and point charges in varying strengths can produce almost any desired shock wave. Shaped charges are possible with a variety of commercially available plastic explosives.

It is best to start with a much smaller charge than is thought necessary and to increase the charge as experience dictates. It takes much less time to set up a charge than to build a new mould.

When working with explosives, great care should be exercised. The mould should be in a cleared area. Observers should stand well back or behind shields. Competent personnel should handle the detonation and placement of the explosives.

DECKS AND BULKHEADS

Once the smooth mesh armature is created, provision must be made for the deck and bulkhead. The mesh and reinforcing that was bolted to the top of the mould to control stretching is bent inward to tie into the deck.

The bulkheads are a problem. The author's experiments indicated that pieces of reinforcing rod could be bent at right angles. One leg of a piece could be placed in the mesh and the other folded flat against the mesh. A line of these pieces could be placed where bulkheads are needed. Some problems are encountered cementing with this system.

Another system is to epoxy bulkheads into the hull after cementing.

Complex bulkheads and the deck may be explosively moulded in separate moulds and attached to the hull after all but their edges have been plastered.

PLASTERING THE HULL

When the armature is shaped, it is plastered in the mould. This was done by hand in these experiments, but it could be done by machine. The cement is smoothed on and vibrated against the hull as in any plastering process.

When plastering is complete a light plastic sheet may be put in the mould and filled with water. A vibrator in the water will vibrate the cement through the mesh and assure penetration. The weight of the water against the hull gives final assurance of shape. This is especially important if there are flat areas in the hull. After the cement has set the plastic sheet may be removed and the water will help the cement cure.

In one experiment the cement was placed in a plastic bag with a stick of dynamite. It was found that the cement splattered and did not evenly penetrate the mesh. No success was indicated.

In another experiment, the cement was spread over the mesh, no attempt was made to force it through, the mould was filled with a plastic liner and water. An explosion was tried to force the cement through the mesh. The cement could not be accelerated by the sudden shock wave of the explosion and only minimal penetration was achieved.

A vibrator in the water achieved the best results. The vibrator used was a low-speed eccentric on a shaft; a higher-frequency vibrator would have been superior. It has been suggested that an ultrasonic vibrator might be especially efficient.

CONCLUSION

Explosive moulding may offer a major breakthrough in the production of ferro-cement boats. It is still a technique in the developing stages, but the experiments described produced promising results.

Improvements on the method could be: (1) the development of a floating dry dock mould that could be sunk away from the hull for launching; (2) the design of hulls especially for the technique; (3) the development of a re-usable plastic membrane; and (4) an improved system of attaching bulkheads.

References

ANON. *Blasters Handbook*. Wilmington, USA: E. I. duPont
1952   Co.

ANON. *Dipont El–506 Flexible Sheet Explosive*. Wilmington, USA: E. I. duPont Co.

ANON. *Primacord Detonating Fuse*. Simsbury, USA: Ensign-Bickford.

COLE, R H *Underwater Explosives*. Princeton, USA: Princeton
1960   University Press.

COOK, M A *The Science of High Explosives*. New York,
1958   USA: Reinhold.

CORCORAN, T, *et al. Explosive Forming*. Dayton, Ohio, USA:
1959   Horox-Herf.

COX, F *Explosive Forming*. Detroit, USA: SP62–03, ASTME.

DUVALL, G E *Some Properties and Applications of Shock*
1961   *Waves*. Interscience.

PEARSON, J Metal working with explosives. *J. Metals* **12**: 673.
1960

PHILIPCHUK, V Fabrication by explosives. *Mech. Engng.*
1960   May, **82**: 48.

REINHART, J S *Behavior of Metals under Impulsive Loads*.
1954   Cleveland, USA: American Society for Metals.

REINHART, J S *Working of Metals via Explosives*. Detroit,
1961   USA: ASTME, Paper No. 61–PET-3.

REINHART, J S and PEARSON, J *Explosive Working of Metals*.
1963   Oxford, England: Pergamon Press.

ROTH, J The forming of metals by explosives. *Eng.* March–
1955   April **37**: 52.

SMITH, C S Metallographic studies of metals after explosive
1958   shock. *Trans. AIME* 214, 574 pp.

A Construction Technique Using Pre-Cast Spans H E Hermanson

The author is the Director of a firm engaged in the commercial production of ferro-cement fishing vessels for the Norwegian fishing industry. The company has constructed and sold a small number of ferro-cement fishing vessels that are in daily use by fishermen around the very rugged Norwegian coast and is actively engaged in research with the aim of improving commercial production in developed as well as developing countries.

WHY PRE-CAST SPANS?

The author felt that pre-cast spans would be beneficial in the commercial production of fishing boats for the following reasons:

Design: Some flexibility in design should be retained, not necessarily in breadth, but certainly in length. This allows more scope in complying with the customer's needs and requests.

Moulds: Most kinds of moulds are very restrictive with regard to changes and the ability to rearrange space. They also require a high degree of skill to construct. Much larger capital outlay is therefore involved in constructing the moulds, more sophisticated building area is required, and heavier equipment is needed to separate mould and shell or turn over the finished product.

Pipe frames: The pipe frame is a very convenient method for one-off boats. However, it does have some disadvantages for commercial production. The frames do not add appreciably to the strength of the boat, new frames are required for each boat, internal bracing is necessary during construction, additional attachment points to the armature have to be placed for inside items such as bulkheads, oil tanks, etc., and engine bedding must be arranged prior to cementing.

Web frames or welded-truss type: The pre-welded zig-zag frame has also been used to good advantage, but has many of the same drawbacks as the pipe frame plus the added area to cement on plastering day, as well as the difficulty of getting a flat enough surface to attach watertight steel bulkheads if needed or wanted. Designers may agree that frames are needed in work boats, particularly in the larger sizes. They also provide very convenient places to attach the many items of equipment which a normal fishing boat needs.

Pre-cast spans: The idea was to develop a method which would meet or at least come close to the following requirements:

Low investment for a series of boats.
Flexibility of deck and wheelhouse arrangement to suit customer.
Maximum use of unskilled labour.
Reduction of number of man-hours required to produce hull.
Minimum amount of expensive yard equipment such as overhead cranes.
Ability to produce a hull with the lines that the architect intended.

Building in an upright position.
Desirability of additional strength in the hull for very hard usage by fishermen.
A method that can be easily taught in developing countries.
An easier method of setting up frame and controlling the scantlings and weight.
A method that would support the wet cement without deforming.
Easier installation of engine, tanks and interior accommodation.
Elimination of mesh build-up.

Some of these requirements have been met and progress is being made on the others.

BUILDING THE MOULD

The dimensions of the largest frame or station are lofted full size. These are then transferred to a set of plywood sheets attached in such a manner that they can be moved in one unit. The lofted frame must be reduced by 2 cm, as this is approximately the thickness of the shell.

After the lines are transferred to the plywood, 2.5 × 2.5 cm aluminium angle is fastened to the sheets with screws. The angle, which follows the line of the loft on the plate will have been pre-drilled with two 3.5-mm holes spaced 50-mm centre to centre for the entire distance around the outer line of the frame. Another aluminium angle is attached to the plywood 100-mm on the inside of the previously-placed angle. The space between the angles is determined by the designer's requirement of the size of the web frame (Figs. 1 and 2).

The plywood sheets can be fastened to a timber framework such as 2 × 4 in and sheets fastened to the

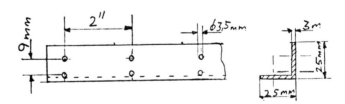

Fig. 1   Hole pattern of aluminium angle

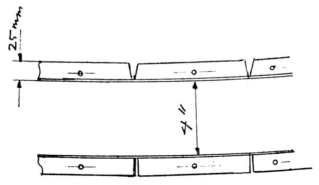

Fig. 2   Typical span width between angles

Fig. 3　Box with frame on each side

other side, so that one box can have two frames attached to it. A web frame is used at each station of the line drawing, so that ten boxes carry twenty full-size frames. Ten frames are fabricated and cemented at a time. They are cured in their forms, and then removed and set in place on the keel (see Fig. 3).

FABRICATING THE SPAN

One problem is immediately evident in trying to pre-cast. How does one achieve any continuity? The author's company uses a large number of 3-mm steel rods in place of wire mesh, thereby eliminating mesh build-up and poor penetration. These 3-mm steel rods are installed in the form previously described. The set-up is as follows:

> A thin layer of plastic is stapled to the pattern between the two aluminium angles.
> Next a flat steel bar, 25 × 3 mm, is installed standing on edge next to the angle that would be on the inside of the boat, and nailed in position.
> A 6-mm round steel rod is then spot-welded to the previously-mentioned flat steel bar. This rod is positioned in the middle of the flat steel bar (see Fig. 4).
> The next step is to lay four layers of wire mesh in between the angles and staple them to the form.
> Then 3-mm steel rods are inserted in the bottom holes of the outside angle, and one end tucked under

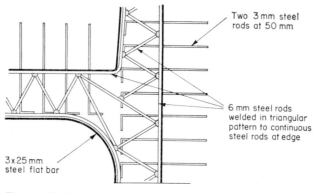

Two 3 mm steel rods at 50 mm

6 mm steel rods welded in triangular pattern to continuous steel rods at edge

3 x 25 mm steel flat bar

Fig. 4　Steel lay-up in typical span

the 6-mm round steel that has been welded to the flat bar.

> A 6-mm round steel rod is laid next to the outside aluminium angle on top of the 3-mm rods and stapled in place.
> Next, the zig-zag-shaped 6-mm steel rod is added and welded to the previously placed 6-mm steel rods that follow the aluminium angles (Fig. 4).
> Then, another layer of 3-mm rods is added in the top holes of the angle.
> Last, an additional four layers of wire mesh are laid on the top of the 3-mm rods and stapled securely, and the frame is ready for cementing.

CEMENTING THE FRAMES

When all frames are fabricated and ready for cementing, procedure is simple. The frames or spans do not have to be watertight, so that a little more water can be used in the mix. However, a normal ferro-cement mix can be used very satisfactorily and penetration is always 100 per cent. This is mainly because the necessary vibration can be used, and it is very easy to work on a flat surface. The time involved is minimal, but the time factor will be discussed later (Fig. 5).

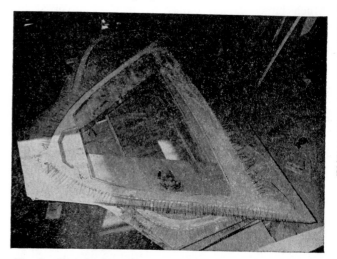

Fig. 5　Cemented frames

ERECTING THE ARMATURE

The next step is a straightforward operation, particularly when a series of almost similar boats is being produced. The length is varied simply by spacing the stations further apart. The keel is generally set up to receive each span, and is prefabricated to a certain degree so that the spans are sitting on a support welded to the keel to help take the weight of the boat (Fig. 6).

Hangers are also used from overhead supports, but any number of methods can be used, depending on facilities. The frames are then tack-welded together to maintain spacing. Rods are placed on the inside of the frames, and tack-welded to the flat steel used when making the frame in the form. These can be very easily removed after the outside mesh is installed.

The mesh on the hull is applied at this time. First of all, the 3-mm rods on the span are bent fore and aft as

Fig. 6   Placement of span on keel

Fig. 7   Installing under-deck forms

close to the span as possible. Then, two layers of square welded mesh are loosely attached to the spans in a horizontal direction. Small pliers that employ a pre-formed wire ring are used to fasten the net to the spans —it is quick and inexpensive. This tool can be found where mink farming takes place. The joints of the mesh are not overlapped but are "mink-ringed" together and the layers are staggered, so that one butted joint is at least 15 cm from the next.

After the two layers of square mesh are hanging in place, 6-mm vertical round steel rods are run from keel to bulwark. These are again fastened with a ringing tool. A 6-mm round steel rod is wired to each span on the outside of the two layers of mesh. This is firmly wired to the span through the mesh and around the span, with approximately 25 cm between each wire. This wiring stays until after cementing and is then removed. Next, the horizontal rods are applied. These can now be welded to the rod just wired to the span, at the required spacing centre to centre. Now, the hull is gaining in rigidity, and the deck forms can be started.

A formwork of 12-mm plywood is mounted between the spans under the deck. First, nailer strips are located on both sides of the span in the deck area 12-mm below the edge of the span, so that when the 12-mm plywood sheets are fitted on top of these nailers, they provide the formwork for the deck mesh and steel, eliminating 25 per cent of the wire tying that is so labour-consuming. These nailers are bolted through the span for later removal if necessary for classification inspection. Here again, 100 per cent penetration is achieved because of an easy work surface. Also the formwork helps to make the armature very rigid (Fig. 7).

At the same time, the bow and stern section forms can be completed. Then, work on the mesh is continued. The next two layers of mesh are square-welded and applied in the same manner as before, except that they are applied diagonally. The last two outside layers are galvanized woven mesh and are applied diagonally on the opposite diagonal. The next two layers are woven mesh and they are applied on the inside of the boat between the pre-cast spans and vertically from keel to deck.

CEMENTING THE HULL

A normal mixture for ferro-cement is used and one of the advantages of this method is that cementing can easily be carried out in two stages. In view of the fact that the frames are already cast, the hull only, or the hull and deck remain to be cemented. On a boat larger than, say, 16-m, it would certainly be easier to do the cementing on two different occasions. The author's company cement the entire unit at one time only because of a climatic and cost difference, but only in the case of boats under 16-m. The formwork under the deck is an advantage for cementing in two operations. It provides a good working surface while cementing the hull above the deck line, and also permits good control of mortar thickness on the deck.

ENGINE BEDS

These are arranged beforehand by providing a place to attach steel angles to pre-cast spans. Figure 8 shows the place provided for in the span. Figure 9 shows the use of a heavy steel plate running the length of the engine room, and this is attached to the span by heavy steel angle iron which is through-bolted to the span (Fig. 10) and welded to the steel plate. These angles and plates are installed before cementing, and are cemented into the keel.

Fig. 8   Space in span for engine bedding attachment

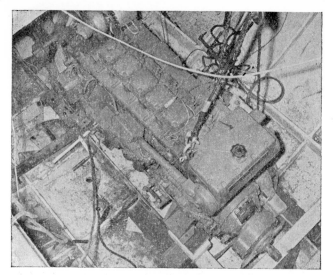

Fig. 9   Engine being mounted

Fig. 11   Fuel tank installation

Fig. 10   Angles bolted to span and welded to plate

OTHER DETAILS

Oil tanks are steel and easily installed (see Fig. 11).

Propeller shaft tunnel is easily accommodated (Fig. 12).

Watertight bulkheads are also easily attached due to a very flat surface (Fig. 13) if steel is preferred. Ferro-cement bulkheads can also be used and they work out very well. This depends on overhead lifting equipment.

Wood nailers are easy to install for interior fitting out. This is done before the spans are erected, and time is saved because it is easier working on a floor than inside a boat (Fig. 14).

The wheelhouse is attached to a coaming which is moulded into the deck (Fig. 15). This has been found to be the best method. The wheelhouse is pre-fabricated in wood or aluminium concurrently with the hull (Fig. 16).

Bulwarks are ferro-cement from the deck right up to and under the wooden railing. This wood is then bolted to the ferro-cement hull (Figs. 17 and 18).

Fig. 12   Propeller shaft tunnel

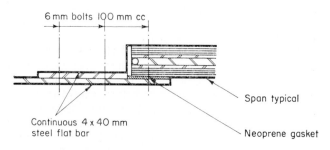

HORIZONTAL SECTION AT WATERTIGHT BULKHEAD

Fig. 13   Typical attachment to span

142

Fig. 14   Nailers installed

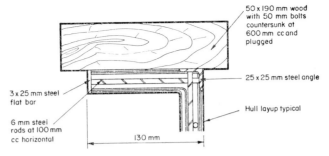

50 x 190 mm wood with 50 mm bolts countersunk at 600 mm cc and plugged

25 x 25 mm steel angle

3 x 25 mm steel flat bar

Hull layup typical

6 mm steel rods at 100 mm cc horizontal

130 mm

VERTICAL SECTION AT RAILING

Fig. 17   Typical railing construction

Fig. 15   Moulded coaming and hatch

Fig. 18   Completed railing

Fig. 16   Completed wheelhouse and cabin

CONCLUSIONS

The pre-cast span method developed by the author's company has in his opinion a very promising future. He considers that they have been able to build faster and cheaper with pre-cast spans than with other methods experimented with.

The entire production for the coming year will use pre-cast spans, and they are selling and designing larger work-boats using the same technique. Much more can be done with this method to increase efficiency.

A Protective Coating System for Ferro-Cement Boats   A R Pavey

Technical expertise in construction of ferro-cement boats has been largely dependent upon self-help and this fact has ensured the success of ferro-cement boat-building associations formed from groups of private enthusiasts. While some information on concrete technology and marine design is available to the novice, no definitive work on protective coatings for these structures has been published.

FERRO-CEMENT AS A COATING SUBSTRATE

Cement is produced from limestone, clay, water and gypsum. Lime constitutes nearly two-thirds of its make-up and has important effects on the properties of the final concrete.

When water is mixed with cement, reactions take place which result in the formation of many compounds, the main ones being tricalcium silicate, dicalcium silicate, tricalcium aluminate and iron compounds. It is the proportions of each of these that give the concrete its properties.

The hydration reaction that causes the concrete to cure produces the greatest increase in strength in the first few days. Full strength is taken as being reached after 28 days. However, the reaction continues indefinitely and the concrete increases in strength for possibly months or years after the concrete has set. Even when the initial water of mixing has evaporated reactions can still occur with water vapour from the air.

The permeability of concrete to water vapour can result in surface effects which complicate coating procedures. Concrete contains soluble compounds which may be leached out. This results in the precipitation of alkali salts on the surface of the concrete and if formed after painting it can disrupt the coating. The highly alkaline nature of the concrete surface can cause a chemical reaction with some types of paint coatings and will lead to their failure. For this reason care must be taken when choosing a suitable protective coating for ferro-cement boats.

NEED FOR PROTECTING FERRO-CEMENT HULLS

It has been suggested that adequately plastered ferro-cement hulls need no protection (Jackson and Sutherland, 1969) and it is popularly believed that paint work is only for aesthetic reasons. This concept is incorrect. Ferro-cement hulls are a composite body of cement-mortar and steel reinforcing wire and mesh. The strength of this composite depends upon the structural integrity of its parts. Any external influence which can lead to the destruction or weakening of either the steel or the mortar must be prevented.

Typical construction methods involve trowelling cement mortar on to tied wire mesh. This technique is likely to result in areas of steel exposed, or protected only by a very thin layer of concrete. Thus there are both concrete and steel surfaces exposed or likely to be exposed to sea water.

The more severe problem arises from its rapid corrosive attack on exposed steel. If allowed to proceed, serious spalling will occur from the increased volume of corrosion products compared to that of the steel. Even minor corrosion can travel along the mesh inside the hull and severely lower its impact strength.

REQUIREMENTS OF SUCCESSFUL PROTECTIVE COATING

The attention of the author's company was first drawn to the matter several years ago, when the epoxy coatings being used were causing severe peeling problems.

To assess requirements the following ideal characteristics of a system were listed:

1. The primer should have extreme adhesion to cement.
2. The primer should be tolerant of alkalinity in the ferro-cement.
3. The primer should contain inhibitors which prevent corrosion of bare steel.
4. The full system should have impermeability to sea water.
5. Single pack products should be used throughout.
6. Simple application technique, preferably brush or roller, should be used.
7. No critical times should intervene between coats.
8. Materials used should be non-toxic.
9. All products should be fast drying.
10. Finish coats should be very durable with a high resistance to chalking in strong sunshine.
11. Antifouling coatings should not be affected by exposure out of the water.
12. Future maintainability easy.
13. A compatible, sanding filler should be available.

These properties were designed specifically to suit the amateur boat-builder who might wish to carry out the operation over several months.

TYPES OF SUITABLE COATINGS

The external protection of marine structures is perhaps the most extreme test that mass-produced applied coatings have to survive today. The advent of steel shipping and, more recently, off-shore drilling rigs and production platforms, has placed much emphasis on the development of high performance coating systems to extend the productive lives of these expensive installations. Almost without exception, the most successful organic coatings so used are vinyl and epoxy coatings. Systems based on these coating types were examined.

CHOICE OF COATING SYSTEM

Epoxy coatings are widely recommended (Jackson and Sutherland, 1969; Hartley and Reid, 1968) for small boats including ferro-cement boats. However, they were ruled out because of several critical aspects of application. They are two-pack products, requiring careful proportioning; they have limited pot life when mixed, usually resulting in considerable waste; and they must be recoated before final cure or intercoat peeling will result. They are suitable for commercial coating work where all factors can be carefully controlled but not for use in "cottage industries".

Vinyl coatings appear to possess most of the desirable properties listed and were investigated further. They are essentially solutions of long-chain polyvinyl chloride molecules, with suitable plasticisers and pigments. They dry entirely by solvent evaporation, like a lacquer, and hence remain sensitive to the solvents in following coats. They are known to be troublefree in recoating after any interval and possess very good resistance to strong sunlight.

However, the adherence of a straight vinyl coating to concrete is not of a high order and a special primer with adhesive and inhibitive properties was required. The primer chosen was a lacquer type coating generally of the vinyl type, but somewhat modified by the addition of several high-adhesion resins and inhibitive pigments. This product has actually been used as an adhesive primer in marine work, both steel ships and concrete barges, for many years and is well known in the marine field.

The balance of the system used in the initial trials and subsequently standardized on, was a straight-solution vinyl with a background of extensive use in sea and fresh water over many years.

The antifouling chosen was a resin-based coating with metallic copper flake as the antifouling component. This can be immersed in 2 h or can be left out of the water for weeks without detriment.

All products in the system are non-toxic, including the antifouling, and are suitable for use by unskilled labour.

RECOMMENDED SEQUENCE FOR COATING

Proper surface preparation is important to the success of protective coating systems. Etching of the exterior hull surface with 25 to 30 per cent hydrochloric acid followed by thorough brushing and rinsing with clean water and then drying is recommended. This removes unsound surface deposits and alkaline salts and provides light surface roughness to improve adhesion. Treatment of the whole surface to be coated with a diluted solution of phosphoric acid is now necessary to convert existing corrosion products on exposed steel to iron phosphate. This is especially important for ferro-cement boats because often the exposed pieces of mesh and protruding tie wires are too small to be seen easily.

The phosphating solution not only removes poorly adhering rust from exposed steel but also provides a thin layer of iron phosphate which prevents rapid rerusting if the surface should become wet prior to applying the prime coat.

First prime coat

The first coating is a proprietary vinyl-based inhibitive primer-sealer thinned 1 : 1. This coating must be capable of sealing the surface concrete by being absorbed into it and must also prevent corrosion of exposed steel frame or mesh. It is upon this primer alone that the success or failure of the system relies.

If adherence to the concrete is poor, succeeding coats will pull away. If insufficient protection is given to the steel, serious corrosion of the reinforcing can occur resulting finally in damage to the concrete.

Filling: At this stage the appearance of the vessel may be improved by applying a high build-up vinyl mastic filler. This product allows single coat applications in the vicinity of 3.175 mm and is very suitable for providing a smooth, even finish to the hull. Its use is only necessary where the aesthetic qualities of the vessel are important.

Such vinyl mastic coatings are usually applied by squeegee or scraper to the desired thickness. They dry within 24 h and may then be sanded to any desired level of smoothness. Filling may be repeated to obtain the finish required.

Second prime coat: A second prime coat is applied to ensure that any exposed concrete or steel uncovered during sanding is properly prepared for topcoating. This coat is usually applied unthinned and is the same type as that of the first prime coat. Four coats of a vinyl copolymer are now applied to all parts of the hull. Alternating the colours of each coat is advisable to ensure complete coverage over the whole surface.

An antifouling compatible with vinyl systems should be applied to the ship's bottom to afford protection against marine growth. The antifouling chosen can be immersed in 2 h or can be left out of the water for 6 weeks.

There are no critical periods between any of the above steps. The coating operation could be spread over 12 months or be completed in one day, with identical results.

PROTECTING THE HULL INTERIOR

In the interior of the hull areas of exposed mesh and reinforcing may again be visible. Because a certain amount of water is always present in this area some means of protecting the steel against rust must be used. A further complication arises in that entrapped water vapour in the concrete must be allowed to escape. If both sides of the hull are sealed by the application of impermeable coatings the only way that vapour can get out is to push off the coating. This effect would be seen as tiny blisters on outside or inside. If these blisters are broken, they are usually filled with water due to the vapour condensing against the cold paint as it leaves the concrete.

The problem can be avoided by using acrylic-based coatings on the inside surface which are permeable to water vapour. Instead of building up pressure beneath the outside coating and blistering it, the water vapour vents through the permeable layer on the inside, leaving the exterior coating intact.

A recommended internal coating procedure is to wire-brush and spot-prime all exposed mesh with the inhibitive vinyl based primer used on the exterior and then to apply two coats of a water-based acrylic coating to the interior of the hull.

Many variations of the basic system are possible, to take advantage of advanced spraying techniques, or to offer high degrees of gloss and gloss retention on above-water areas. Variations are available as non-skid deck coatings. Used over galvanized or zinc-coated steel fittings the same coatings are suitable for protection or decoration.

PERFORMANCE HISTORY

The system described has been used in Australia for over 3 years by a number of owner builders and has proven virtually trouble-free in practice.

Adhesion problems have not developed and the little hull maintenance necessary has been simply and successfully carried out using the same coatings.

The antifouling coating used has been most effective in all Australian waters and is also simple to repair and recoat.

Owner-builders or owners taking delivery of a semi-finished hull from commercial builders have found the system simple to use, and without any critical aspects.

As a matter of interest, the identical system is being successfully used on steel hulls but over a prime coat of inorganic zinc silicate applied directly to the steel.

CONCLUSIONS

It is believed a system has been developed to meet the requirements set out earlier. This system should be entirely suitable for use in developing countries in the Pacific area, where ferro-cement boat-building is likely to be carried out by owner-builders.

The protective coatings tested are available world-wide and can be supplied in the Pacific area from several separate manufacturing and supply depots.

References

CEMENT AND CONCRETE ASSOCIATION OF AUSTRALIA *Seminar*
1970   *on Protective and Architectural Coatings for Concrete.* Concrete Institute of Australia, December.
HARTLEY, R T and REID, A J *Ferro-cement Boat Building.*
1968   London, England: Boughwood Printing House.
JACKSON, G W and SUTHERLAND, W M *Concrete Boat*
1969   *Building.* London, England: George Allen and Unwin.
MURDOCK, L J *Concrete Materials and Practice*, 2 ed. Rome,
1970   Italy and London, England: Butler and Tanner.

Acknowledgements

The author is indebted to Dimet Corrosion Pty. Ltd., of 166 Albert Road, South Melbourne, Australia, for permission to publish this paper.

Protection and Finishing of Ferro-Cement Hulls   P B Hunt

The excellent alkali and seawater resistance of epoxy resins, combined with their outstanding adhesion to concrete, metal and wood, make this class of compound eminently suitable for use on ferro-cement hulls.

Suitably formulated products can be used not only for sealing in preparation for painting but also for filling and fairing and for the fixing of timber bulkheads, furniture, etc., during fitting out. Epoxy resin tie coats ensure good adhesion between old and new areas when major repairs and modifications are required.

SEALING OF THE HULL

Until curing is complete and an equilibrium moisture content has been reached, no form of surface coating should be applied.

Early trials where the outside surface was sealed with an amine adduct cured epoxy resin soon after steaming failed due to loss of adhesion of the coating. Many hulls were moved out of doors immediately after sealing. The accumulated rainwater would certainly aggravate the problem.

Current New Zealand practice is for inside or, at least, protected storage for a period of several months. The inside surface should then, after a thorough brushing to remove laitence, receive a coat of a slightly porous epoxy undercoat. This should be formulated to be as impervious to ingress of liquid water as possible whilst allowing the passage of water vapour.

Advice against use of latex paint

An alternative specification using latex paint to achieve the same purpose has very serious disadvantages. These are:

(a) Latex paint films are notoriously unsatisfactory under wet conditions such as those met with in bilge areas. When immersed for any length of time they tend to soften and lose adhesion because of the presence of surfactants, thickeners and stabilisers which are so necessary for preserving stability in the can.

(b) The existence of a latex film on the surface would preclude using epoxy resin glues or fillers which are advantageous during fitting out.

Priming of exterior

The same type of coating as has been recommended on the inside can also be used for priming the outside, after removal of laitence and before filling or fairing takes place. Such a film, when cured, is hard, easily sanded, has excellent adhesion and can readily be applied by brush, roller or spray. It should be formulated to have a relatively long pot life so as to make application easy but should be touch-dry overnight. This point raises the matter of low ambient temperatures in work areas. Though, in the light of present knowledge, it is possible to produce epoxy systems which will cure down to temperatures of 0°C and below, their rate of cure at such low temperatures is slow and they really need a period at round 10°C for completion of the reaction. For this reason, winter warming of work areas where finishing is taking place is strongly recommended.

Pre-treatment of exterior: Two schools of thought on the removal of laitence appear to exist. One favours no more than mechanical wire brushing and the other acid treatment. One thing is certain, the hydrochloric acid etching normally used on massive concrete structures must not be used on ferro-cement. Too much steel is too near the surface and is subsequently attacked and corroded by the traces of calcium chloride left behind after even the most elaborate washing. Phosphoric acid etching appears to be safe and any residual calcium phosphate, being virtually insoluble, would, if anything, tend to render the surface denser than it would otherwise be.

FILLING AND FAIRING

After the epoxy undercoat has been applied and allowed to cure it is imperative that the exterior surface should be critically examined all over for areas where wire ties are on or very close to the surface. To prevent formation of corrosion craters all such areas should be raked out, the wire well punched home and the resulting cavity filled flush with an epoxy filler. Such a product must have a high enough mineral and pigment loading to make for ease of sanding, must be non-sagging on vertical surfaces and, probably most important of all, must be free of unreactive volatile matter such as solvents. Even a shallow filling carried out with a material containing solvents will stay soft owing to slow evaporation and will subsequently shrink. For this reason liquid grades of resin should be used and they should be cured with combinations of amines and polyamide resins. For use under these conditions, polyamides have a further advantage—they are anti-corrosive materials in their own right. A properly formulated filler will, when mixed in the specified proportions with its hardener, have a slight residue of polyamide and the cured material will not only adhere well to concrete and/or exposed steel-work, but will help to protect the steel against rusting.

Advice against using polyester fillers

Though polyester-type fillers customarily used in automotive repair cure quicker (can be sanded faster) than epoxies they are not to be recommended on ferro-cement for the following reasons:

(a) Polyester resins are less resistance to alkali than epoxies and the types used for automotive fillers are worse than average in this respect.

(b) Polyester-type fillers do not have the high adhesive properties of epoxies.

It is usually necessary to go over the whole area several times to make sure that craters will not subsequently appear due to expansion on rusting. When stopping-up has been completed and the filler has cured overnight all filled areas should be sanded smooth. Early sanding, as soon as the filler has become reasonably hard and before curing is complete, will save both time and labour.

"Fairing" of pleasure craft

On pleasure craft a further coat of epoxy undercoat should be applied. As this is to used as a guide coat for subsequent sanding, it is an advantage for it to be tinted grey. All hollows and "flats" should now be filled using an epoxy fairing filler. This is a specially designed material which is far more thixotropic than a normal stopping grade. It is a soft but non-sag paste in the can and re-attains this state within a very few seconds of being allowed to come to rest after mixing or application. When applied with a float or doctor blade, however, the high shearing forces break down the gel structure and make application on large areas easy. Though every effort should be made to fair-up in one application, it is usually necessary to sand and re-apply further quantities of material.

It is not only wasteful in time, material and money to apply an all-over layer of filler, it is a positive disadvantage, owing to the very big difference in the thermal co-efficient of expansion of concrete and an epoxy resin even when filled with minerals such as talc or calcite. Areas even up to 1 m in diameter pose no problem but a continuous coating several mm thick over the complete hull is likely to lose adhesion in service.

FITTING OUT

Where portholes, etc., are cut after plastering, or even where they are merely trimmed, the raw edge and the exposed reinforcing should be sealed off and made good with epoxy filler. The frames can be set in the same material or, if preferred, a polysulphide sealant may be used. The flexibility of the latter after curing is probably advantageous. Under no circumstances should any form of orthodox putty be used though butyl rubber sealants are satisfactory in non-critical areas. All other skin fittings should be set down with either epoxy compounds or polysulphide. If the latter is used on bare concrete, the special primer recommended by the manufacturer for use on porous surfaces must be applied. Epoxy bedding compounds or fillers do not require the use of primers on sound surfaces.

Engine beds, etc

Fully-cured epoxy fillers/bedding compounds develop crushing strengths in excess of 450 kg. This property makes them ideal materials for use as load transfer media on engine beds, under winches, etc. After "shimming", all irregularities should be filled with the epoxy material and the holding down bolts brought up finger-tight. After curing for 48 h, the bolts can be finally tightened in the sure knowledge that there is 100 per cent registration with no point loading. There is no danger of "creep" even in layers approximately 5 mm thick under loadings likely to be met in practice.

Securing bolts

Any securing bolts which need to be installed during fitting out should be grouted in with epoxy resin. Vertical holes in horizontal surfaces should be filled with a liquid mixture but it is essential that it should be solvent-free. Epoxy undercoats or other forms of purely surface coatings are quite unsuitable. Where the gap between concrete and bolt is only a few mm, unfilled mixtures are best since they tend to be lower in viscosity, but for gaps of 5 mm upwards, clean, dry silica sand or crushed quartz should be added equal in dry volume to the total volume of resin and hardener. This will increase the rigidity of the cured compound (and hence the tensile strength of the joint) as well as cheapening the job. Where bolts are to be installed into vertical surfaces, the above mixture may be used if the holes are drilled sloping downwards and the bolts are "cranked" but if this is not convenient, the same type of epoxy filler as was used on the outside of the hull will prove admirable. The bolts must be cleaned free of grease before installation and should be held lightly in position for at least 24 h before tightening.

Timber fittings

The tensile strength of a timber-to-timber joint glued with an epoxy resin is of the order of 80 to 100 kg and between clean steel surfaces up to twice this figure. When gluing to concrete, however, the controlling factor is the tensile strength or, more properly, the "peel" strength of the concrete. Even then an assured joint strength of, say, 25 kg is usually more than enough for timber fittings, particularly if reinforced with relatively minor mechanical fixings. For the installation of bunks, cupboards or other timber items, a normal grade of epoxy boat-builder's glue may be used but, equally well, the same epoxy filler or fairing filler as was used elsewhere will be found to have excellent adhesive properties. Epoxy gluing of untreated or Tanalized timber yields first class joints but Boric treated timber is not so satisfactory.

Bilge areas, chain lockers, etc

To prevent the possibility of diesel oil contamination of bilge areas which could lead to penetration and possible subsequent failure of the exterior paint system, at least two coats of epoxy coal tar should be applied and allowed to cure for a week or more under well-ventilated conditions. Epoxy coal tar may also be used for lining sewage tanks but, for all enclosed spaces such as tanks, it is essential that curing conditions should include good ventilation. Without this, solvent vapours will condense in the upper part of the tank and lead to "washing off". The same treatment is recommended for chain lockers and similar spaces.

Fuel, water and sewage tanks

Diesel oil, petrol and drinking water tanks are best lined with fibreglass using epoxy resin or polyester resin. If the former is used, a special amine-type hardener is essential. Normal hardeners are quite unsuitable for drinking water in particular since they tend to leave a residual odour in the cured film. If polyester is used it must be a chemical-resistant grade. In view of the inevitable poor adhesion to the concrete the use of chopped strand mat is recommended so that the lining is strong enough chemically to stand on its own and, in fact, form a tank within the tank. Flanged lids and fittings are essential to prevent possible attack at the margin of the lining.

Use of epoxy tie coat

Major re-plastering and modifications or additions should always be accompanied by the use of an epoxy tie coat. These mixtures have been specially designed as bond or tie coats between old and new concrete. The mixed tie coat is applied, usually by brush, to the clean dust-free old surface at a spreading rate of 2 or 3 m²/l. The new plaster must then be applied before the tie coat has set. This will usually mean within 2 h in winter or 1 h in summer. Unfortunately, tie coats are very susceptible to slow curing under cold conditions and every effort should be made to ensure that the ambient temperature when they are used is not below 10°C. A properly used tie coat will yield a joint between old and new application which is the strongest part of the structure. A deliberately contrived break will always occur in the plaster and never in the joint itself.

EXTERIOR FINISHING OF WORK BOATS

The exterior of work boats should receive two coats of epoxy coal tar after the filling operation is completed. Fairing is generally ignored.

If black is acceptable, the topsides may safely be left in this state. Chalking with loss of gloss and some browning occurs after a few months, but the film will retain its integrity for long periods and can be recoated with the same material. If a different colour is required the thick protective film of coal tar epoxy may still be applied. The application of a 2 pot epoxy sealer coat to prevent bleeding a day or so later may be followed by use of orthodox topside paints. Over a period of months there will be slight dulling of bright colours and a slight yellowing of white, but the total system is stable and, after the first re-paint, no further discolouration occurs.

Below the waterline, the coal tar coating will accept anti-fouling paints of the soft leaching types but, when using heavy duty vinyl materials, caution must be exercised. Many vinyl anti-foulings contain "strong" solvents and these will certainly soften coal tar epoxy. A preliminary test should be carried out on a small area or the manufacturer's advice should be sought on a suitable grade.

EXTERIOR FINISHING OF PLEASURE CRAFT

Over the past few years in New Zealand, an increasing number of ferro-cement hulls have been fibreglass-sheathed using lightweight cloth and epoxy resin. An outstanding example was Doctor Robert Griffith's "Awahnee" which circumnavigated in Antarctic latitudes unscathed in spite of ice floes.

Owing to their relatively poor alkali resistance, polyester resins are not recommended for ferro-cement hulls.

Fibreglass sheathing

It is essential that routine epoxy filling should be carried out as normally. Scrim woven glass cloth of about 60 to 80 g/m^2 or glass tissue should then be cut to suitable lengths, placed dry against the hull and well saturated with mixture of liquid epoxy resin and an amine-aduct hardener. The best method of application is with a mohair paint roller and about 250 ml/m^2 of the mixture are required. It will be found that, even on overhang, the wetted cloth will cling well. After curing overnight at a minimum ambient temperature of 10°C, light sanding, particularly on joints, should be followed by a second resin application at about half the above rate to complete weave filling. When using tissue, the second coat of resin may be omitted.

After sheathing has been completed, the hull should be finished in the same way as for a laminated wooden one. Anti-fouling may be applied direct to the underwater areas without further preparation providing a sufficiently substantial layer of epoxy resin has been applied to prevent migration of dissolved copper ions from the anti-fouling into the ferro-cement. Normal air drying undercoat and gloss finish may be applied to the topsides or, if desired, 2-pot polyurethane may be used.

Decks

Decks may be treated in the same way as topsides but, if a heavily non-skid finish is required, an epoxy coating is essential. Nothing else will give the same wear-resistant type of finish. After applying an epoxy undercoat and checking for exposed ties as usual, a heavy roller-coat of the same epoxy resin mixture as recommended for fibreglass sheathing should be applied, but without the use of cloth. Whilst this is still wet, silica sand, crushed quartz, granulated cork or sifted sawdust should be sprinkled on. After overnight hardening, the excess should be swept off and another coat of the same resin mixture applied. If sand or crushed quartz has been used, this second coating should be stippled so as not to fill the texture which has been achieved. If cork or sawdust have been used, a light sanding should be followed by removal of dust and then the second coat of resin which should be a generous one so as to saturate the texturing material. In all cases, the final treatment consists of one or more thin coats of decorative wear-resistant paint.

Cabin exteriors, deck houses, etc., should receive the same treatment as topsides.

Cabin interiors

After any surface filling necessary has been carried out a second coat of epoxy undercoat should be applied. When this has cured, the surface may be treated as if it were a normal, sealed timber one, i.e. it may be decorated with normal air drying alkyd systems.

Finishing without fibreglass

Providing filling has been systematically carried out and at least one further all-over coat of epoxy undercoat applied the topsides may be finished with normal air drying systems. Below the waterline, at least one and preferably two coats of 2-pot epoxy enamel should be applied over the undercoat to prevent the possibility of copper ion migration. When this has cured normally, copper anti-fouling may be applied.

REPAIR

For emergency repairs below the waterline, special underwater curing epoxy resin compositions are available. They are soft, sticky compositions based on liquid resins and containing a fairly high percentage of mineral filler. The curing agents are invariably polyamide resins. The high percentage of mineral filler is necessary to bring the specific gravity up to a figure where floating off in the uncured condition is unlikely. The sticky nature serves the same purpose while the particular type of polyamide hardener helps to displace water from the surface of the damaged area and also acts as an anti-corrosive material on any exposed steelwork. Resin and hardener should be mixed very thoroughly, placed in a polythene bag and carried down to the repair by divers. Application is best made with a gloved hand. Depending on the water temperature the material will set hard enough to withstand wave action in 2 to 6 h. The finally cured product never achieves anything like the hardness of a normal epoxy filler applied and cured above water but it sticks well and will make a good, temporary repair. When the time comes for permanent repair, the area is cleaned down to bare concrete and re-plastered using an epoxy tie coat as set out earlier.

Minor repairs to the topsides or other parts of the hull can be carried out at any time using epoxy filler. All loose particles must be removed and efforts should be made to get rid of rust on exposed metal.

Repainting

When repainting time comes, a sound paint system can be treated in the normal way as for a wooden boat. Wash down, sand where necessary and repaint. If the condition of the coating is bad or corrosion has become apparent, it is essential to clean down to bare concrete. Careful sand blasting is the best way. By the use of the appropriate type of epoxy-resin composition, the hull can usually be brought back to a sound condition providing there is no serious structural deterioration.

CONCLUSIONS

It is a mistake to think that a ferro-cement hull can be treated in the same way as a normal timber one.

Massive timber can be left virtually untreated for long periods without deterioration. Massive concrete requires no protection but ferro-cement needs painting in the same way as does steel and for the same reason—unless protected it will speedily deteriorate. The important difference is, however, that where steel can be chipped, flame de-scaled or sand-blasted during subsequent maintenance, the original treatment of a ferro-cement hull should be, as near as possible, for the expected total life. The most durable available type of finish must be used and from both theoretical and practical points of view epoxy resin compositions should be employed.

Ferro-Cement Fishing Vessels
Designed by FAO   J F Fyson, Ø Gulbrandsen and A F Haug

It has long been recognized that fishing boat development cannot be regarded in isolation. The boat is a part of a complex system consisting of many more or less known variables such as abundance of fish, fishing methods, distance to grounds, skill of crew and market conditions. The success of a boat will depend on how well it fits into this system.

In a developing country we usually find an existing fishery utilizing small boats, or canoes maybe powered with outboard motors. The production per unit is low, but so is the investment, and in economic terms this might not be as bad as it would appear to the casual observer. In trying to decide on the next step up from such a traditional fishery, difficult decisions are necessary to determine what fishing method, what size and type of boat can profitably be introduced. Due to the complexity of the factors involved and lacking basic information, it is often necessary to adopt a "trial and error" method: have a boat built, fish with it and, in the process, obtain answers to some questions. The next boat might be a modified version, bigger or smaller, and the process should lead to a boat that has a demonstrated profitability. From there on, the fishing industry can often take over. The difficulty lies in starting the ball rolling— proving the profitability of a certain boat in a certain country. This is a "hit and miss" job that the existing fishing industry will often not have either the know-how or the capital to perform. The government, with outside assistance, will therefore have to bear the greatest part of the burden in the initial stage of the development and FAO has been assisting in this task, through research, to determine the abundance of fish and through practical experimental fishing.

INITIAL ACTION TAKEN

The experimental fishing can of course be carried out with a vessel that is brought into the country, but for smaller vessels there are often advantages in constructing them in the country itself, providing a visible demonstration of the possibilities of local construction and giving "on the job" training to the local boat-builders. The cost of sending an expatriate boat-builder to supervise such construction on the spot is, of course, considerable, but importing boats can also be very costly and does not provide the ancillary advantages mentioned. FAO has, therefore, in many cases recommended this course of action and assisted in constructing prototype fishing boats in countries lacking established boat-building facilities and skilled boat-builders. Wood has been the material mainly utilized so far and designs have been developed specially to avoid some of the complications of conventional wooden boat construction. However, one cannot escape the fact that wooden boat-building requires certain skills and ability to handle tools and to fit together the many pieces that a wooden hull consists of to make a tight and solid job. In areas where this skill, together with a good supply of suitable timber at acceptable cost is available, there is still scope for wooden boat-building, and up to recently there has not been any alternative construction method that could be utilized in the same circumstances. With the corrosion problem caused by tropical salt water, steel is not an attractive alternative for smaller fishing vessels, unless built in boatyards which can assure proper sandblasting and protective paint application on all exposed surfaces. On the other hand, steel has given good service on freshwater lakes and rivers. FRP (fibreglass reinforced plastic) is not considered suitable for construction of prototype boats, since the cost would be high for the mould. For series production of fishing vessels FRP offers, of course, many advantages.

When ferro-cement started to gain popularity in the mid-sixties as a construction material for boats up to 17 m, it seemed to present a possible alternative to wood as a material for fishing vessels in tropical areas. One of the authors of this paper had the opportunity to study closely the construction method during a visit to New Zealand, one of the pioneer countries where this material was further developed after the initial experiments of Professor Nervi of Italy. A "Report on Ferro-cement Construction for Fishing Vessels" was written as a result of this study, and published by *Fishing News International* from April to June 1968.

This report emphasized the low capital investment needed to set up a boatyard and the high proportion of unskilled labour which could be used for this type of construction. As these factors correspond closely to the basic requirements needed to set up a boatyard in a developing country, particularly in one with no tradition of wooden boat-building, it was decided to carry the investigation further by building a fishing boat and thereby gaining further experience in the construction and operation of a ferro-cement vessel. At that time, the author concerned was stationed in Thailand and, under his supervision, a 16-m stern trawler was constructed by the Fisheries Department of Thailand in 1968–69. A film was also made during the construction of this boat. A number of ferro-cement boats have been designed and built under FAO supervision during the following years as a consequence of this first FAO contact with this novel construction technique.

PRESENTATION OF BOAT DESIGNS

The general arrangement plans of the following boats are shown in Figs. 1 to 6 and Table 1 gives their main particulars.

7.5-m UAR-1 and 10.0-m UAR-2

These boats were designed for fishing and transport in the open waters of Lake Nasser, the Arab Republic of Egypt. The prototypes were built in 1970 in Rome in cooperation with Professor Nervi and transported to

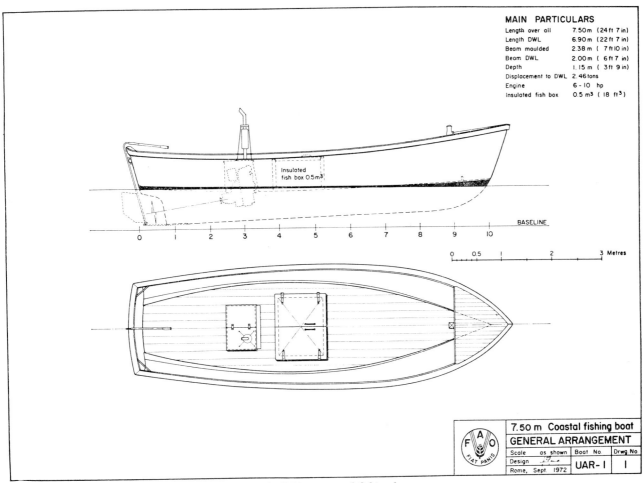

MAIN PARTICULARS

Length over all	7.50 m (24 ft 7 in)
Length DWL	6.90 m (22 ft 7 in)
Beam moulded	2.38 m (7 ft 10 in)
Beam DWL	2.00 m (6 ft 7 in)
Depth	1.15 m (3 ft 9 in)
Displacement to DWL	2.46 tons
Engine	6 - 10 hp
Insulated fish box	0.5 m³ (18 ft³)

Insulated fish box 0.5 m³

BASELINE

7.50 m Coastal fishing boat
GENERAL ARRANGEMENT

Scale	as shown	Boat No	Drwg No
Design		UAR-1	1
Rome, Sept. 1972			

Fig. 1   7.50 m coastal fishing boat

Egypt. Two similar boats were later built in Egypt. The boats, although heavy compared with wooden hulls, have been satisfactory in operation and plans exist for construction of a series of the 10-m boat and several larger boats for service on Lake Nasser.

10.6-m trawler/purse seiner MAG-1

Fishing in Madagascar is mainly carried out with traditional type outrigger canoes, apart from a number of large shrimp trawlers. A need was felt for an intermediate type of decked boat that could perform multiple tasks such as trawling, purse seining and handlining. The hull of this boat was built in a local boatyard with FAO assistance and the boat will be used for experimental fishing. The construction method aroused great interest in Madagascar and a fishing company built two 12.6-m shrimp trawlers according to design UGA-2, in the same yard.

11.0-m coastal fishing boat DAH-6

The boat is designed for fishing with handlines, gillnets and can also handle a small purse seine. The wheelhouse has been placed to port to give more effective deck area to starboard. A crew of six men can be carried and trips of 2–4 days' duration are envisaged. The prototype was launched in 1971 but had to be taken out of operation after only one year due to leakage and corrosion of the steel mesh caused by faulty plastering. Too coarse

sand particles were used in the mix and proper penetration was not achieved. This incident has clearly demonstrated the need for careful supervision by an experienced ferro-cement boat-builder at the plastering stage.

12.6-m trawler UGA-2

The design was prepared for trawling in Lake Victoria and the hull of the first boat was built during a two-month FAO/Swedish Boat-building Training Centre in Uganda in 1971. The boat has, after completion, been utilized for experimental trawling and has performed very well.

16-m trawler FC-1

The first ferro-cement boat built under FAO supervision was launched in Thailand in 1969. The boat is at present being utilized by the Fisheries Department of Thailand for experimental fishing.

DESIGN CONSIDERATIONS

Weight

Over the last five years, numbers of books and magazine articles have been published dealing with ferro-cement construction. Much of this literature is biased and gives incorrect information regarding the weight and strength characteristics of the material. It has been stated that above 10.6 m ferro-cement could be built as light as

151

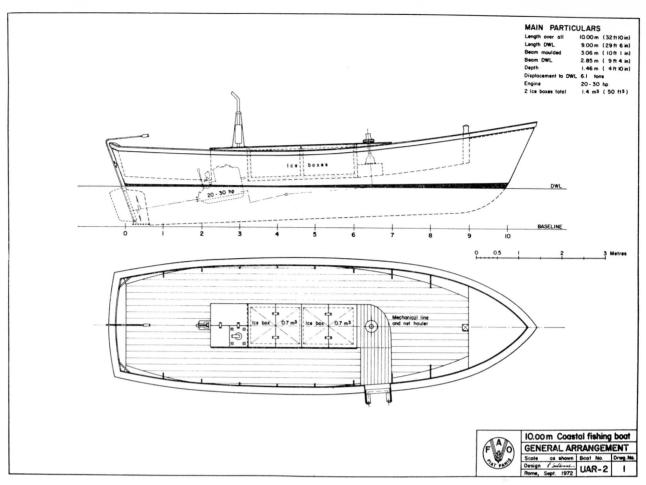

MAIN PARTICULARS

Length over all	10.00 m	(32 ft 10 in)
Length DWL	9.00 m	(29 ft 6 in)
Beam moulded	3.06 m	(10 ft 1 in)
Beam DWL	2.85 m	(9 ft 4 in)
Depth	1.46 m	(4 ft 10 in)
Displacement to DWL	6.1 tons	
Engine	20 - 30 hp	
2 Ice boxes total	1.4 m³	(50 ft³)

10.00 m Coastal fishing boat
GENERAL ARRANGEMENT

Scale as shown	Boat No.	Drwg. No.
Design	UAR-2	1
Rome, Sept. 1972		

Fig. 2   10.0 m coastal fishing boat

wood and steel, and this belief undoubtedly has led to many ferro-cement boats being designed at too low displacement and the builder getting some surprises at launching, finding the boat floating deeper than the designed waterline. It is now recognized that, at least for fishing boats up to 16-m, ferro-cement is heavier than wood and steel, and considerably heavier than FRP. A comparison for a 12.6-m trawler gave a light ship displacement of 9.4 t for the FRP boat, 13.1 t for the wooden boat, 15.1 t for the steel boat and 16.3 t for the ferro-cement boat. It is evident that this heavy weight must be taken into account in the design phase and limits the use of ferro-cement to displacement-type vessels. Most fishing vessels operate as purely displacement hulls at speed length ratios ($V/\sqrt{L}$) under 1.3, where the extra weight of ferro-cement fortunately carries little penalty in speed.

The question of converting a design for a wooden vessel into ferro-cement is often raised. This might or might not be possible, depending on what displacement the wooden vessel was designed at and whether ballast was included. Only a naval architect will be able to judge this on the basis of the line drawing of the wooden boat.

Scantlings

Ferro-cement is a new material for fishing boat construction and rules and regulations for scantlings published by the various classification societies and marine departments are still provisional in character. So far, only the New Zealand Marine Department have, in their provisional requirements (1970), given minimum finished mortar thicknesses for various hull sizes, ranging from 25 mm for a hull between 10.7-m and 12.2-m, 41 mm for a 19.8-m hull. The minimum steel content is given as 385 kg/m³. The type of reinforcement has followed the usual practice in New Zealand and other parts of the world: Table 2 gives details about steel reinforcement on the various vessels built under FAO supervision.

The experience over several years of operation of fishing vessels and work boats shows that the critical design factor for vessels up to 18-m is service loads and in particular resistance to impact and not overall strength in bending as determined from laboratory tests.

Resistance to impact can be improved by increasing the shell thickness or by a superior type of mesh, but specific data useful to the designer have not yet been published. Until this is available it is wise to adhere to the hull thicknesses proposed by the New Zealand regulations and design the boat for the extra weight. In addition, heavy wood fenders should be fitted in the areas most prone to impact, the bulwarks are probably better made of another material than ferro-cement. Figure 5 shows an example of a bulwark consisting of tube railing through-bolted to the deck with a wide plank fastened along the lower part of the stanchions.

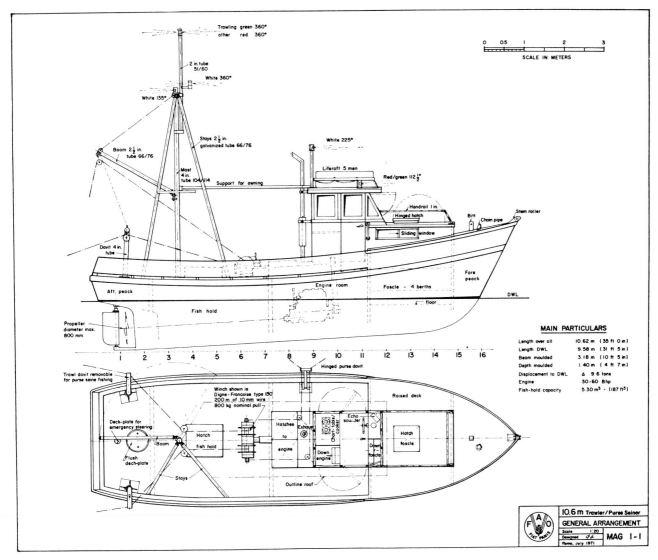

Fig. 3   10.6 m trawler/purse seiner

The heavy weight of ferro-cement does not make it very suitable for decks for the smaller vessels although sufficient stability can be assured through adequate design to counteract a high centre of gravity in light ship condition. A conventional planked deck has been used on several FAO designs under 13-m length. Bulkheads and deckhouses are of conventional wood or plywood construction. Each material can be utilized where its properties suit best—ferro-cement for the curved and "difficult" parts of the hull and wood for plane surfaces such as deck, bulkheads and deckhouse.

CONSTRUCTION METHODS

A number of different methods have been evolved in various parts of the world to form the hull shape and provide the metal reinforcement which holds and strengthens the mortar matrix of a ferro-cement boat. These methods range from a form work of pipe frames, through steel web frames supported on a pipe stem and keel to open wood moulds and solid moulds of the mass production methods. Three of these methods have been utilized in boats built under FAO supervision and the pros and cons of these in the light of experience are discussed here.

Suspended pipe frames

This is one of the original methods used by Professor Nervi and many ferro-cement builders in New Zealand and elsewhere. Two variations of the method have been used, in one of which the pipe frames are covered with mesh and left embedded in the mortar matrix, while in the second, the pipe framework is removed once the hull has been cured and any voids patched.

Pipe frames left in the mortar

The pipe frames are intended as a form work only and do not provide much additional strength to the hull except for the additional rigidity provided by the mesh fold over the pipe itself. The folded mesh layers over the pipes can cause difficulty when the time comes to ensure a good void-free filling of mortar through the mesh. It is not easy to ensure that this thickened area is completely filled unless a vibrator is used. Unsealed

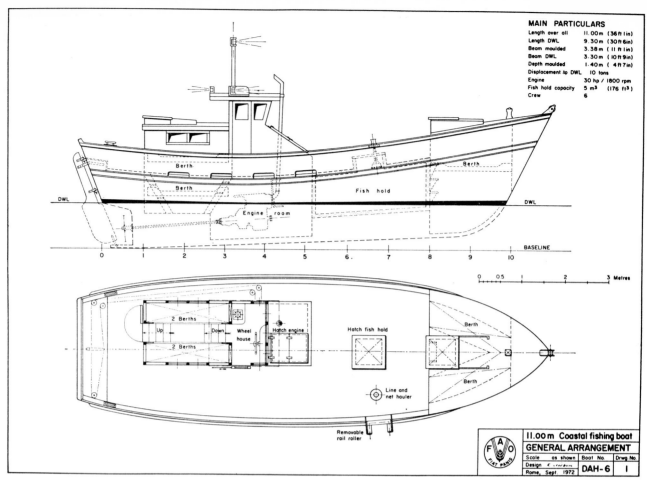

MAIN PARTICULARS

Length over all	11.00 m (36 ft 1 in)
Length DWL	9.30 m (30 ft 6 in)
Beam moulded	3.38 m (11 ft 1 in)
Beam DWL	3.30 m (10 ft 9 in)
Depth moulded	1.40 m (4 ft 7 in)
Displacement to DWL	10 tons
Engine	30 hp / 1800 rpm
Fish hold capacity	5 m³ (176 ft³)
Crew	6

		11.00 m Coastal fishing boat	
FAO FIAT PANIS		GENERAL ARRANGEMENT	
	Scale as shown	Boat No.	Drwg. No.
	Design C.	DAH-6	I
	Rome, Sept. 1972		

Fig. 4   11.0 m coastal fishing boat

pipes can also provide a channel through which water can pass both internally and in small longitudinal voids left where the bond between pipe and mortar is not completely watertight. The pipe can sag under the weight of mortar or by careless workmen stepping on the hull, and needs to be well braced to hold the hull in shape.

Pipe frames removed after curing

This method has some advantages in small boats in which hulls only are built in ferro-cement as the pipe framework can be removed as an integral mould and used again in succeeding boats.

The major disadvantage with both methods is the lack of fixing points for joinery and equipment and, unless starters are designed into the hull at positions at which attachments are to be made, much time can be lost during fitting out.

Inverted pipe frames

Not recommended under any circumstances; the method provides for pipe frames to be fixed upside down in holes in a pair of base bearers. These are difficult to brace and align and provision for the fixing of internal fittings and installation of engine beds is difficult and time-consuming. This is a poor method and results in unfair hulls and is very time-consuming in fitting out.

Suspended web frames

Frames made up of rod reinforced with trusses of similar or smaller section rod are suspended from an angle iron or channel to form the hull shape. This method, although time-consuming in the making up of the frames, results in considerable savings in fitting out time, provided that interior joinery, fuel tanks, etc., are positioned to take advantage of the webs at the framing positions. The web frames are also useful as tying-off points for the internal lining of the insulated fishhold. In hulls to be provided with ferro-cement decks, deck beams of similar web construction at each frame provide a good base for the longitudinal rods. Provided battens are used to true in the deckline and care is taken to keep workmen from walking directly on the rods and mesh, a fair deck can be achieved.

MATERIALS

Steel reinforcement

Both mild steel reinforcing rods 6 mm in diameter and high-tensile rods 5 mm in diameter have been used. Longitudinals of high-tensile or hard drawn rod have considerable advantages over ordinary mild steel, not only for strength but also in ease of fairing. Distortion caused by any accidental stepping on unsupported hull

154

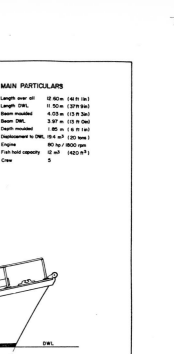

MAIN PARTICULARS

Length over all	12.60 m (41 ft 1 in)
Length DWL	11.50 m (37 ft 9 in)
Beam moulded	4.03 m (13 ft 3 in)
Beam DWL	3.97 m (13 ft 0 in)
Depth moulded	1.85 m (6 ft 1 in)
Displacement to DWL	19.4 m³ (20 tons)
Engine	80 hp / 1800 rpm
Fish hold capacity	12 m³ (420 ft³)
Crew	5

Fig. 5   12.6 m trawler

panels is also minimized by the resistance to bending. Transverse rods of mild steel bent around the longitudinals and tied in place with 18-gauge tie wire complete the steel reinforcement.

Mesh

Both square welded mesh and hexagonal (chicken) wire have been used. Tests carried out by the Applied Scientific Research Corporation of Thailand and others indicate the greater strength of square welded mesh and, where available, this would appear to be the best material. Hexagonal mesh has and is being used successfully, however, for *small* workboats provided the gauge of the wire used is sufficient to achieve the design weight of steel reinforcement per unit volume. Nineteen gauge, 12 mm mesh is considered to give the minimum acceptable weight of mesh. Twenty-two gauge, 0.7 mm, is too light to achieve the desired strength.

Tie wire for fastening the mesh to the rod framework should be galvanized or stainless steel if available as this helps to reduce rust spots should an occasional tie wire be left exposed during plastering. Tying of the mesh can be quickly achieved by teams of two men, one pushing precut loops of wire through the mesh and the other twisting up and cutting off with a pair of carpenter's pincers.

Cement and sand

Cement used has been Portland type 1 or 2 in all cases. Sieved river sand, 100 per cent passing a No. 7 sieve with a maximum of 5 per cent passing sieve No. 100, has been used for construction.

Additives

No pozzolanic additive has been used in any of the boats built but water reducing and retarding agents have been used.

Tests (ASRCT, Bangkok) showed that reduced water content and increased strength could be achieved with the use of lignosulphonate plasticizing additives and the

155

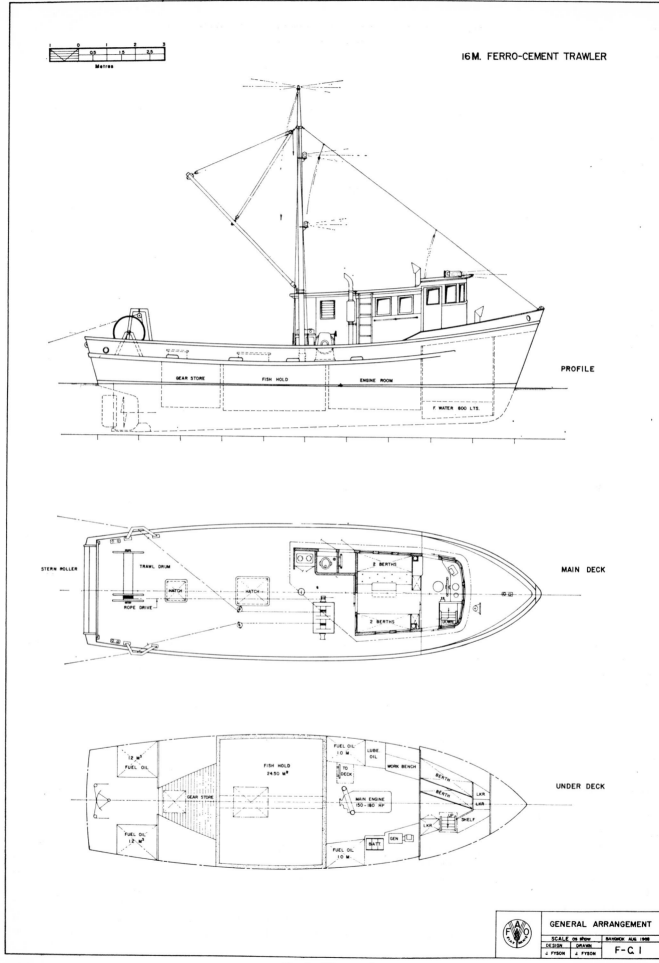

16M. FERRO-CEMENT TRAWLER

PROFILE

GEAR STORE   FISH HOLD   ENGINE ROOM

F. WATER 800 LTS.

MAIN DECK

STERN ROLLER   TRAWL DRUM

HATCH   HATCH

ROPE DRIVE

2 BERTHS

2 BERTHS

DOWN

UNDER DECK

12 M³ FUEL OIL

FISH HOLD 24.50 M³

GEAR STORE

FUEL OIL 10 M.

LUBE OIL

WORK BENCH

TO DECK

BERTH

MAIN ENGINE 150-180 HP

BERTH

LKR

LKR

SHELF

UP

FUEL OIL 12 M³

FUEL OIL 10 M.

BATT.

GEN

GENERAL ARRANGEMENT

SCALE as show   BANGKOK AUG 1969

DESIGN   DRAWN

J. FYSON   J. FYSON

F-C.1

Fig. 6   16 m trawler

TABLE 1. MAIN PARTICULARS OF BOATS PRESENTED IN FIGURES 1-6
(ALL DIMENSIONS IN METRES)

Data	Boat					
	7.5 m UAR-1	10.0 m UAR-2	10.6 m MAG-1	11.0 m DAH-6	12.6 m UGA-2	16 m FC-1
Country	A. R. Egypt	A. R. Egypt	Madagascar	Dahomey	Uganda Madagascar	Thailand
Fishing method	gillnets handline	gillnets handline fish transport	trawl purse seine handline	gillnets handline	trawl	trawl
Cubic number (CUNO) Loa × B × Dm (m³)	20	45	47	51	94	152
Length over all (Loa)	7.50	10.00	10.62	11.00	12.60	16.9
Length dwl (Lw)	6.90	9.00	9.58	9.30	11.50	14.50
Beam to outer surface of hull (B)	2.38	3.06	3.18	3.38	4.03	4.54
Beam dwl (Bw)	2.00	2.85	3.05	3.30	3.97	4.42
Depth amidship (Dm)	1.15	1.46	1.40	1.40	1.85	2.10
Draft amidship (d mean)	0.57	0.72	1.02	0.90	1.37	1.40
Draft aft (d aft)	0.70	0.90	1.20	1.05	1.60	1.65
Minimum freeboard (F min)	0.66	0.82	0.50	0.57	0.73	0.75
Displacement to dwl (△ wl tons)	2.5	6.1	9.6	10.0	19.4	35
Fishhold capacity (m³)	0.5	1.4	5.30	5.0	12	24.5
Engine Power Pb/rpm Hp/rpm	8/2000	20/2000	50/1800	30/1800	80/1800	150/1800
Pb/△ Hp/ton	3.2	3.3	5.2	3.0	4.1	4.3
Lw/▽ 1/3	5.1	5.0	4.6	4.4	4.3	4.4
Speed (knots)	5.7	6.5	7.3	6.6	8.1	8.8

TABLE 2. SCANTLINGS AND WEIGHTS

	7.5 m UAR-1	10.0 m UAR-2	10.6 m MAG-1	12.6 m UGA-2	16 m FC-1
Frame construction	Web frames	Web frames	Removable wooden moulds	Web frames	Pipe frames
Longitudinal rods	5 mm HT	5 mm HT	6 mm MS	6 mm HT	6 mm MS
Longitudinal rod spacing, mm	75	80	50	50–75	75
Transverse rods	4 mm HT	5 mm HT	6 mm MS	6 mm MS	6 mm MS
Transverse rods spacing, mm	75	80	150	75	100
Mesh type	Welded	Welded	Welded	Welded	Hexagonal
Wire size	1 mm 19 gauge	1 mm 19 gauge	1 mm 19 gauge	1 mm 19 gauge	1 mm 19 gauge
Mesh dimension, mm	12 × 12	12 × 12	12 × 12	12 × 12	15
Number of layers	3 + 3	4 + 3	4 + 3	4 + 4	4 + 4
Thickness of shell, mm	22	25	27	29	29
Weight of shell, kg/m²	57	63	70	75	75
Hull area, m²	27	42	52 excl. bulwarks	76 excl. bulwarks	120
Deck area, m²	8	16	18	31	40
Weight shell, t	1.6	2.7	3.7	5.7	9.0
Weight keel, bulkhead, etc., t	0.5	0.9	1.5	2.2	3.6
Weight deck, t	0.3 wood	0.5 wood	0.6 wood	1.4 wood	3.0 FC
Weight deckhouse engine outfit, t	0.3	0.6	2.2	5.9	9.5
Light ship displacement △1 t	2.6	4.7	8.0	15.2	25.1
Cubic number (CUNO)	20	45	47	94	152
△1/CUNO	0.13	0.10	0.17	0.16	0.16

HT = High tensile
MS = Mild steel

addition of a retarding agent in hot climates also assisted by giving more time for the application of the mortar and fairing.

Mixing of mortar

Sand and cement were measured by weight in the proportion of 1.75 : 1 in one case and 2 : 1 in others. Due to variation in the amounts of water in the sand, a check was kept on uniform consistency of the mix by carrying out slump tests at frequent intervals.

For plastering by the single application method, a slump of 7.5 cm was found necessary to ensure proper penetration of the mesh. A lower slump resulted in voids, in part due to the work force tiring as the day progressed with a consequent drop in efficiency despite maximum efforts by the supervisors.

The outer layer of the plaster in the double application method could be applied with proper penetration using a slump of 5 to 6.5 cm.

Paddle mixers were not available in most cases so that tilting-drum mixers and hand-mixing had to be used.

Applying the mortar

Both single and double application methods have been used. Working with unskilled or semi-skilled labour in tropical climates, one major advantage of the double application method is that it is much easier to ensure that the outer layer of mortar is applied without voids.

In the single application method considerable force is necessary to push the mortar right through the layers of mesh to the inside of the hull and at the end of a long hot day it is all too easy for the quality of the work to drop. In the double application method, less physical force is necessary to bring the mortar through the outer layer of mesh and rods and up to the inner surface of the inside layers. The inner mesh is still not covered and the supervisors can see any areas which need more mortar to fill voids. As already mentioned, with the double application method it is possible to use a mix with a lower slump and still obtain proper penetration. With the lower water content, one could, therefore, expect a higher strength and fewer problems with shrinkage.

In order to ensure a proper penetration of the inner layer of mortar, small vibrators such as flat-bed vibrators or a heavy-duty orbital sander converted by the addition of a base plate of plywood have been used.

Curing the mortar

Both water spray and steam curing have been used. Some difficulty has been found with achieving a sufficiently high temperature with steam generators. For example, in one case, two steam generators of the type used in steam cleaning plants for automobiles were needed to achieve a temperature of 70°C and it was not possible to go any higher despite an air temperature of 24 to 27°C. Where larger steam cleaning equipment capable of bringing the temperature up to 80°C and holding it there for 6 h is not available, it is felt that curing by water spray is the best solution, provided the work plan can be programmed around this. For example, deck-house and joinery work can be undertaken during the curing time as was done in Fiji with the construction of a 10.7-m fishing boat.

Painting

Considerable difficulty has been experienced with flaking paint and rust marks on ferro-cement hulls.

Best results to date have been achieved with tar-epoxy coatings on a thoroughly dry hull.

A proprietary tar-epoxy coating containing a micaceous ferric oxide has the additional advantage of good corrosion resistance and appears to prevent the rust stains which may occur due to strands of mesh or tie wire exposed at the surface of the hull.

The tar-epoxy coatings are covered with a suitable primer to prevent bleeding and can then be overcoated with conventional marine paints.

Engine installation

Best results have been obtained with engine beds which are formed integrally with the hull by reinforcing rods covered with mesh. Beds are 10 cm in thickness and the outside of the mesh of the beds is plasterd first and then the interior filled and vibrated at a later date.

Provision is made during alignment of the beds for a 5 to 7.5-cm wooden packing piece to be bolted to the top of the ferro-cement bed. This allows for any minor trimming of the beds which may be necessary during final alignment and helps to absorb vibration.

Holding-down bolts are allowed for by casting blocks into the bed which are later removed to leave a space for the insertion of a steel plate drilled to the size of the bolt and with a nut welded on the underside. The beds are then drilled when the engine is in position and the holding-down bolts tightened down on the nuts.

Blocks inserted in the beds can be of wood greased to facilitate removal or made of offcuts of styrofoam from the hold insulation, the advantage of the latter being that they are easily broken out after plastering.

Fitting out

Unless proper provision is made in the design and during the construction of the ferro-cement hull, fitting out can be a time-consuming operation which can more than make up for any saving achieved in the hull construction.

Ferro-cement upstands to which cabins and deck-houses are bolted are much easier to keep tight than wooden sills and coamings bolted directly to the deck.

Plugs for skin fittings and deck openings such as fuel filler pipes, pump suctions, etc., must all be incorporated before plastering.

Time required for the fitting of rubbing strakes can be cut considerably if wooden battens are fastened to flats designed into the hull and prebored for the location of bolt holes. Plasterers can then work to these battens leaving a flat surface to which the belting can be fastened. Four or five 16-mm laminations, the first two glued and bolted, and the remainder screwed and glued to this base, will provide a good belting to protect the hull against impact damage.

Interior joinery, fuel tanks, inner linings of fishholds, exhaust piping, etc., all need fastening points which should be arranged in the hull either as starters cast into the hull or using the web frames. Unless these are allowed for, the builder is obliged to go to considerable trouble to obtain rigid fixing points (it is considered that through-bolting the hull is not a satisfactory method of obtaining fixing points).

EXPERIENCE

Ferro-cement has proven well suited for the purpose of constructing hulls of prototype fishing vessels of 10 to 16-m in developing countries where boats of this size had never been built. An example of this is an FAO project in Uganda where the hull of a 12.6-m trawler was built in two months starting from lofting. To achieve this, *it is essential to have a well experienced ferro-cement boat-builder as a construction supervisor.* This is necessary not only to speed up the construction but mainly to achieve a satisfactory quality. Especially in the critical plastering operation, fatal errors can be made, as occurred in one FAO project where an 11-m coastal fishing boat had to be scrapped after one year in operation due to voids in the mortar leading to leaks and corrosion of the steel reinforcement. The main reason was the use of too coarse sand in the mortar causing penetration problems. The assistance of an experienced ferro-cement boat-builder will be the best guarantee against failures like this and in a developing country this assistance should cover the construction of three to five hulls to ascertain that the correct technique is well assimilated. In projects involving construction of prototype fishing vessels it is also well to remember that the hull is only a part of the finished boat and that trained people are required for the installation of engines, fuel tanks, winch, electrical outfit, etc. Apart from initial penetration problems, operational experience with the ferro-cement boats built under FAO supervision has been good. The ease of repair has been demonstrated in several cases where damage has occurred due to grounding or collision with other boats. It is, however, necessary that the persons responsible for the operation of the boat know the correct repair procedure and that damage is repaired relatively quickly. In tropical salt water, corrosion of the steel reinforcement will take place quickly once the mortar is cracked and water seeps in. Several ferro-cement boats have been observed with damage above the waterline that has been left unattended, causing the exposed steel mesh to rust away. If the cracks had been properly repaired in the first place a more extensive repair later would have been avoided. This is to a large extent a question of the owner's attitude to maintenance, but more practical training in the correct repair procedure for ferro-cement hulls would improve matters.

As happened with FRP in its earlier days, the field of ferro-cement construction has been rather dominated by claims asserting that the material excels in all ways—strength, cost, maintenance and ease of construction. FAO has felt a need for a more rational assessment of the material as applied to fishing-vessel construction. Like all construction materials, ferro-cement has its strong and weak points and objective information is needed to assure satisfactory results.

Weight and Cost Estimates for Small Fishing Vessels Ø Gulbrandsen

The ability to predict the floating waterline of a ship before it is launched has always been one of the naval architect's main tasks and well suited to impress the layman. With larger ships, this has been carried to a fine art and there are seldom any unpleasant surprises at launching. With smaller fishing boats, the issue is complicated by the variations in scantlings, construction materials, main proportions and a general lack of data, and the launching becomes the "moment of truth" for the naval architect's more or less reasonable guesses. In most cases the builder is happy if the boat floats at the designed waterline or higher—adding ballast will bring her down to where she should float. If she floats deeper than designed, the problem is not so easy to solve and the designer gets most of the blame.

A method is clearly needed which will give a reasonably correct weight for the completed boat without too laborious calculations—but flexible enough to take into account the most important factors. It will also give an indication of what happens to the displacement when one wants to use, say, a design of a wooden boat for construction in ferro-cement.

A measure for size

First, a scale is needed for measuring the size of boats. Length overall has long been the term known to seamen and builders for expressing size. However, as a basis for comparing the size of boats, the length overall is crude; with the same length, a boat can have varying beam and depth which will, largely, influence size.

Size can best be figured out as a volume and if we take the length, multiplied by the beam and the depth, we get the volume of a square box having the overall dimensions of the boat. This volume expressed in cubic metres is called the cubic number, or CUNO. Boats having the same CUNO will approximate the same size. Note that this is approximate and that a square barge can have the same length, beam and depth as a fishing boat with sharp bow and stern and consequently the same CUNO, but the size and carrying capacity will be very different. In fact, only boats of fairly similar shape can be compared by using the CUNO and this holds true for most fishing vessels. Figure 1 shows how the various dimensions are measured. The depth moulded is measured from the top of the deck at the side to the

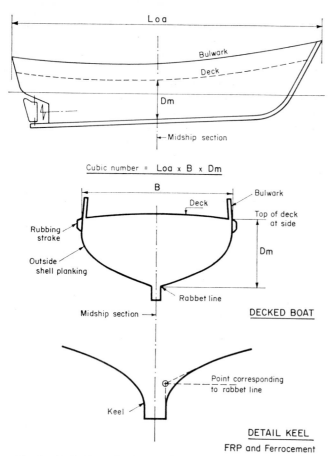

Fig. 1 Definition of cubic number

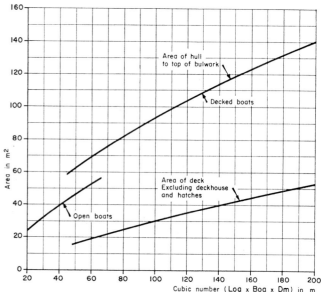

Fig. 2 Area of hull and deck

If the shape of the midship section is not known, an estimate can be made based on the cubic number (CUNO). Figure 2 shows the relation between CUNO and surface area of the hull and the deck.

The weight per unit area can be calculated when the scantlings for the skin and the frames are known. As an example, Table 1 shows the shell panels of a 13-m boat built in various construction materials. Based on specific scantling rules, it is also possible to calculate the

point where the bottom and the keel meet. In FRP and ferro-cement hulls the latter point can be difficult to define and Fig. 1 indicates how it can be located on the drawing of the midship section.

Methods for estimating weight

Since the CUNO gives a measure for size it can also be used as a basis for calculating hull weight. Multiplying the CUNO by a coefficient depending on boat size and type of material provides a quick method for obtaining the hull weight. This approach has been used by Benford and Kossa (1960) to obtain steel weights for larger fishing vessels.

The method works well where a standard set of scantlings has been established. With smaller fishing vessels there is a lack of standardization of scantlings and, especially with wooden vessels, there is a large variation between countries.

For smaller vessels a better result is obtained if the weight calculation is based on surface area of the boat and weight of material per unit area. This will enable a fair approximation of weight changes introduced by utilizing new construction materials and methods.

The surface area of the boat can be determined in various ways. Exact calculations can be made based on the lines plan. An estimate can be made by taking the full girth midship multiplied by the length overall and by a coefficient. This coefficient is about 0.93 for normal proportioned fishing vessels with transom. The approximate surface area is therefore: full girth midship × length overall × 0.93.

TABLE 1. CALCULATION OF SHELL WEIGHT PER M² FOR 12.6 M FISHING VESSEL

	Wood	Steel	FRP	Ferro–Cement
	50x100 400 35	60x40x7 380 5	450 9.5 mm	Frames spaced 1150 80 284 7 lay. mesh 2 lay. rod 6 mm
Specific gravity	0.75	7.8	1.5	2.6
Weight of skin per m²	26 kg	39 kg	14 kg	70 kg
Weight of frame per m²	19 kg	17 kg	7 kg	6 kg
Weight of panel per m²	45 kg	56 kg	21 kg	76 kg

weight per m² of various construction materials and boat sizes. Figure 3 gives the basic weight per m² of the shell in relation to CUNO based on the scantlings as given by Lloyd's Register of Shipping for FRP, Rajendran and Choudhury (1969) for wood, Hanson (1960) for steel and New Zealand Marine Department for ferro-cement. It must be noted that for wood, the line shown is below what is practised in several countries. A wooden vessel built according to Danish rules would, for example, be considerably heavier than indicated by the line in Fig. 3.

In addition to the weight per m² of the shell panel comes the weight of keel, stem, engine beds, stringers, bulkheads and local stiffening. The weights of these items are cumbersome to calculate and as a first estimate one can reckon with 40–50 per cent of the shell weight.

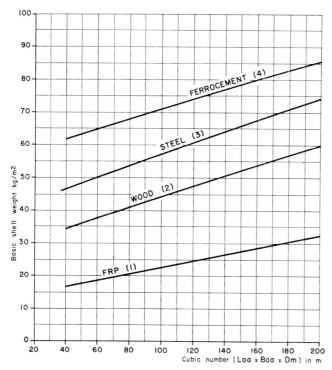

Fig. 3 Weight per square metre of hull and deck (excluding keel, deadwood, bulkheads, stringers and local stiffening).

The method for calculating the light ship weight is shown in Table 2. A detailed subdivision for weight and cost calculation is given in Appendix 1.

Design Consideration

Table 3 shows an example of calculation for a 12.6-m trawler.

The light ship weight will, in this case, vary between 9.4 and 16.9 t, the FRP boat being lightest and the ferrocement boat heaviest. It is evident that this large difference in weight will have to be taken into consideration when the design is prepared. If, in this case, both boats are built after the same lines plan, the FRP boat will float much higher than the ferro-cement boat. This often leads to low initial stability and the need for ballast to bring the FRP boat down to the designed waterline. If the FRP boat is to be designed without ballast, this will require a new shape of the midship section. Taking the 12.6-m trawler again as an example with the same prismatic coefficient of 0.58, the immersed area of the midship section for the FRP boat is 1.3 m² and for the ferro-cement boat, 2.4 m². The influence of this on the design is shown in Fig. 4.

In most cases FRP boats have been produced with conventional midship section and ballast is added in order to have the boat floating at the designed waterline. A recently built 16-m FRP fishing vessel carries, for example, 9 t of ballast.

If the bulwarks and deck of the ferro-cement version of the 12.6-m trawler were made of wood instead of ferro-cement, a weight saving of 1.2 t would be achieved. Since this is weight situated above the centre of gravity, this weight saving would have a marked influence on the initial stability of the vessel, especially in light ship conditions.

It is not yet clear to what extent the saving in weight of the FRP boat can be beneficially utilized in the design of displacement fishing vessels. There is, on the one hand, a gain in still water speed from approximately 8.5 knots for the ferro-cement boat to 9.2 knots for the FRP boat. On the other hand, the lighter FRP boat will have more violent movements in a seaway than the heavier ferro-cement boat. Heavy displacement means

TABLE 2. ESTIMATE OF LIGHT SHIP WEIGHT
(For breakdown of divisions, see Appendix 1)

Division			Items included	Weight calculation
1	Hull	Shell	Skin, frames	Area of shell (m²) × weight per m² from Fig. 1 from Fig. 2 or calculated or calculated
		Strength members	Keel, deadwood, bulkheads, engine bearers, stringers, local stiffening	Percentage of shell weight steel, wood, 40–50%
		Deck	Deck, deckbeams	Area of deck (m²) × weight per m² from Fig. 1 from Fig. 2
2	Deckhouse		Deckhouse—wheelhouse	Weight = C_2 × Cubic content of deckhouse Wooden deckhouse C_2 = 60 × 80 kg/m³ Steel deckhouse C_2 = 140 kg/m³
3	Outfit		Joiner work, fish hold lining, masts, rigging, fuel tanks, anchors, chain, life-saving equipment, galley equipment	Based on Cubic Number Outfit weight = C_3 × CUNO For decked boats: C_3 = 25–40 kg/m³
4	Machinery		Main engine, shaft and propeller	From manufacturer's leaflets
5	Auxiliaries		Generators, pumps, refrigeration machinery	Only include for larger vessels weight from manufacturers' leaflets
6	Electrical		Batteries, installation, deck-lights, electronics	From manufacturers' leaflets or included in 3
7	Deck equipment		Winches, power-blocks, anchor winch	From manufacturers' leaflets
8	Cargo		Ballast, fishing gear	Determined by designer

TABLE 3. WEIGHT CALCULATION 12.6-M TRAWLER

Loa = 12.6 m
B = 4.03 m
Dm = 1.85 m

Cubic Number (CUNO) Loa × B × Dm = 94 m³
Area of hull (Fig. 2): 90 m²
Area of deck (Fig. 2): 31 m²

Division		Wood	Steel	FRP	Ferro-cement
	Weight per m² (Fig. 3)	43 kg/m²	56 kg/m²	21 kg/m²	70 kg/m²
	Shell (90 m² × kg/m²)	3,900 kg	5,000 kg	1,900 kg	6,300 kg
	Keel, bulkheads, etc.	2,000 kg	2,500 kg	900 kg	2,500 kg
	Deck (31 m² × kg/m²)	1,300 kg	1,700 kg	700 kg	2,200 kg
1	Hull	7,200 kg	9,200 kg	3,500 kg	11,000 kg
2–8	See details below	5,900 kg	5,900 kg	5,900 kg	5,900 kg
	Light ship displacement	13,100 kg	15,100 kg	9,400 kg	16,900 kg

The following groups will give approximately the same weight for all materials:

2	Deckhouse—wood 60 kg/m³ × 13.5 m³ =	800 kg
3	Outfit—30 kg/m³ × 94 m³ =	2,800 kg
4	Machinery—80 hp/2000 rpm, shaft and propeller	700 kg
5	Auxiliaries—omitted =	0 kg
6	Electrical (included in 3)	0 kg
7	Deck equipment—winch =	800 kg
8	Ballast—designer's margin	800 kg
	Divisions 2–8 Total	5,900 kg

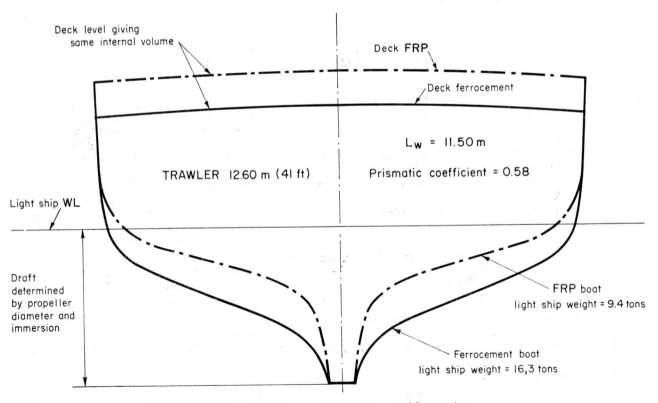

Fig. 4   Influence of light ship weight on midship section

increased resistance to disturbance and will provide a better working platform for the crew. In displacement-type fishing vessels, the penalty in speed for increased displacement will be slight compared with the improvement in motions. For faster semi-planing boats, however, the increased weight of a ferro-cement hull will give a substantial reduction in speed compared to an FRP hull.

COST ESTIMATE

Variations in building costs

Construction of large fishing vessels is a field of international competition, hence, within this sphere we do not find major price differences from one country to another. Smaller fishing vessels are, however, rarely exported and the type of vessels, construction methods and materials are very much influenced by local tradition and resources, with the result that one finds great variation in cost and quality. Basically, this has been governed by economic factors: in areas with rich fishing grounds, we find sophisticated, well-equipped and expensive vessels. The fisherman can afford to pay the extra cost since the reward in increased production justifies it. In areas with poor fishing and low prices, the vessels have been correspondingly cheaper, more simply equipped and often of low quality. The cost of small fishing vessels therefore aligns itself to the general economic level of the fishery and only a major breakthrough leading to higher catches or better prices will provide the required incentive toward introduction of better built and better equipped boats.

Especially for wooden fishing vessels, which probably constitute more than 90 per cent of the world's fleet of smaller fishing vessels, there is a great variation in cost between areas. Any attempts to arrive at a generally valid standardized cost for various sizes of small fishing vessels will, therefore, be futile. One can, however, arrive at a standard method for calculating costs which facilitate comparison between various alternative materials when sufficient data are known in a specific country.

Method for cost estimate

For a fishing vessel, the cost differences between alternative materials will mainly be limited to division 1, Hull structure.

The more detailed the cost calculation for this division, the more reliable the result. However, it is often necessary to make rough cost estimates before construction has started, and Table 4 provides a system for doing this.

The labour requirement is given in man-hours/ton, using the weight calculated according to Table 1 as a basis for labour cost. The range indicated is very wide—the lower figure is representative for efficient yards with skilled workers, while the higher figures are more appropriate in countries in the starting-up phase of a boat-building industry. Only experience and data will indicate which figure to apply.

The remaining costs can be calculated according to Table 5. The same grouping as in the weight calculation (Table 1) and in Appendix 1 has been utilized.

In addition to the direct costs of materials and labour come the overheads which are usually taken as a percentage of the labour cost which might vary from 50 to 150 per cent, depending on the type of operation, administrative costs and depreciation and interest on investments in buildings and machinery.

The profit is usually taken as a percentage of the net production cost of the boat—often around 10 per cent.

An example of a cost calculation for a 12.6-m trawler is given in Appendix 2. The costs are based on local prices in East Africa and the result is not valid in other areas.

Hull cost as part of total cost

From the cost summary in Appendix 2, one will note that the direct cost of divisions 2–7, which is common for all materials, is 55 to 65 per cent of total cost. Therefore on a vessel of this type and size, fairly large variations in the cost of division 1 will not have a great bearing on total cost. The total savings that can be obtained by using cheaper construction materials for the hull should, therefore, not be exaggerated. In trying to save costs on a fishing vessel of this type, it might be equally rewarding to investigate possible savings when selecting the engine and equipment.

Wood, steel, aluminium, FRP and ferro-cement have all been successfully employed for the construction of smaller fishing vessels. All of them have their strong and weak points, and none can claim a general advantage over another. The dominance of wood for small-boat

TABLE 4. BASIS FOR COST ESTIMATE—HULL (Division 1)

	Wood	Steel	FRP	Ferro-cement
Basic cost per ton	Cost/m³ sawn planks specific weight	Average cost/t plates and profiles	$0.30 \times$ cost/t glass $+ 0.70 \times$ cost/t resin $=$ cost/t laminate (30% glass content)	Mesh: cost/m² × No. of layers + rods: cost/m × length of rods/m² + cement and sand = cost/m² $$\text{cost/t} = \frac{\text{Cost/m}^2 \times 1{,}000}{\text{thickness, cm} \times 24}$$
Wastage	30–50%	20%	15%	15%
Fastenings, paint, etc.	20%	10%	5%	10%
Labour man-h/t	200–550	150–350	150–350	150–350

(See Appendix 2 for example of cost estimate)

construction is being challenged, especially by FRP. In the pleasure-boat market there has been a rapid changeover from wood to FRP, but this has not yet happened in fishing vessels. This cannot simply be attributed to traditions and stubbornness among fishermen; rather, it is due to the fact that wood has given a reasonably good service and no other material has yet convincingly demonstrated an overall superiority with regard to price, longevity, maintenance and resistance to shock and abrasion. However, the situation is not static and, depending on prices and technological development, one material may gain ground and another lose, but due to the differences between areas and countries in economic and technological development, the situation will probably not arise where one material has gained universal preference. For a long time to come, there will be a place for each of the hitherto known materials utilized in fishing vessel construction.

TABLE 5. COST OF MATERIALS AND LABOUR

Division		Cost calculation	
		Materials	Labour
1	Hull	See Table 4	See Table 4
2	Deckhouse	Wt × mat cost/t	Wt × man-h/t Est. 200–500 man-h/t
3	Outfit	Wt × cost/t	Wt × man-h/t Est. 300–800 man-h/t
4	Machinery	Makers quote	Wt × man-h/t Est. 200–600 man-h/t
5	Auxiliaries	Makers quote	Included in 4
6	Electrical	Makers quote	Firms quote
7	Deck gear	Makers quote	Included in 3 and 4
8	Cargo	Ballast and gear	Omitted

APPENDIX 1

(SUBDIVISION FOR WEIGHT AND COST CALCULATION)
(GROUP 1 AS FOR WOODEN HULL BUT CAN BE ADAPTED FOR OTHER MATERIALS)

Division	Group	Item
1 Hull	10 Keel, stem, stern-post	101 Keel-shoe
		102 Stem-apron
		103 Sterntimber-horntimbers
		104 Dead woods
		109 Miscellaneous
	11 Frames	111 Floortimbers
		112 Frame
	12 Planking	121 Planking bottom
		122 Planking sides
	13 Stringers, etc.	131 Bilge stringers
		132 Beam shelves
		133 Ceiling
		134 Bulkheads
		135 Engine stringer
		136 Engine beds
		137 Rubbing strakes
	14 Deck	141 Deck planking
		142 Deck beams
		143 Covering board
		144 Bulwark
		145 Hatch coamings
	15 Fastenings, paint	151 Nails
		152 Bolts
		153 Paint

Division	Group	Item
2 Deckhouse	21 Deckhouse	211 Framing
		212 Planking
		213 Windows-portholes
	22 Open bridge	
	23 Awnings	
3 Outfit	31 Joiner work	311 Cabin lining
		312 Cabin flooring
		313 Cabin berths
		314 Lockers
	32 Fish hold	321 Insulation
		322 Lining
		323 Partitions
		324 Boxes
	33 Tanks and piping	331 Fuel tanks
		332 Oil tanks
		333 Fresh water tanks
		334 Fresh water piping
		335 Bilge pump piping
	34 Ventilation	341 Air ducts
		342 Air conditioning
		343 Heating
	35 Rigging	351 Masts
		352 Booms
		353 Standing rigging
		354 Rope
	36 Safety equipment	361 Navigation lights
		362 Lifeboats, rafts
		363 Rockets
		364 First aid
		365 Anchors
		366 Anchor chain
		367 Mooring ropes

Division	Group	Item	Division	Group	Item
	37 Steering gear	371 Steering wheel		62 Installation	621 Wiring
		372 Steering transmission			622 Switchboard
		373 Rudder-rudderstock			623 Switches
		374 Rudder tube-stuffing box			624 Lamps
	38 Galley	381 Stove		63 Decklights	631 Floodlights
		382 Sink			632 Searchlights
		383 Cutlery		64 Electronics	641 Radio-telephone
4 Propulsion machinery	41 Main engine	411 Engine			642 Radar
		412 Reverse/reduction gear			643 Echo-sounder
		413 Fuel piping	7 Deck equipment	71 Trawl winch	711 Winch
		414 Exhaust piping			712 Transmission
		415 Starting equipment		72 Anchor winch	721 Winch
		416 Engine controls			722 Transmission
	42 Shaft and propeller	421 Propeller	8 Cargo	81 Ballast	
		422 Tail shaft		82 Fishing gear	
		423 Intermediate shaft		83 Fish—ice	831 Fish
		424 Couplings			832 Ice
		425 Sterntube		84 Bait and water in bait tanks	
		426 Shaft bearings			
5 Auxiliaries	51 Generators	511 Generating set		85 Fuel—water	851 Fuel
		512 Fuel piping			852 Lubricating oil
		513 Exhaust piping			853 Fresh water
	52 Pumps	521 Bilge pump		86 Crew	861 Crew members
		522 Clutch-transmission			862 Crew effects
	53 Refrigeration machinery	531 Refrigeration compressor		87 Stores	
		532 Refrigeration pipes			
6 Electrical	61 Batteries	611 Batteries			
		612 Battery box			

Appendix 2

EXAMPLE: ESTIMATE OF STRUCTURAL HULL COST OF A
12.6-M TRAWLER BASED ON COSTS IN EAST AFRICA (US $)

Division 1

	Wood	Steel	FRP	Ferro-cement
Basic material costs (East Africa)	135 m³ sawn to size specific weight: 0.75	230/t	Mat = 1700/t Resin = 850/t	Weldmesh 12 mm galvanized 19 gauge = 0.80/m² rods, high tensile 6 mm 0.15/m rods, mild steel 6 mm 0.05/m
Material cost/t	$\frac{135}{0.75} = 180$	230	Mat = 0.3×1700 = 510 Resin = 0.7×850 = 600 cost/t: 1110	Mesh 7 layers $0.80 \times 7 = 5.60$ 14 m high-tensile 0.15×14 = 2.10 14 m mild steel $0.05 \times 14 = 0.70$ Steel reinforcement 8.40 Cement, sand, etc. 1.00 Cost/m² 9.40 Cost/t = $\frac{9.40 \times 1000}{2.8 \times 24} = 145$
Wastage	30% of 180 = US $54	20% of 230 = US $46	15% of 1110 = US $167	15% of 145 = US $22
Fastenings and paint, etc.	20% of 180 = US $36	10% of 230 = US $23	5% of 1110 = US $56	10% of 145 = US $15
Total material cost per ton	270	299	1333	182
Estimated man/h/t	550	350	350	350
Direct labour cost/t US $0.40/h	220	140	140	140
Hull weight (from Table 3)	7.2 t	9.2 t	3.5 t	11.0 t
Material costs	$270 \times 7.2 = 1940$	$299 \times 9.2 = 2750$	$1133 \times 3.5 = 3970$	$182 \times 11.0 = 2000$
Direct labour costs	$220 \times 7.2 = 1580$	$140 \times 9.2 = 1290$	$140 \times 3.5 = 490$	$140 \times 11.0 = 1540$
Division 1 Total direct costs hull	3520	4040	4460	3350

The following divisions will give approximately the same cost for all materials

Division 2–8

Division	Item	Materials and equipment	Labour
2	Deckhouse, wood	0.8 t × US $270/t = US $ 200	0.8 t × 500 m/h/t = 400
3	Outfit	2.8 t × US $800/t = US $2,200	2.8 t × 800 m/h/t = 2,200
4	Machinery 80 HP/7800 rpm	US $6,500	0.7 t × 600 m/h/t = 400
5	Auxiliaries	US $ 100	Included in 4
6	Electrical	US $1,000	Included in 3
7	Deck equipment	US $2,000	Included in 3 and 4
8	Cargo	Omitted	Omitted
	Subtotal	US $12,000	3,000 m/h × US $0.40 = $1,200
	Total, Divisions 2–8	US $13,200	

COST SUMMARY (US $)

	Wood	Steel	FRP	Ferro-cement
Division 1	3,500	4,000	4,500	3,500
Divisions 2–8	13,200	13,200	13,200	13,200
Total, Direct Cost	16,700	17,200	17,500	16,600
Overheads	2,000	3,000	5,000[1]	2,000
Profit	2,000	2,000	2,000	2,000
Total	20,700	22,200	24,500	20,700

[1] Depending on number of hulls.

References

BENFORD, H and KOSSA, MIKLOS An analysis of US fishing
1960   boats—dimensions, weights and costs. *Fishing Boats
of the World*, vol. 2. London, England: Fishing News
(Books) Ltd.

HANSON, H C Steel and wood scantling tables. *Fishing Boats
1960   of the World*, vol. 2. London, England: Fishing
News (Books) Ltd.

LLOYD'S REGISTER OF SHIPPING *Provisional Rules for the
Application of Glass Reinforced Plastics to Fishing
Crafts.*

NEW ZEALAND MARINE DEPARTMENT *Provisional Requirements for the Construction of Ferro-cement Boats.*
Wellington.

*Proceedings Conference on Fishing Vessel Construction
Materials.* Montreal, Canada: Fisheries Service,
Department of Fisheries and Forestry, Fisheries
Report No. 12: 31.

RAJENDRAN, R and CHOUDHURY, R L *Scantlings for Small
1969   Wooden Fishing Vessels. Fishery Technology*, vol. VI,
No. 2. Ernakulam, Cochin: S. Gopalan Nayar.

The Cost of Ferro-Cement Boat Construction in India M A K Tayab

In India there are about 8000 mechanized boats and other craft, besides a large number of traditional craft. In Tamil Nadu State, about 1200 mechanized boats are engaged in fishing. The Department of Fisheries, Government of Tamil Nadu (Madras) has been active in helping to increase the number of mechanized boats in operation. Most of these mechanized boats are derived from designs proposed by FAO.

FERRO-CEMENT PROJECT INITIATED

The Indian Department of Fisheries was very much concerned over the ever-increasing cost of construction of wooden fishing boats and was on the lookout for an alternative cheaper material. The cost of raw materials for fibreglass boats is very high in India, though all the required raw materials are produced locally. So ferro-cement was chosen. Research on the determination of various characteristics of ferro-cement was done by producing test slabs and finding the proper rod/mesh combination, mortar mix, etc. After these tests were done, a small row boat was built as a pilot project on the basis of the test results and the published literature. This pilot boat was successful and it helped greatly in having workmen and other persons connected with the project getting the feel of the new medium.

Though it would have been possible to commission a naval architect locally to prepare a design for ferro-cement boats and if necessary tank testing could have been done at Madras itself, it was decided to buy commercial designs which were readily available at a reasonable price to save time. All the rest of the research and development work was done by the Department of Fisheries (Madras). Several ferro-cement boats including a 38-footer have been built so far. Here, mainly the cost of the 38-ft (11.6-m) ferro-cement boat which was built recently will be discussed.

The principal dimensions of the boat are as follows:

Length over-all	37 ft 6 in	11.45 m
Length at W.L.	35 ft	10.65 m
Beam	10 ft 10 in	3.3 m
Draught	5 ft 9 in	1.75 m
Depth moulded	6 ft 3 in	1.9 m
Hold capacity	460 ft^3	13.00 m^3
Fuel capacity	510 gal	2300 l
Water capacity	250 gal	1100 l
Accommodation	5	

DETAILS OF CONSTRUCTION

For the keel a mild steel channel 150 × 75 mm was used weighing about 125 kg. The stem was made out of 25 mm mild steel rod and stem post and shaft, etc., were fabricated out of 18-mm rod. Galvanized iron pipes 25 mm in diameter were used for frame work. For both vertical and horizontal frame work 10-mm rods were used at a spacing of 75 mm centre-to-centre. Admittedly this was a very cautious approach and in future, after further experimentation, a lighter rod with wider centre-to-centre spacing could be used. The utility and advisability of adopting deformed mild steel bars and medium high-tensile steel could also be investigated.

For meshing, ordinary hexagonal 12 mm (chicken) mesh, 22 gauge (galvanized) was used. For this boat the deck and wheelhouse were of wood. An Ashok Leyland ALMU 370, 6-cylinder marine diesel engine rated at 80 hp at 1800 rpm (made in Madras) was used. The boat was equipped with fish-finder, a winch, insulated fish-hold, trawl gallows, etc.

CEMENTING OF THE BOAT

A paddle type and an ordinary pan-type mixer were employed. The work was commenced from the stem and finished at the transom. The conditions of humidity and temperature are such that it appears that it is advisable to have a small quantity of mortar, say, 1 ft^3 (0.028 m^3) mixed at a time. The cementing was commenced by about 09.00 h and completed by 12.00 h of the next day, i.e. it continued for 36 h, though the batches of workmen were being changed frequently.

Pencil vibrators were used during the cementing. Ordinary portland cement conforming to ISI (Indian Standards Institution) was used. However, it had 10 per cent pozzolana ground and incorporated along with the clinkers at the factory itself. No other additives were used. Clean well-sieved river sand was used. Two truck loads, i.e. about 12 t of sand was procured for Rs. 120

and the required quantity was utilized. Four and a half tons of cement worth Rs. 900 was used. Hence the total cost of sand and cement was about Rs. 1000, i.e. 4.5 per cent of the cost of materials for the entire hull. A water : cement ratio of 0.45 was used. One full bag of cement of 50 kg was mixed with 100 kg of sand with 45 l of water. Though about 20 to 25 workers were engaged on cementing day per shift, it is hoped to economize on this by another system and it is anticipated that the entire cementing could be done in 8 to 10 h with a smaller labour force.

ANALYSIS OF COST FACTORS

		Rs.	Rs.
Steel items:			
1. M.S. rods for vertical and horizontal framing			
(i) Frame work 10 mm 1500 kg		2,500	
6 mm 50 kg		80	
25 mm 50 kg		80	
			2,660
2. (i) M.S. channel 150 × 75 mm, 160 kg		400	
(ii) M.S. plate 6 × 10 mm, 100 kg		300	
			700
3. (i) Pipes, G.I. 25 mm Ø, 120 m		660	
(ii) Pipes M.S. 25 mm Ø, 35 m		180	
			840
4. Mesh:			
(i) Hexagonal 20 mm, 22 gauge, 26 rolls		2,800	
(ii) Welded mesh 25 × 25 mm, 14 gauge/60 ft^2		70	
			2,870
5. Welding materials, etc.		1,000	
6. Galvanized mild steel binding wire 20 gauge, 60 kg		200	
			1,200
Total cost of steel items:			8,270
7. Cementing:			
(i) Portland cement, 4.5 t with about 10% of pozzolana ground in factory itself		900	
(ii) Two truck loads of river sand, about 12 t		120	
			1,020
8. Paint		2,800	
			2,800
Total cost of materials for the hull			12,090
9. (a) Stern tube, gland and other brassware			1,500
(b) Rudder assembly, etc.			900
10. Miscellaneous items of equipment			3,420
11. Fish-hold (thermocole insulation, fibre-glass facing, complete)			2,400
12. Cost of furnishing for wheel house			2,000
13. Cost of timber, for wheelhouse, deck, etc.			9,540

Total cost of materials for hull, including wheelhouse, etc.		31,850
14. Cost of labour, 10,000 m/h		12,500
Total cost of hull		44,350
15. Cost of engine, including propeller, power take-off, etc.		45,000
16. Other equipment, fish-finder, compass and navigational aids, etc.		11,500
17. Overheads, 50% of the labour charges		6,250
		107,100
18. Profit, 7½%		7,900
Total cost of boat	Rs.	115,000
	or, say, US$	15,400

The cost of the hull itself was only about 12,500 + 12,500 = Rs. 25,000. The labour cost given here is the total labour cost including cost of finishing the boat.

The above table shows that the more expensive items were as follows:

		Rs.
1. Engine including propeller (15)		45,000
2. Labour charges (14)		12,500
3. Other equipment, fish-finder, etc. (16)		11,500
4. Cost of timber (13)		9,540
5. Cost of steel (1–6)		8,270

The timber bill alone came to Rs. 9,540; substituting a ferro-cement deck for the wooden deck could result in savings. However, timber may continue to figure as a fairly large item of expenditure in the total cost. Steel accounted for Rs. 8,270, and, as suggested above, by reducing the quality of steel used, the cost on this item could be reduced by, say, about 10 to 20 per cent. Hence, though our present boat did cost us around Rs. 115,000, or about US$15,400, a further reduction in cost is possible.

COMPARATIVE COST USING VARIOUS MATERIALS

Taking boats of more or less same size, the approximate market price of boats utilizing various materials can be compared. At present a manufacturer is offering at Madras a 32.5-ft (9.90-m) fibreglass boat for about Rs. 150,000 (US$20,000). A 38-ft fibreglass boat may cost not less than Rs. 200,000 (US$26,666). A 38-ft (11.60-m) wooden boat may cost Rs. 150,000 (US$20,000). A 36-ft (11.00-m) steel boat is available for about Rs. 180,000 (US$24,000). However, a 38-ft steel boat is likely to cost Rs. 210,000 (US$28,000). Not only is the capital cost of a ferro-cement boat lower but also its maintenance will no doubt be cheaper. Though in the operation of a fishing boat the cost of fuel and labour is a major cost and is more or less constant in any type of boat, in a ferro-cement boat, since the initial capital cost is lower, the over-all cost of operation will be lower.

RESPONSE FROM THE FISHERMEN

The response from fishermen for the ferro-cement boat was very enthusiastic and it is thought they will take to it readily.

The developing countries with denser populations are in urgent need of larger supplies of foodstuffs, especially those richer in protein. Their fishing industries have great scope for development and they should rapidly expand their fleets. The cheapest and best solution appears to be the use of ferro-cement boats on large scale. The raw materials required are more easily available than those for other types. The skills required are not so critical and production does not demand highly capital-intensive structure. A good labour force could be trained at a relatively small outlay. If a Research and Development Service is set up and if it supplies good designs and offers training facilities, it may be possible to popularize the technique of building ferro-cement boats on a large scale at a relatively low outlay compared to other alternatives.

Discussion Covering Construction Methods and Costs

Moar (Rapporteur) noted that Leonard described design problems and construction experience during the building of a 27.4-m (90-ft) fishing boat which was probably the largest boat built in ferro-cement to that date. An interesting feature was the use of steel bulkheads welded to the reinforcement; it would be valuable to find out how a ferro-cement hull with a steel bulkhead welded to the reinforcing would stand up, and whether problems could occur with electrolysis. The hull thickness of this large boat was only about 32 mm (1¼ in), which seemed rather light and could be the reason for some of the damage the boat sustained during a typhoon.

Noble and **Cleaver** mentioned refrigerated fish carrier barges. This was a very interesting development which might appeal to countries having limited capital available for investment in fisheries. Leaving catcher boats on the fishing grounds, rotating their crews and collecting the fish from the boats by using barges of this type would assist in making maximum use of the available equipment. **Nontanakorn** discussed flat-sided barges built in Thailand for river work. Apparently these had been very successful and, in the light of discussion during previous sessions on the essential requirement of curved surfaces, it would be important to hear whether the flat-sided barges had given any problems. Sutherland described a number of construction techniques, most prominently the sandwich construction method, consisting of a steel jig made up of web frames, like the pipe frame method. Longitudinal battens of timber were attached to this jig and layers of mesh stapled to the battens on the outside. The outside layers of mesh were then plastered. After the mortar had cured, the jig was removed, the mesh stapled to the interior and then the inside plastered. The timber was left inside the mortar. The method saved a lot of labour and was useful for low production runs.

Behnke and **Doleman** elaborated on the female mould technique. This was a very interesting method, but would it not have been easier to make a male plug first of ferro-cement and fair that, rather than to fair the interior surface of a female mould? **Carkeek** discussed the merits of pipe frames, timber frames and, in particular, truss frames. It appeared that his company was successful in making up truss frames, but amateurs had had a lot of trouble with welding stresses and fairing. **Gulbrandsen** on costs and weight had two well made comments; firstly, only hulls should be made in ferro-cement and not decks and cabins and appendages—there seemed to be general agreement on this point, substantiated by a lot of service experience; the second point was that the cost savings made by using ferro-cement were not startling. By the time all equipment was installed and the boat finished they could turn out to be very small; American and Canadian experience may even indicate that a ferro-cement boat could be more expensive in first cost because of labour costs. Ferro-cement boats cannot easily be justified on cost alone, and consideration needed to be given to other, more decisive, advantages of the material. Moar was convinced that there were many other advantages—some were listed in several of the papers—and he thought that these could be stressed. If low initial cost was to be of paramount importance, prospective boat owners would be better advised to consider other methods of saving money, such as reducing or simplifying equipment.

Pavey, discussing painting of boats, maintained that paint was necessary to cover the various areas of bare steel left after a boat is plastered. This appeared to be a strong condemnation of bad amateur practices; a well made boat, properly plastered, should not need painting.

Tayab recounted his experience in building a fishing vessel, using a pipe frame; he also reported the boat's success in practice. This was encouraging news from India where someone had started from scratch without apparent outside help and had successfully made and operated a fishing boat of ferro-cement.

It was suggested that the discussion should touch primarily on the following points, apart from considering the multitude of different construction methods identified and described in the papers;

(a) The lack of technical data and information as an inhibiting factor, delaying commercial acceptance of ferro-cement.
(b) The use of mixers. One paper claimed that drum mixers were perfectly acceptable while other experience has been that these produce very poorly mixed mortar patches that could produce weak spots in the hull.
(c) Curing. Various curing techniques were suggested, including chemical, steam, water and saltwater curing.
(d) The advantages of ferro-cement.
(e) The extent to which ferro-cement should be used for vessel parts other than the hull.

CONSTRUCTING THE ARMATURE

A number of different construction methods had been described in the papers presented. Discussion on the geometry of the skeletal steel and methods of tying the mesh, on what may be described as the classical constructional system were commented on by a number of participants.

Roberts (New Zealand) described the skeletal steel used in recent boats built by his Association as consisting of 5 mm (6 gauge) longitudinal rod at 38 mm (1½ in) centres with 2.6 mm (12 gauge) transverse rods at down to 25 mm (1 in) spacing. With three layers of 0.7 mm (22 gauge) hexagonal mesh on either side of this skeletal steel, plaster penetration was better and the armature was sufficiently rigid to avoid deformation when applying the mortar.

Donovan (New Zealand) said that with such an extensive skeletal steel structure and a reduced number of layers of light mesh, Roberts was perhaps getting away from the concept of ferro-cement, defined as a finely divided mesh reinforcement in a hydraulic mortar.

Walker (Australia) quoted Nervi's original work in which the number of layers of mesh were increased until penetration became difficult. Where thicker shells than could be obtained by mesh alone were required, it was found that the same properties could be achieved by opening up the mesh and putting rods in between. However, it was imperative to have finely divided mesh near the surface to stop cracking. If four small section rods could be used as a replacement for one of large section with similar strength, this also resulted in improved crack control.

Bowen (New Zealand) noted that a strong feeling existed in some areas in New Zealand, that transverse framing of one type or another was a vital part of a ferro-cement boat and requested opinions from participants.

Boden (Australia) considered that amateur builders and small yards, used to conventional construction techniques in wood or steel, find transverse framing advantageous as a form on which they can build, and he also noted that in steel construction, experience had shown that it was not sufficient to rely on the strength given by the steel fabric of the shell but that framing was necessary to maintain transverse strength.

Fyson (FAO) said that for vessels built in developing countries FAO had chosen either the pipe or truss frame methods, largely because of the relative simplicity and the relation to conventional setting-up techniques already familiar to local boatbuilders. Other advantages were low tool costs and suitability for building small numbers of boats. This problem existed especially in countries where modern fishing techniques were not well established and the construction of prototype vessels was often necessary to determine suitable boat types before any large-scale production could begin. The transverse framing system had further advantages in assuring a rigid armature less susceptible to deformation during the plastering stage, plus the use of the framing to provide fixing points for bulkheads, internal fittings, engine beds, etc.

Hermanson (Norway) said that in his opinion internal framing in fishing boats helped in localizing impact damage. In his own area problems were experienced with ice, and wooden boats required protective sheathing at the waterline. This had not been found necessary for the transverse framed ferro-cement boats which had been able to break up the ice without problems.

O'Kell (Australia) considered that the method of frame erection in which the frame is suspended to overhead trusses is, to the amateur, a very tough proposition—one involving many weeks of work, with usually only a mediocre job of fairing. He proposed the upside down method on all but the larger vessels and described the method and its advantages as follows:

169

The builder, following offsets given on lines plans, erects a jack-post framework, upon which the temporary pipe frame is raised and, having a fixed and steady base, this is a simple job of fairing.

Pipe frames are erected and pipe stringers are fixed inside the structure to initially fair the frame which is then ready for mesh-work. This process is usually completed by two men in six days.

All mesh-work is placed from the outside of the hull—which makes for speedy and neat construction. Gravity is on the side of the builder with this method—not against him—very important in the plastering stage, and even the pinning or stapling is speeded up.

There is a large tolerence for fairing the hull as this process goes on right through the job. Even if the builder has made a poor job of frame bending and erection, this is still easy to overcome. The framework is not restricted by preformed web frames, but is adjustable throughout. Starters are placed ready, and *after* all hull fairing is complete any web frames required are spot welded into position and meshed.

The mesh-work is packed clear of the framework by 19 mm (¾ in) which allows the plasterers to work easily around the frames. The small wooden packing pieces are removed after the curing process and the indents are made good. The plastering procedure is a simple and light job compared to the overhead method—by which the toughest part of the job is reached when the men are tiring. The one-shot method is thus more easily achieved. After water and weather curing, the hull is rolled to an upright position and completed normally. Man-hours involved to hull finish in this method are consistently 20—25 per cent lower and the cost of rolling the hull is more than compensated by the fact that a heavy and expensive overhead frame is not needed.

Fyson (FAO) agreed that the upside down method might have some advantages for amateurs, but the commercial builder of fishing boats (unless engaged in series building using a mould) would probably prefer the upright method because of the ease of installing frames, bulkheads, engine beds, stern tube, rudder shaft tube, etc. Most experienced boatbuilders would be familiar with the methods of setting up framing and should have little difficulty in obtaining a fair hull.

One of the most time-consuming jobs in the construction of the armature is the tying of the mesh to the skeletal steel and a number of methods of speeding up this process have been used.

Donovan (New Zealand) described a modified pneumatic stapling machine in which the staple was curled over behind the wire somewhat similar to the principle of the hog ring which was also used by some people. He personally favoured the use of 1.6 mm (16 gauge) black iron wire with a machine developed for use with an electric drill. This consisted of a small vice grip wrench to grip the tie with a short length of rod welded to one arm of the wrench which could be fitted into the chuck of the drill. He was impressed by the strength and tightness of the tie achieved. He also considered that by extending the length of the twisted part of the tie and bending it back into the mesh the problem of protruding wires was almost eliminated.

Walker (Australia) favoured the use of a reel to hold the wire which could be bent over with one hand, pushed through the mesh and pulled back using a pair of pointed nose pliers which are then used to twist up the tie. In this way the wire and tool are held in the hands and there is no changing from tie to pliers to cutters. He did remark, however, that his company had found considerable variation in tying time de-

pending on the composition of the tying team and that pairs of workmen one on each side of the hull with one acting as a pacemaker had given the best results. He used light tie wires, down to 1 mm (20 gauge) depending on the gauge of the mesh and tied on the lower of the cross wires of the square welded mesh so that when the tie was folded over, it lay flush with the surface.

Rossiter (Australia) considered that with 20–25,000 wire ties in a boat the use of labour-saving devices could be most attractive and described a method of forming closed ties pneumatically using standard staples in conjunction with a hand held mandrel. The advantages to be gained being high-speed fixing of the mesh and the elimination of twisted tie ends which could protrude and cause corrosion.

Wheeler (New Zealand) said that his company's experience over ten years had shown that the pincer type end cutter gave the best results. By using the pincer as a lever as the twisting of the wire loop progresses, it was possible to pull the mesh firmly together. They had used the staple or hog ring system but found it difficult to get the mesh tight enough with this method. They had also used ordinary pliers to twist the ties and cut them off later but found this slow. He considered that if the ties were wound up, cut off fairly long and then hammered back as Donovan suggested, when the hull was being faired up the long ends would tend to turn around and protrude from the mesh surface.

Recently his company had used 0.7 mm (22 swg) stainless steel wire with satisfactory results, and even if there was slight exposure of an occasional tie there was no rust problem.

Donovan (New Zealand) asked whether the stainless steel ties in the presence of moisture without air in the curing mortar mix might be liable to corrosion.

Wheeler (New Zealand) considered that there would be 20–25,000 of these ties in a boat to hold the armature together and he did not think that more than minor corrosion could occur during the mortar curing stage, so that the problem was unlikely to be serious, if it occurred at all.

Boden (Australia) asked what was the real function of the tying, just to hold the mesh in place until the mortar was applied or was it intended to transfer some stress from the main rods to the mesh and thence to the mortar?

Pama (Thailand) said that in compression tests he had noted a tendency for the wire mesh to buckle causing premature spalling. Ties holding the mesh together would tend to prevent this.

Perry (Australia) agreed with Pama that in compression tests the mesh tended to buckle. However, he considerd that one seldom got this direct compression stress on a boat, there were usually bending stresses as well and the failures he had seen had been through bending of the ferro-cement membrane itself in conjunction with compression. He had not seen a failure in which ties would have prevented this.

Moar (New Zealand) replied to a suggestion that staples might be considered as a structural element between layers, acting much as a stirrup in a reinforced beam. He agreed that this effect could occur but, as most construction codes specify a maximum spacing of ¾ of the effective depth of the beam between stirrups, this would mean that ties would have to be at about 13 mm (½ in) spacing in both directions to make them effective. He considered that the major value of ties was during construction, otherwise there had to be fairly serious damage to the hull before they could provide any assistance.

Both **O'Kell** (Australia) and **Donovan** (New Zealand) stressed the importance of tight tying to prevent distortion of the mesh during the plastering stage. Forcing of the mortar through mesh which is not tightly tied, resulted in an unfair hull, and increased shell thickness where mortar layers were forced apart.

A method of applying netting to a ferro-cement hull was described by an amateur builder from Auckland, New Zealand. This method resulted in an even tightness of mesh all over the hull and saved labour, as application was carried out four layers at a time and fastening took place at each application.

Space was required on the site for a bench made of used ply sheets 1.2 m (4 ft) wide and about 1.2 m (4 ft) longer than the longest length of mesh required, measured vertically from sheer to keel. This bench should be marked off in feet and four rolls of mesh set up at one end above each other on a rack. About 25 mm (1 in) clearance was left between each roll and the rolls staggered over each other by 76 mm (3 in). This staggering of the rolls ensured that as the four layers were pulled out together on to the table there were four 76 mm (3 in) overlaps on each sheet. A template of scrap wood 76 mm (3 in) wide was used to test the amount of overlap along the most even side of the mesh and as adjustments were made the four layers were tied temporarily together with light gauge wire 0.7 mm (22 gauge). Ties were fixed in about four places, one each end and two in-between. The opposite edge of the panel was similarly tied. To assist in hauling out the layers over the bench, two battens were placed one under and one over the layers and lightly nailed together. The battens were moved each time a new length was cut off.

The panel on the bench, cut to length, was prepared by cutting off all selvedge edges except one. This was the "working edge" top selvedge which finished the join of the preceding panel, being the edge to cover, hold and conceal the raw edges of the overlaps of the preceding panels.

The mesh was applied to the hull from the forward end, each panel overlapping in turn. The amount one panel overlapped the next varied but a minimum of 6 mm ($\frac{1}{4}$ in) was required. A typical overlap amidships could be as follows: 38 mm ($1\frac{1}{2}$ in) at sheer line; 19 mm ($\frac{3}{4}$ in) at turn of the bilge; 57 mm ($2\frac{1}{4}$ in) at the keel. With this method of applying mesh, the overlap takes care of any shape required and no cutting to shape was necessary.

The panel was rolled up very loosely from the bottom, tied with wire and hoisted to the sheer. A temporary hook should be in position on the sheer to take the top of the panel which should be secured with a temporary wire tie near the hook.

Rather than hang panels vertically, it was found better to have the keel or bottom end about 46 cm (18 in) further forward than at the sheer, this allowed the selvedge edge to lie off-line with the vertical transverse wires and the frames, thus making it easier to tie. The amount of overlap on the preceding panel is important so the panels should be temporarily tied in about four places as the overlap is adjusted. Panels were fastened from the centre line outward so that they became tight and free from sags and wrinkles, 1.2 mm (18 gauge) tie wire was passed through the mesh by a tool made for the purpose which had a pointed end to open up a way through the mesh. The wire was placed at right angles to the tool engaging a shaped barb rather like a crochet needle in reverse and pushed through by means of a pistol grip handle. The wire then had a U end which was held in position on the inside of the mesh whilst the threading tool was removed. The length still outside was used to twist and position the U inside to pick up the inside layers of mesh, passing over the horixontal rod and out in such a position that it picked up all the outside layers. The wire was cut off long enough to twist up with mole grips and ratchet. The pigtail thus formed was cut off

at a convenient distance, the end turned inward through the open way of the mesh and using a 4 mm ($\frac{5}{32}$ in) hollow-faced nail punch chased right through the mesh into the inside—thus making absolutely certain that the tie ends did not protrude through the plaster. Margins such as around stem, keel and rudder post and transom were phased out so that a similar overlapping occurred. From both sides, layers were cut to match each layer from the other side and, in this way, a neatly formed rounded stem resulted with no more than one extra layer on an overlap.

The same system could be used inside the boat. By placing a four-layer panel temporarily on the outside of the hull, but exactly where it is to go inside, it was possible to shape it exactly for the inside, cutting the mesh to fit around bulkheads and floors, etc., which can be easily followed from outside. The mesh was then twitched to itself whilst in this position. The shaped panel was lowered and loosely rolled, sheer end up and placed inside the sheer end and then released so that it dropped down like wallpaper on the inside. Floor timbers or floor gussets can be covered four layers at a time by cutting a template in thick brown paper, allowing for turnback. Usually it is better to commence with floor gussets, frames, etc., and fill in between with the panels afterwards.

The 4-layer system was devised and first used on a 15 m (49 ft) auxiliary ketch so that the 1.0 m (3 ft) wide panels were not difficult to fasten against the steel framework. For the more complex curves of smaller hull shapes it is, however, not so easy to do this. Darts can be used to overcome some of the problems of pulling a 90 cm (36 in) wide panel against the framework, but in general it is easier to reduce the width of the panel to 50 cm (18 in).

Half panels are made by placing and lightly tying the four selvedge edges together and then hauling out along the table the required length of panel and cutting down the centre to produce two panels 46 cm (18 in) wide. Panel sheets are separated by releasing ties and sliding across each other to form the normal overlap. To assist the sheets to slide over each other and overcome the entanglement of the raw cut edges, place lengths of approximately 15 cm (6 in) widths of plywood, hardboard, or tin between them before sliding them across each other.

Covering web frames or deck beams can be carried out with a series of overlapping sheets with a minimum of waste. A small panel of four sheets is cut widthways across the mesh having sufficient length to cover both sides of the frame and enough extra for a turn-back each side. This small panel is bent into a U shape, formed around the frame and tied in place.

Roberts (New Zealand) said that using the older method of netting for an 11.3 m (37 ft) boat took 1200 hours to set up the frames, put on the stringers, apply the netting to the hull, floors, frames, engine beds, etc., and then tie the hull and plaster it. With the method described it took half this time.

CONSTRUCTION METHODS USING MOULDS

Behnke (USA) discussing the cavity mould method stated that although most ferro-cement builders agreed on the advantages, there was considerable disagreement on the disadvantages of the method. Sutherland, for example, listed worker expertise, very high mould costs and complete standardization as disadvantages of the method. These were contrary to his (Behnke's) experience as he found unskilled labourers could be trained in the process in a few hours. The cost and expertise required to build a mould, furthermore, are virtually the same as building a ferro-cement hull of the same size using conventional techniques. The cavity mould method is, therefore, as well suited for developing nations as industrialized ones. Up to now, three or four identical hulls were required to economically justify the use of a mould. A method has recently been developed, however, to build low-cost moulds that will also make the method suitable for one-off construction.

Walker (Australia) described a male mould method used by his company in the building of small lightweight boats, in which the hull thickness did not exceed 9 mm ($\frac{3}{8}$ in). For larger thicker-hulled vessels this method was not used due to the difficulty of achieving complete penetration. Polythene was first placed over the mould and the mesh stretch-formed into place using a four-part block and tackle at each side of the mesh to exert the necessary tension. The mesh used being the 0.7 mm (22 gauge) hexagonal (chicken wire) type.

With the thin shells, penetration was achieved by forcing the mortar through the mesh with conventional steel trowels following up and consolidating the mortar with vibrating trowels. Plasterers then finished the hull to the required surface and penetration was nearly 100 per cent with perhaps one or two spots to touch up inside.

Richardson (New Zealand) mentioned the problem of joining in bulkheads, engine beds, etc., with a hull constructed on the male mould principle and outlined a way of preventing complete penetration in the way of bulkheads or other such items by laying a 15 cm (6 in) or 30 cm (1 ft) width of polythene on top of the first two layers of mesh so that when plastering was complete, these two layers were not penetrated and could be split and folded back to permit the insertion of bulkhead grounds, precast frames or wooden bulkhead panels. When the item had been inserted, the mesh was folded back onto the bulkhead and plastered giving a continuity of reinforcement with a good bond right through. The application of the male mould method to barge construction in Tonga was described.

Two types of barge hulls were envisaged, one 16.5 × 4.6 × 1.09 m (54 × 15 × 3½ ft) for general cargo and freezer containers. The second 12.8 × 3.48 × 6.9 m (42 × 12½ × 3 ft) for houseboat hulls or other general purpose work. The former to be double ended with the V corrugations extending up the bow and stern, the latter, a conventional rounded bow and flat stern for propulsion, if required.

The type of mould construction used, generally know as the "Cedar Mould Method", was built up by making 14 wooden station frames, mounted upside down on bed "plates" and covered with 75 × 25 mm (3 × 1 in) battens placed longitudinally. Clear plastic sheeting over the mould was followed by 12 layers of wire mesh on 12.2 m (40 ft) and 15 layers on 16.5 m (54 ft) barges using alternate layers of 13 mm (½ in) and 25 mm (1 in) galvanized wire mesh. This type of construction was chosen for two reasons. Firstly, the box-like shape of the barge with straight sides and corrugated bottom, lent itself to easy removal of mould frames, and secondly, six hulls were envisaged as coming off the one set of frames—thus keeeping cost down to a minimum. All the initial building up to the wiring stage was carried out over a period of approximately three months by two local carpenters under European supervision.

Plastering the hull posed some problems as there is nothing but soft coral sand in the Tongan Islands, and very little fresh water and with tools and equipment at a minimum. The problem of sand was overcome by shipping a good hard silicone sand from Fiji. The water problem was more than adequately solved by sinking a well where there was surface seepage and pumping up to 14 ft high header-tanks for pressure.

Plastering the first 54 × 15 ft hull was accomplished by a 05.00 h start and 17 hours of non-stop work with a labour force of 16 unskilled Tongans.

The plastered hull was cured for 28 days being kept damped-down by water spray day and night for 21 days.

During this time, fore and aft combined deck/bulkheads were prefabricated, also side deck/bulkheads. These four were to act as bouyancy tanks in the event of accidental holing. After the turnover of the plastered hull had been effected by the use of 5.5 m (18 ft) high coconut-log gantry frames, chain, blocks and tackles, the inside frames of the hull were stripped out and the prefabricated, water-tight end and side bulkheads fitted. These parts, together with the floor panels were all of ferro-cement construction and all bonded to the hull-shell with cement to make a very strong box-section structure. Heavy hardwood toe-rails and beltings completed this part of the construction.

The barge was fitted out with a 9.1 × 3.7 × 2.1 m (30 × 12 × 7 ft) high, 2-room fibreglass freezing chamber and a 3.7 × 3.0 m (12 × 10 ft) after welldeck, housing the generator and twin compressor units. A galavanized pipe framing was fabricated on top of the freezer to support a canvas awning beneath which the fish were to be processed before being placed in the chamber.

The first 42 × 12½ ft barge was built for a supply storage vessel; mainly diesel fuel for generator motors. It was envisaged as having to stand a great deal of hard work and a very solid strong floor was necessary in the hold. A lightweight concrete of local pumice aggregate was used, to fill the 15 cm (6 in) deep V corrugations, and over this were laid four layers of 13 mm (½ in) mesh followed by 10 cm (4 in) square mesh and another four layers of 13 mm (½ in) mesh, all of which were tied to the concrete slab by wire ties buried in the concrete. This was plastered with a 2–to–1 mix of sand and cement, the resulting sandwich being extremely strong and solid, capable of withstanding the impact of 200-litre (44-gallon) drums of fuel. The hold was finished with conventional wooden hatches and canvas cover. This vessel had a draft of 38 cm (15 in) unladen, rather more than expected—due mainly to an inferior grade of pumice. The watertight flotation bulkheads were built *in situ*, as the handling of prefabricated sections proved to be a problem without suitable lifting equipment.

During plastering, successful penetration of 12 and 15 layers of mesh was achieved by the use of an electric vibrator. The finish was such as to give a glazed surface against polythene sheeting on the inside of the barge.

MIXING AND APPLICATION OF THE MORTAR

Various mixing methods were discussed and the effectiveness of the various types of mechanical mixers commented on.

Fyson (FAO) described the mixing of mortar by hand in an isolated area in a developing country where a suitable mechanical mixer was not available. The sand:cement ratio was reduced to 1.75 from the more usual 2.1 and the water:cement ratio held at 0.4. A plasticizing additive was used and compression tests on the mortar gave a value of 560 kg/cm² at 21 days. Experience with different types of mixers had shown that a satisfactory mix could be obtained with drum mixers provided the rpm was controlled, while paddle mixers gave the best mix of all.

Walker (Australia) agreed that a paddle mixer gave better mixes but added a warning on the necessity for meticulous cleaning of the blades to avoid the possibility of hard lumps falling into later mixes.

Hall (New Zealand) said that paddle mixers used in his area were equipped with rubber belting on the blades which kept the mixer clean. When the rubber wore out it could be simply replaced.

Wells (New Guinea) noted that some drum mixers turned too quickly for satisfactory mixing of a ferro-cement mortar, with a tendency to a centrifugal action keeping the mix to the sides of the bowl instead of dropping and mixing it. Therefore, a mixer in which the rpm could be varied to suit the mix type should be chosen.

Hall (New Zealand) pointed out that if a paddle mixer was not available, the designed water:cement ratio could be maintained by reducing the aggregate slightly. If a drum type mixer was used then the mix should have the aggregate reduced and, in this way, strength permeability and durability could be retained but with higher slump and slightly greater shrinkage due to the reduction in aggregate. He also proposed a method of mixing in which nearly all of the water was put into the mixer and half the sand and all the cement added. This, when mixed, gave a liquid paste to which the remainder of the sand, and finally the last of the water, was added slowly to bring the mix to the correct consistency.

Pama (Thailand) considering the question of which type of mixer to use, remarked that as a designer he was not over-concerned with the type, provided that after 21 days his test specimens gave him the correct compressive strength as designed.

O'Kell (Australia) in discussing the mixing of mortars in tropical conditions suggested that, when the temperature was over 27°C (80°F), ice could be used with advantage in the mixing water to slow down the initial set so that the plasterers could complete the job without having to rush the finishing operation. Crushed or block ice could be used provided that it was completely melted before the mixing operation began. The mesh could also be hosed down thoroughly to clean and cool it off and then allowed to dry before plastering.

Hall (New Zealand) added that there could also be a strength advantage in using ice in mixing water in high temperature areas; the strength of concrete or plaster being affected by the mixing temperature; the lower the mixing temperature the higher the final strength.

Fyson (FAO) suggested that a chemical retarding agent could also be used with advantage in tropical conditions either by itself or in conjunction with ice.

Janes (Australia) asked if a slump test provided a reliable guide to the workability of mortar.

Buckner (Australia) in replying stated that the whole question of workability in mortar and concrete was complicated and the slump test was a very limited test on which to predict workability. There are a number of other methods, for example, the VeBe test, the Kelly Ball test, the Flow Table test, etc. The latter is the most consistent predictor of workability but it is not easily used by the boatbuilder. Probably the most useful method was the practical knowledge of an experienced plasterer who could, by working up the mortar with a trowel, decide when the mix was producing the surface he wanted and he would then have the correct workability.

Eyres (New Zealand) remarked that regulations in New Zealand required a slump test to prevent the plasterer making his job easier, improving penetration by using a very wet mix which would have a low strength figure.

Fyson (FAO) said that a useful way of training plasterers not accustomed to working with ferro-cement type mixes, was to make up trial hull sections, determining the workability necessary to get proper penetration in practice according to the materials available and then using a slump test to check continually on the mix to ensure that it remained consistent. With such a trial section, using the two-shot method, the mortar could be forced through from one side with a supervisor on the other to check penetration. If the mix was too wet there would be a tendency for the mortar to slump away from the reinforcing rods on vertical sections. If too dry, the mesh would divide up the mortar to such an extent that there would be a lack of adhesion with loss of strength. By varying the water:cement ratio on the trial section, it is possible to arrive at the correct workability, verifying the results with compression tests on standard cubes and controlling the consistency with slump tests.

Walker (Australia) said that on small boats built over a male mould, he used a hopper with a pencil vibrator and got good penetration. However, he only used this method on light hulls up to 9 mm (⅜ in) thick and would not like to use the same method for a larger boat with reinforcing rods. For the small boats he had also applied the plaster with a vibrating trowel, adjusting the vibrations per minute and then backing up with a steel trowel and a wooden float to level off. The plaster was allowed to dry considerably before using the steel trowel again; if the steel trowel was used too early it tended to bring the reinforcement to the surface. The hull was finally gone over with a hard sponge float with a slightly dimpled finish which left a roughish surface and gave good paint adhesion.

Fyson (FAO) added that, in addition to pencil vibrators, he had found flat plate vibrators useful. An orbital sander with a plate on the bottom had been used, but best of all were small electrical external vibrators such as those used in the concrete industry to vibrate long beams. Several of these had been used with considerable success in the two-application plastering method. By using these vibrators on the second internal application a good bond was obtained between the inside and the outer layers.

Roberts (New Zealand) described the two-application method of plastering practised by his Association. Plasterers worked on the outside of the hull with supervisors inside the boat checking on penetration. The aim was to get penetration to 75 per cent of the thickness. At this stage, the interior plaster was not touched because they had found that, if they tried to smooth it off in any way, air bubbles or voids were formed, which would not come out. After the plaster had cured for a couple of days, a light man was sent in to carefully knock-off with a trowel any pieces of plaster that had penetrated too far into the hull. These pieces were left until the boat was fully cured and then removed with a vacuum cleaner. The second coat of mortar was applied after 10 to 14 days of curing. A very liquid grout was splashed into the cavities with a whitewash brush. About two gallons of this grout was required per foot length of a 40-ft boat. This was allowed to stand for a time so that the excess moisture could dissipate, some of it soaking into the previous coat, some of it evaporating. The internal layer of mortar was then vibrated into place with an orbital sander.

Wheeler (New Zealand) described the mortar application used in his company's construction of 12.2 m (40 ft) yachts built upside down following the sandwich construction method. A heavy duty orbital sander with a plate on the bottom was used as a vibrator. They used vibrators working at different speeds as they found that in some areas a high-speed vibrator giving a lighter action was required, while for thicker areas a slower speed geared-down version forced the mortar through better. In application, the mortar was simply shovelled on to the hull and spread with the vibrators.

Wooden floats were then used and battens about 2.4 m (8 ft) long faired the hull in the fore and aft direction. Thinner, lighter battens were used in the transverse direction for checking the shape and cutting off or adding on where required. The hull was finally sponged using long sponges backed by boards which gave a fairly coarse texture to the surface for good paint adhesion. After the mould was turned over and the jig removed, a pencil vibrator was used to fill the heavily reinforced sections of the keel. The hull sides were filled internally with the orbital type vibrator.

Richardson (New Zealand) mentioned the use of similar plate vibrators on a male wooden mould. He had had trouble on the sides of the hulls but had obtained penetration through the extra layers of mesh by throwing the mortar through the reinforcement.

Roberts (New Zealand) said that his Association had also tried throwing the mortar through the mesh and had encountered a serious problem, the bigger particles of sand and aggregate were heavier than the smaller lighter grains, and they had found that on the inside they had almost pure sand and on the outside almost pure cement.

Wells (New Guinea) mentioned the problem of obtaining correct cover over the mesh when using inexperienced labour. He had overcome this by using a tyler's trowel, one side of which had a serrated edge. When sufficient mortar had been forced through the armature the trowel was turned on edge and swept across the reinforcement. Depending on the depth of the serration on the edge of the trowel, a build-up of 3 to 6 mm ($\frac{1}{8}$ to $\frac{1}{4}$ in) was obtained with a series of valleys cut by the serration. This gave a very even distribution of mortar on top of the mesh and when the surface was then finished with a wooden float, it was possible to obtain a very even cover.

Rossiter and **Perry** (Australia) described the application of mortar under pressure. The application of mortar to the membrane of reinforcement was one of the most critical operations in the manufacture of ferro-cement. In hand-compacted methods the builder must rely on the skill of a large workforce. A number of attempts had been made to use gunite or other spray equipment, but these had not generally been successful, due to problems associated with rebound from the reinforcement and the provision of backing forms. These problems had been overcome through the development of a pumping technique which transported the mortar to the hull and used the pump pressure to squeeze it through the reinforcement. The nozzle was held in contact with the mesh and the pump had been geared so that the operator at the nozzle could traverse the hull in approximately 7.5 cm (3 in) wide sweeps, maintaining full control of penetration. The hoses were 3.8 cm (1$\frac{1}{2}$ in) diameter glass reinforced plastic and light enough even when full of mortar to be readily handled by the operator with one assistant. It had been found that two skilled nozzle operators working in turn could apply the material to a 15-m (50-ft) hull in approximatley 5 to 6 hours.

This method of application had the advantages of:

(a) Obtaining satisfactory penetration without hard manual work, giving a reduction in fatigue of the work force.
(b) Reducing the man-hours in applying the mortar, and the number of men working inside the hull.
(c) Using only skilled labour in the application of the mortar.
(d) Providing a better control over the concreting process, in that, because the placing of mortar was rapid, it could be stopped for periods if necessary without extending the overall plastering time.

Behnke (USA) had made some tests on spraying mortar and had experiences similar to those reported by Roberts in throwing the mortar against the mesh. There was a definite separation and the process was discontinued. Since then, he had applied the mortar coat first and pushed the mesh reinforcing into the wet mortar.

O'Kell (Australia) loaded the mortar onto the mesh from the outside of hulls which were built upside down, spread it out by trowelling and then used steel scrubbing brushes to force the mortar through the mesh.

Hall (New Zealand) remarked that cement technologists agreed that vibrators should be used to compact rather than to make the concrete or mortar flow. The objection to using a vibrator to make the plaster flow was that it could cause segregation within the mix.

Walker (Australia), referring to Perry's comments about the application of mortar using a pump, said that he had used a similar method with simple nozzles with the same surface area as the 3.8 cm (1$\frac{1}{2}$ in) diameter hoses coming from the pump. This had been successful but he had found that it was not possible to go below a certain water content without clogging up the first foot of hose. There was a lot of wastage and two or three people were needed to collect the droppage and take it back to the pump for recirculation.

Perry (Australia) considered that Walker's problem of wastage could have been overcome if the gearing of the pump had been altered. He had experimented with pump gearings and had been able to get good penetration with very little drop-off. Problem areas were along the frames, either pipe or truss type. In areas where access could only be obtained from one side he still used vibrators to obtain penetration. Apart from this he had found the pump successful in reducing the hard work involved in applying the mortar and enabled them to leave the application of mortar to two skilled pump operators with one supervisor on the other side of the hull. He used a water:cement ratio of approximately 0.4 with well graded sand and a small amount of plasticizing additives.

CURING

Hall (New Zealand) in pointing out the need for adequate curing of ferro-cement hulls said that the main object was to prevent loss of the original mixing water. Provided that mixing water was retained over a 28-day period complete hydration should be assured. The curing water, fog spray, steam curing or the chemical use of membrane compounds were merely to offset the loss of water due to the evaporating processes. He also suggested that, in the future, carbon dioxide curing might well be practical probably in conjunction with steam.

Walker (Australia) said that his company used water curing and felt that the more water that could be passed over or through the boat, the more watertight the hull after curing. They put hessian completely over the boat right down to the ground and soaked the hessian to keep the hull glistening wet.

Bowen (New Zealand) remarked that problems had occurred in some cases where water curing had been used, due to slipping of the foundations caused by large amounts of run-off water and he asked whether a recirculation system had been tried instead of a continual supply of fresh water.

Roberts (New Zealand) said that it was his Association's practice to leave a hole in the bottom of the boat from which the water drained back into a receptacle. The rate of flow was regulated. As water rose in the container, a float switch was activated, adjusted so that spraying could be continued for periods of $\frac{1}{2}$ min, 1 min or longer as necessary. At night, for example, only one spray might be needed every three or four hours, but during the middle of a hot day it might be necessary to set the spray for a 1 minute period in every ten.

Carkeek (New Zealand) observed that it can take thousands of gallons of water to cure a hull if the curing water was allowed to drain away on the ground, not to mention the problems that the drainage could create on an open site. For curing boats, his company placed a galavanized tray made up in overlapping sections under keel. This was sloped so that the water ran down into a sump where an electrical or petrol operated pump returned the water through a perforated hose on the gunwhale of the boat. In each recirculation the water passed through a filter to remove any sand. To replace lost water, a simple ballcock valve was used with just enough pressure to maintain the water level in a reservoir. By these means they were able to cure a boat with only 50 to 60 gallons of water.

Wells (New Guinea) used steam curing and wished to know how long one should wait after the initial set before beginning curing.

Hall (New Zealand) said that provided steam curing commenced before there was a heavy loss of water, the time delay was not important. In general, concrete product manufacturers used steam curing and to cut down loss of time they began a cure as soon as possible after the initial set. It had been found that a delay of about four hours was necessary, principally because the humidity, which is part of the steam curing, could possibly cause slumping of their products if curing was begun earlier.

Moar (New Zealand) considered it preferable to start curing within four hours after the last mix had been made and increase the temperature gradually to avoid cracking, after which the curing should be continued until the hull was as strong as required and then the temperature reduced slowly back to air temperature. He considered the normal duration of the cure would be about 12 hours. With a ferro-cement hull one should still water cure for a further three days after steam curing,

O'Loughlin (New Zealand) agreed with Moar that it was important to avoid rapid changes in temperature and considered that the time required for steam curing should be of the order of 800–1,000 degree-hours (this referred to degrees centigrade).

Moar (New Zealand) in answer to a question about costs of steam curing said that a suitable plant could cost about NZ$ 8000. Running costs would include employment of a boilerman plus 50–100 gal of diesel oil fuel per boat. The economic viability would naturally depend on the number of times the plant was used per month.

Walker (Australia) asked whether water curing would, in fact, result in a better hull than steam curing.

Perry (Australia) said that some references indicated that steam curing reduced shrinkage while others claimed an increase in shrinkage. The Australian code of practice for prestressed concrete required an additional allowance for shrinkage when steam curing was used.

Kidson (New Zealand) asked about the possibility of using non-shrinkage additives in the mix and what effect they would have on the bond between mortar and reinforcement.

Moar (New Zealand) said that his company was using such additives in their present mix and considered them useful provided they were used only to inhibit shrinkage and not to such an extent as to start chemically stressing the boat. There was a certain stage at which expansion could cause loss of bond and the aim should be limited to the stopping of shrinkage. Chemical prestressing experiments had been carried out in various countries, particularly in the USSR and the USA, but knowledge of the subject was, as yet, limited.

Ellen (Australaia) said that his experience with expanding cements in ferro-cement construction had not been favourable and agreed that only small dosages of such additives should be used. He considered the principal method of controlling shrinkage was to stop moisture evaporating from the mortar and this was perhaps best done by wax emulsions and acrylics.

Hunt (New Zealand) asked what was likely to happen to the nature of the cured mortar in its final properties if wax or acrylic emulsions were added and how they would affect the painting of the cured hull.

Ellen (Australia) agreed that wax emulsions could affect painting if they were left as a skin on the surface. Sand blasting was the best method of removing them for painting and this had been common practice for many years in the building industry for wall panels and thin concrete sections.

Moar (New Zealand) considered that membrane curing was a second-rate method and only to be used if no other was available. He felt there was too much surface area to stop water loss. There was also a risk of cracking and considerable problems later with the painting of the hull.

Walker (Australia) said that he used membrane curing in only one area of the hull and that was when pouring a ballast keel as it was inconvenient to water cure. Two coats of chlorinated rubber were used to reduce moisture loss.

O'Kell (Australia) pointed out that in addition to the curing methods discussed, the hull should be weather cured to an equilibrium moisture content before painting, otherwise escaping moisture could lift the paint film.

VOIDS AND GROUTING

Bowen (New Zealand) remarked that problems had been encountered in some cases with corrosion of reinforcement due to voids in the hull. These voids were the result of insufficient compaction of the mortar and poor plastering techniques. In New Zealand, ways had been devised to eliminate the problem by improved plastering techniques and the use of a locally designed hand grout pump. Plastering was usually now carried out by what was known as the "two-shot" or "double-application" method which resulted in a generally void-free hull. The only problems being in the vicinity of frames, keel and stems where grouting had been successfully used. Some controversy had been generated on the advisability of grouting boats. One school of though considered that mortar could be forced off the hull by the application of a grout under pressure, but this did not appear to have been borne out in practice. There had, however, been a safety problem, as one man had lost the sight of an eye for 18 months due to grout under pressure impacting into his face.

Fyson (FAO) confirmed the finding of voids, even in carefully plastered hulls and agreed that the major problem was in thickened areas such as around the stem, stern post and bottom of the keel. Care should be taken to avoid excessive mesh

175

build-up around the stem and keel as this would cause difficulties with penetration and result in voids. The judicious use of pencil and flat plate vibrators in such areas was important to ensure proper penetration. Voids could be located by sounding the hull with a hammer. The difference in sound between a fully compacted area of mortar and an area containing a void was easily recognized with practice and could be marked out with chalk. To fill these voids, 6 mm ($\frac{1}{4}$ in) holes could be drilled to a depth of three quarters of the hull thickness at 20 to 30 cm (8 to 12 in) centres in the area of a void. Depth of hole could be controlled by using a block of wood on the drill bit as a stop. When drilling, it was possible to feel when the drill entered a void. If the drill hit a reinforcing stringer (which would be recognized by the increased resistance) the drill should be withdrawn and a new hole started. Partly drilled holes could be plugged with epoxy mortar. A suitable grout was made up of cement and water mixed to the consistency of porridge. The cement should first be passed through a fine sieve to remove lumps and in order to facilitate mixing a suitable wetting agent should be added, in the proportion of 1 per cent by weight of cement. When mixed, the grout could be thinned for injection. A suitable consistency could best be arrived at by trials with the pump, the grout should be thin enough to penetrate the void but not so liquid that there was a tendency to flow back through the entrance hole after the nozzle was removed. Hand pumps suitable for injection of grout could be found in the construction industry where they were in use for the grouting of prestressing cables. Alternatively, a pump could be made up on a similar principle to that used in New Zealand.

Donovan (New Zealand) mentioned a method of locating voids by rolling an iron bar across the hull, a void being indicated by a change in the ringing tone produced by the bar. Some investigation was also being carried out on the possibility of ultrasonic location of voids. Another problem, which he believed was due to voids, was blistering of the paint layers on a ferro-cement hull. He had discussed the question with paint manufacturers and suppliers and had come to the conclusion that blisters frequently occurred in areas where there were voids.

Carkeek (New Zealand) added that he had also been concerned with the problem of blistering paintwork and had noticed that when broken, such blisters were usually found to contain water. On testing, he had discovered this water to be free of salt which would indicate that this was fresh water that had come from the mortar layer and not sea water that had penetrated the paint surface.

It was agreed that further investigation should be made into the problems of voids and the penetration of moisture causing blistering of paint.

PAINTING AND COATING SYSTEMS

Hunt (New Zealand) said that Pavey's paper advocated the use of hydrochloric acid etching. Although this was used extensively for massive concrete, it had been found in New Zealand that in ferro-cement with steel very near the surface it was extremely unwise, due to corrosion of the steel and the difficulty of removing the products of attack. The corrosive effect of calcium chloride left on the surface could be extremely serious. Phosphoric acid was safer since any residue was insoluble calcium phosphate. He could see little point in following an etching of hydrochloric acid by a phosphoric acid treatment.

The paper discussed requirements for successful coating in detail but dismissed the advantages of epoxy coatings in a few words. He agreed that recoating with epoxies was not as easy as with a permanently solvent sensitive vinyl resin system but the latter had disadvantages also. Vinyl resins generally tend to suffer from poor adhesion and to bond satisfactorily to concrete they have to be considerably modified as Pavey indicated, was the case with his primer system. Vinyl coatings are all low in solids so film build-up is also low. On such a rough surface as a plastered hull, many more coats would be required. Another point was in the recommendation of a vinyl mastic filler which he considered was a contradiction in terms. A filler needs to be a material with maximum active solids content and minimum solvents—in other words, minimum possibilities of shrinkage due to loss of solvent and minimum loss of time during the period when a solvent slowly evaporates from an applied film. With a vinyl mastic filler the period is relatively long and should a second application be needed the very fact that vinyls are easily recoated means that they remain permanently solvent sensitive. Therefore, the first sanded down coat of filler would be softened by the second application.

He agreed with Pavey in recommending that the internal coating should be capable of transmitting water vapour, but was surprised that a vinyl primer previously stated as being impervious to water, was recommended as the first coating. It was suggested that a latex paint should be applied over the primer. He disagreed because latex was a material which softened in wet conditions even if it were a so-called 100 per cent acrylic, and this would cause failure of the coating in areas in contact with bilge water. He felt that too strong a case had been made against epoxies from the point of view of critical recoating time, toxity, etc. Properly handled and applied, epoxies could quite safely be used and people were now accustomed to the use of two-pot materials. Epoxies had inherently good adhesion to concrete, there was no problem from alkalinity and they could be made into filling and fairing compounds which contained 100 per cent solids, could be relied upon not to shrink and not to be affected by anything applied over them.

Worsnop (Australia) agreed that epoxies were entirely suitable where conditions were well controlled, particularly in a commercial operation but said that the purpose of the coating system recommended in Pavey's paper was to find a simpler system which could be used by people not familiar with two-pot materials. The coating devised had been used on about 30 ferro-cement boats without problems. The vinyl system had been well proven over the last 30 years and some of the largest ships in the world had virtually the same coating system. He could not agree that exposed steel was an unlikely occurrence as had been suggested. Many owner-built and some professional boats did have steel on or near the surface. For this reason, anti-corrosive pigments had been included in the primer and any proposed coating system should take this into account. The vinyls proposed had certainly been considerably modified and, in fact, contained natural rubber and epoxy materials. The system had been developed about 30 years ago and extensively used in the marine field. The vinyl mastic filler suggested was intended only to fill the surface roughness of the ferro-cement and was not intended as a fairing filler. If a filler was required for fairing, he would recommend using a solvent for epoxy which was compatible with this coating system. The filler should be applied between two coats of primer. It was correct to say that vinyls were softened by following coats but this did not effect the form or shape of the underlying vinyl. Regarding the internal coating system, the primer itself was not impervious so that even with two coats on the interior surface, it was still porous. On the hull exterior, it was the primer plus the vinyl finishing coats together which provided an impervious coating.

Hall (New Zealand) said that cement contains dicalcium silicate and if this was mixed with 70 per cent of its own weight of water, it would achieve 80 per cent of its strength in four years. The cement in the mix, therefore, must be considered as being chemically active long after a boat was painted and in the water. If this chemically active material was on the surface then surely it must have some effect on paint. Acid etching bares the sand in the mix and hence protective coatings go on a chemically inert surface rather than on a chemically active element. This was one of the main reasons for using acid etching. In connexion with adhesion of paint he raised the question of alkali-active aggregates. In some parts of New Zealand, for instance, the local aggregate had a high alkali content so that, in these areas, low alkali cements were specified for concrete work. If low alkali cement was used it kept the alkali content of the mortar down to an acceptable level. If, however, an alkali reactive sand and a cement other than the low alkali type were used, problems of paint adhesion could occur.

Moar (New Zealand) said that he had done some research on bonding concrete with epoxies and had found that one should never acid etch concrete before using epoxies because the resultant bond was not as good. Apparently the acid tended to stay in the interstices of the concrete thus causing an inferior bond. He doubted whether hydrochloric etching should be used in conjunction with epoxy resins. He had also discovered that, by applying the right type of epoxy curing agent while the concrete was green, a far more durable bond could be obtained.

FITTING OUT OF FERRO-CEMENT HULLS

Janes (Australia) considered it desirable to reduce the number of through-bolts required in a ferro-cement hull to a minimum, nevertheless, rubbing strakes, skin fittings, chain plates, etc., still required through-bolting. He asked how leakage and corrosion problems could be overcome when fitting these bolts.

Carkeek (New Zealand) said that in his company it was standard practice to cut a hole through the hull larger than the fitting and line this hole with epoxy mortar to bring it down to the size of the fitting, thus isolating it from the reinforcement. They also used a fairly large backing plate under the nut to spread the load.

Fyson (FAO) in fishing boat construction in developing countries, had used inserts of plastic pipe through holes in the hull with galvanized iron bolts which were a close fit in the plastic. A large flat plate washer was used as backing and the fitting was well bedded in mastic. When the nut was taken up, the plastic swelled slightly making a tight fit in the hole. The result being that the bolt was isolated from the hull reinforcement and no leakage could occur.

O'Kell (Australia) said that his practice when installing skin fittings had been to weld perimeter rods to the longitudinal reinforcing and wrap the mesh around these. Flanged skin fittings were then bolted straight through the ferro-cement and no problems had been encountered. Recent regulations in Australia required round flanges of 25×13 mm ($1 \times \frac{1}{2}$ in), steel drawn, tapped and then inserted and welded into the reinforcing. He considered this an expensive and unnecessary complication.

Watkins (Australia) said that compensation on openings was a strength requirement covered by a mathematical formula. However, such compensation was not required on skin fittings with a hole diameter of 50 mm (2 in) or less. O'Kell had mentioned the problem of excessive point loading by having to run a rigid pipe system to a predetermined opening in the hull. With fishing vessels it was possible to incorporate a short length of approved flexible material in the suction and discharge lines.

Walker (Australia) referring to the fitting of chain plates in yachts, said he used strips of stainless steel fitted to the hull internally, set in epoxy concrete and through-bolted with bolts countersunk into the top sides. In answer to a question about the use of stainless steel embedded in cement and subject to saline conditions, he confirmed that he had had no problems probably because the epoxy concrete in which the bolts had been set, sealed them against such a reaction. He did point out, however, that if stainless steel was used for chain plates, then rigging screws, shackles, etc., should also be of the same material to avoid electrolysis.

Donovan (New Zealand) had experienced difficulties with stainless steel embedded in ferro-cement and had since used galvanized mild steel bolts and galvanized iron fittings, setting them in a polysulphide mastic or in epoxy mortar with no corrosion problems. Discussing bulkheads and their installation, he said that various methods had been used to reinforce and plaster ferro-cement bulkheads. Wooden bulkheads were also frequently used where weight was an important factor. He pointed out that the force on a bulkhead tended to be in the fore and aft direction rather than athwartships, and stiffening and strengthening the bulkheads was necessary to prevent collapse under water pressure. He did not consider that boats under 12.2 m (40 ft) in length needed bulkheads, at least not ferro-cement ones, as they were generally too heavy. In this case, he used timber or heavy plywood with a hinged tab system with fairly long legs for fastening the bulkhead into the hull. The tabs were tied into the structure and there was no actual movement after the boat was plastered. The hinge could move independently of the rods in the hull reinforcement. Such bulkheads could be made watertight by using silicone rubber or polysulphide mastics. For ferro-cement bulkheads in larger boats he left starters in the hull and made up the bulkheads after plastering with welded square mesh and expanded metal on either side. He also incorporated stiffeners as the flat panels would not stand up to the weight of water pressure, should a section of the hull become flooded.

Walker (Australia) described the various systems used by his company to fit bulkheads. For smaller lighter boats they prefabricated plywood bulkheads on trestles with all cross reinforcement in, varnished trim fitted and the bulkheads painted and completely finished before installation. About 20 mm ($\frac{3}{4}$ in) around the edge was left unpainted and the bulkhead was simply filleted into the hull with an epoxy concrete which contained sand and no-sag fillers in the mix. No screws, bolts or any other fastenings were used to fix the bulkheads into the boats and they had had no problems with this method. In building larger boats, such as fishing vessels, they would normally use ferro-cement bulkheads and decks. Stiffening frames and floors would also be used and the backbone run right through as a girder tapered off into the hull following through the stem. Like Donovan, he felt that the spaces in the boat should be as large as possible so that the plasterer could get in to work. Many designs had been based on wooden boats which were restricted by timber size to a maximum of, say, 30 cm (12 in) keel width. His keels were usually three times this and tapered off fore and aft so that, although the ballast was 300 lb per ft^3 instead of, say, 730 lb per ft^3 for lead, the centre of gravity was lower than that of the lead keel boat. Extra displacement could go in ballast or extra water or fuel. The engine could be put lower down and, therefore, more usable space was available in the hull.

Boden (Australia) pointed out that licensing authorities in Australia were very concerned about watertight subdivision of fishing vessels or vessels carrying passengers commercially. This meant, in general, that at least four bulkheads were required, or perhaps three on small vessels, one being a collision bulkhead at about 5 per cent of the length from the forward perpendicular, one forward and one aft of the engine-room and one at the stern. These bulkheads should be strong enough to withstand water pressure should any of the compartments be broached. He felt that a considerable amount of the development work in ferro-cement had been done by yacht and small-boat builders where bulkheads had been of lesser importance. It should be realized that, in larger boats and for commercial use, suitably stiffened and strengthened bulkheads were most necessary.

Anderson (New Zealand) said that regulations in New Zealand required only a collision bulkhead below 15 m (50 ft) and below 9 m (30 ft), these were not mandatory. Above 15 m (50 ft) bulkheads were also required fore and aft of the engine-room.

Behnke (USA) said that he had begun by fabricating ferro-cement bulkheads which were intended to be tied into the hull, but they had proved to be too heavy, so plywood bulkheads were used instead. These were fitted into the hull using fibreglass and an epoxy cement. They had been tested by filling several compartments on the vessel with water and no leakage had occurred.

Wheeler (New Zealand) mentioned the sandwich construction his company was using for the building of 12.2 m (40 ft) yacht hulls in which bulkhead grounds were cast into the actual structure. Floors were not used but the area where the lead keel was bolted on was thickened and heavily reinforced. This reinforcement was carried up the side of the hull for quite a distance.

Norris (Canada) discussing the fitting of starter rods for bulkheads, suggested that the leg lengths of the rods wired into the longitudinals should be varied in length to avoid the tendency to get a line down the ends of the starter rods. If leg lengths were varied from 10 to 30 cm (4 to 12 in) in 5 cm (2 in) increments, they formed an undulating curve which was much less likely to cause cracking.

Fyson (FAO) was not enthusiastic about the use of starter rods for internal fittings because these rods tended to be disturbed during the plastering operation, leaving small voids along the rods which could allow moisture penetration. He considered that web frames incorported into the structure provided better fastening points for internal fittings.

O'Kell (Australia) disagreed saying that, in the method he used, the starters were fixed and wired to the longitudinal rods. As plastering was mostly done from outside, the starters were not disturbed.

Boden (Australia) referring to a previous discussion on painting of ferro-cement hulls and the suggestion that internal coatings should be porous to permit the escape of moisture, asked what precaution should be taken when coating the inside of a tank or fishhold with an impervious material.

Eyres (New Zealand) said that certain local builders were in favour of an air gap in a fishhold between the insulation and the hull for this very reason.

Wells (New Guinea) raised the point that, with fish held in a hold for some time, the drainage of digestive juices and body acids could attack concrete even more than diesel oil, and he considered it essential to keep the fishhold bilges pumped clean.

Fyson (FAO) had used plastered fishholds with styrofoam insulation and had applied a thick layer of a bituminous coating on the hull before fitting the foam without encountering problems with paint blistering. Sump wells were provided to allow the melt water and fish juices to be washed down and pumped out. A good coating of white epoxy paint on the interior of the plaster made for a hard, easily cleaned surface resistant to fish juices.

COSTS OF CONSTRUCTION

Behnke (USA) complimenting Gulbrandsen on his paper, said that one point made concerned the cost of the hull which was given as of the order of 15–20 per cent of the total cost of a fishing vessel. A previous paper (Traung and Gulbrandsen 1968) provided a table which gave the average distribution of total expenditure of 102 Canadian vessels, broken down into percentages between maintenance and repair, other operating expenses, fixed charges, crew share, etc., The conclusions suggested that, reducing the crew by one, might result in more saving than a large reduction in initial hull cost. In developing countries, labour costs were lower so this relationship might not be the same. He would like to have some data that gave a cost breakdown for typical developing countries together with percentage costs of the hull annually in comparison with those of an industrialized country.

Gulbrandsen (FAO) said that it was difficult to compare costs from one area to another. For instance, one would probably find in a developing country that machinery and equipment were relatively more expensive than the hull, so that the cost of the hull in porportion to the total cost would go down when compared with that of an industrialized country. He would also like to have the type of operational cost breakdown requested by Behnke, but sufficient data were not yet available. Amplifying his paper, he said that Fig. 3 gave the weight of a shell based on specific requirements outlined in various scantling rules. For example, for fibreglass the figure referred to Lloyds scantling rules, while for wood he had selected that outlined in an Indian trade journal. Steel was based on scantlings for steelboats on the west coast of Canada and ferro-cement on the New Zealand Marine Department provisional requirements. As these scantlings might change, however, he had provided in Table 1 a method to calculate the basic shell weight, based on the actual materials utilized.

Hermanson (Norway) considered that ferro-cement lent itself very well to use in developing countries because of the labour intensive factor. Even with double the man-hours, it was still cheaper to build boats in such countries rather than to import them.

Fyson (FAO) gave costs for a 16-m (52 ft) fishing boat built in Thailand, in which material costs per square metre came to approximately US$13.18 (US$1.14 per ft²). Construction time for the ferro-cement hull, decks and bulkheads was about 22 man-hours per square metre (2 man-hours per ft²). He compared these costs with those quoted by Noble for a 16-m (52-ft) ferro-cement fishing boat built on the Pacific Coast of North America, which gave a comparable figure for material costs of about US$12.64 per square metre (US$1.17 per ft²).

Reid (New Zealand) compared costs in New Zealand for his own company's 12.2 m (40 ft) ferro-cement hull at under NZ$ 3000 without decks and keel to that of a wooden hull at the same stage costing over NZ$4500 and a steel hull more than NZ$6000. In fibreglass the price probably, would be just under NZ$5000.

Brekveldt (New Zealand) found it difficult costwise to justify commercially built ferro-cement boats. He used an approximate rule in steel fishing boat construction which allowed one third of the total cost for hull, deck, wheelhouse, bulkheads, tanks, engine beds, mast, etc., another third for machinery and engineering items and the last third for outfitting including winch, fishhold installation and refrigeration. If decks, wheelhouse, tanks, etc., were not built in ferro-cement, an appropriate allowance would have to be made when calculating costs in this material. The value of the hull relative to the total cost might, therefore, end up at about 20 per cent. If this was the case, he could not see any great cost saving in building in ferro-cement.

Behnke (USA) felt that insufficient information was available on costs of fishing boat construction and operation to justify selecting ferro-cement over other boatbuilding materials without careful analysis. A study of the operational requirements, enviromental factors, and the availability of labour and raw materials should all be considered before a project is started. Because of the high interest rates prevalent in many developing countries, the cost of capital should also be considered. Although a 90 per cent reduction in the manhours required to build a ferro-cement boat using the cavity mould method may not seem particularly important in developing countries where labour rates are low, the savings can be very significant over the life of the vessel if the interest rates are high.

Moar (Rapporteur) in summing up the discussion said that somebody had enquired as to how big one could go with ferro-cement boats. He considered that if some reinforced concrete was used in the interior and prestressing was allowed, it should be possible to have ferro-cement boats built to a size comparable to the largest tankers today. It was interesting to note that there was a ferro-cement submarine container being designed to transport liquefied natural gas. Ferro-cement boats would get bigger and bigger and there was no reason why the material should not equal steel in size and capacity. The tendency would be for application of prestressed concrete in combination with ferro-cement and the vessels would probably be submarines because of the natural advantages the material presents in this field. He felt that ferro-cement development was just beginning.

There was evidence of a divergence of opinion on many points, with Behnke disagreeing with Sutherland on moulding costs and the disadvantages of the cavity mould process. Behnke also suggested that developing countries should approach ferro-cement boatbuilding cautiously and be wary of salesmen from ferro-cement companies and amateur ferro-cement enthusiasts whose recommendations may not be unbiased. Hunt was not in favour of using hydrochloric acid for etching of ferro-cement boats, and it was generally agreed that there was a lot to be done on working out a suitable painting system for ferro-cement. Various methods of fitting frames and bulkheads were proposed; this could be done by precasting, casting with the hull, casting after the hull was completed using starter bars, or by bonding timber or steel frames or bulkheads into place using fibreglass and epoxy compounds. Mortar mixing, plastering and fairing techniques were extensively discussed. The most favoured method was to mix the mortar in a paddle mixer, apply it by a two-stage method using vibrating orbital trowels for the second stage. An excellent suggestion was the use of a serrated edged trowel in order to achieve a uniform cover over the steel. Behnke suggested that steel rods were not an essential component in the reinforcing of ferro-cement hulls, the need for their use depending more on the construction method adopted. It was generally agreed that large rods should be avoided, small rods should be well covered with mesh and all changes in steel quantities should be phased over a large area to avoid stress concentration. Agreement on the need for proper curing was registered, using either steam or water. Tamura suggested a combination of a very high temperature and pressure to assist in producing a new form of extra-strong concrete. The cost of ferro-cement boats was generally considered to be favourable, though the advantage was reduced by restricting the ferro-cement content in the total structure to the bare hull. It was agreed that in some countries ferro-cement boats could be built indigenously, while boats of other materials would have to be imported at a much higher cost involving greater expenditure of foreign exchange.

Part IV—SERVICE EXPERIENCE

Survey of Ferro-Cement Fishing Boats Built in New Zealand   D J Eyres

It is mandatory for any fishing boat built in New Zealand to be surveyed by the New Zealand Marine Department if its registered length is 10.67 m or greater. Further, at the time of writing plans and specifications of fishing boats at 6.09 m or greater registered length, are required to be approved by the department before building may commence. All of these boats are built under survey and those of 10.67 m and greater registered length are also inspected annually.

The Department became involved in ferro-cement boats for the first time in 1964 when the construction of two fishing boats of sufficient length to fall within the department's jurisdiction was commenced. A number of yachts had already been build in this medium and, having some success, it was natural that ferro-cement would be tried in commercial craft. Neither the builders nor the department at that time had any clear guidelines to work to and with one of these craft close liaison was maintained between the builder and department's staff and each problem discussed as the work progressed.

Since that date, ferro-cement fishing boats have been built spasmodically, a number of them being built professionally by contractors experienced in concrete technology. These contractors usually adopt quality control procedures and construction was under the supervision of a Registered Engineer whose certification was accepted by the Department as evidence of satisfactory construction in respect of the hull. However, the contractor and engineer often had little experience of boat-building practice and although familiar with concrete technology, were nevertheless finding their way with respect to the application of ferro-cement to boats.

A large number of amateur yachtsmen were building ferro-cement boats themselves from stock plans and by early 1969 an increasing number of approvals were being sought by fishermen to build their own boats in this medium from modifications of the same stock plans. The Department, having already drawn up requirements for wood and steel fishing boats, considered it necessary at this time to prepare similar requirements for ferro-cement fishing boats. It was fortunate that a code of practice for the construction of ferro-cement boats had already been issued by Lloyd's Register of Shipping. Taking this as a basis, the Department attempted to expand the code of practice in the light of our experience and observations at survey of boats coming under our jurisdiction and to be more definitive about the actual construction. This did not prove an easy task; being a new medium there was much experimenting with different techniques and widely differing opinions held about the merits of these techniques. As more boats were built and the performance of those in service and those which failed were examined, the requirements which are quoted on page 105 of this book, were established.

CONSTRUCTION REQUIREMENTS

Building and workmanship

The site of construction is required by the department to be acceptable to a surveyor as being compatible with good boat-building and ferro-cement practice and this does not preclude the amateur builder. Professionally-built boats are as a rule constructed under cover in permanent buildings with various facilities at hand.

Most ferro-cement boats built by amateurs in New Zealand are constructed under temporary roofed building frames. This is particularly true of the large number built in the North Island, where year-round climatic conditions are suitable. The building frame is strong enough to support some of the weight of the plastered hull—more than one suspended hull has collapsed under the weight of newly-applied plaster.

All the boats which the department has surveyed to date have been built upright, using the "suspended hull method". To obtain the hull form, use is made of removable wood frames, fabricated wire rod frames or pipe frames which may be retained or cut out after plastering. The fabricated frames or removable wood frames prepared by an experienced boat-builder appear to be the most popular.

Various hulls have been built in New Zealand on moulds which would be economically justifiable for a production run of standard boats. The author has inspected one boat built on a solid wood male mould, sometimes referred to as a "cedar mould" and found, after the boat was plastered, had been turned and the mould stripped out, that it was possible to sit inside and watch what was going on outside, due to the lack of any penetration of the mortar over large areas. This would seem to bear out the experience of builders using this method in the North-West of the USA where Benford (1971) claims the method has died a natural death. Attempts have been made in New Zealand to lay up hulls in solid metal female moulds without any success, due mainly to the problems of removing the hull from the mould. The department would be unlikely to accept either method for a surveyed boat.

The development of a sandwich form of construction is reported by Moar (1972) and this utilizes a jig-and-wood-batten-type mould. No surveyed boats have been constructed to date using this principle and the department would have to make a thorough examination before approving any fishing boats in this form.

MATERIALS

Steel: Mild-steel hard-drawn wire stringers are usually used for reinforcement but high-tensile steel wires have also been used and may give a fairer curve when laid around the framing. The mesh, which is laid inside and outside of this reinforcement, is often 0.711-mm or 1.016-mm galvanized wire netting with a 13-mm or 19-mm hexagonal or square mesh. Welded square mesh has also been used, the number of layers of mesh in each case being dependent on the wire size. A new patented mesh is now available in New Zealand and is reported on by Moar (1972). This mesh may be used without wire stringers but has not been evaluated in a surveyed boat by the Department.

Cement: Ordinary Portland cement only is used in New Zealand for boat-building mortar.

Water: The department's requirements call for fresh water only to be used.

Aggregates: It is very important that a good-quality aggregate be used and this is obtained in New Zealand from river shingle, free from deleterious materials. Under no circumstances should beach sand be used and there has been some concern in New Zealand with aggregate taken from a known volcanic area rich in pumice. The hull of one surveyed fishing boat had deteriorated to an extent where it was necessary to condemn it and withdrew survey. Tests of hull samples revealed a high pumice content of the aggregate used in the original mortar mix. We are told that where wet pumice is added to the mix it may react with the mixing mortar and produce a high water : cement ratio and subsequently an inferior plaster. Where the pumice is dry before addition to the mix, it can absorb water from the mortar and there will not be enough water to hydrate the cement.

Additives: It is common practice in New Zealand to add Pozzolan to the mix at the rate of about 10 per cent by weight to aid densification of the mix and also combine in slow reaction with the free lime to give the stable compound impervious to sea water. Benford (1971) has given the results of bending tests on ferro-cement planks which indicate that the strength is reduced progressively by the addition of pozzolan and 10 per cent is probably the maximum that should be added. The Department's requirements do not specifically call for the addition of pozzolan as some builders believe it should, since perfectly good mortar mixes are produced with or without other various proprietary additives. Approval of any additive is given where it can be shown that it may directly or indirectly reduce the water : cement ratio and where approved standards are published for the additive.

Strength requirements: A reasonable amount of information has been published concerning the strength of ferro-cement panels and beams but literature on the strength of ferro-cement hulls is negligible. To lay down requirements for the scantlings of ferro-cement boats was therefore a difficult proposition without theoretical guidelines and some service experience which had proved invaluable in establishing scantling requirements for wood and steel fishing boats.

Early tests on panels by Collen (1958–1960) showed that there was a direct relationship between the ultimate bending stress and steel content of ferro-cement with considerably improved extensibility of the reinforced mortar where the steel content exceeded about 320 kg/m^3 of mortar. With this information the Department has asked throughout for a steel content of not less than 385 kg/m^3 of mortar (i.e. 24 lb/ft^3, which represents 2 lb of steel/inch of mortar thickness using Imperial units employed in New Zealand). Initially the reinforcement was required to be equally distributed fore and aft and transversely, but considerable controversy arose over this requirement as many smaller boats had been built with longitudinal stringer wires only. To establish the validity of this argument a study was commissioned by the Department (Scrivener and Carr, 1971), of the stresses due to transverse loading experienced by ferro-cement boats varying in length from 10.67 m to 19.81 m. In this study, the load pattern adopted was that used by Saethre (1968) to study the strength of various frame types in wooden fishing boats. The results tended to confirm the belief that additional transverse wires were unnecessary in craft of less than 13.72 m length. It is interesting to note that the early Nervi yacht *Nenelle*, as reported by Bezukladov *et al.* (1968), had an overall length of 12.5 m and the reinforcement consisted of only longitudinal stringers 6 mm in diameter, set 50 mm apart with three layers of mesh inside and four layers of mesh outside these stringers. This boat was built in 1948 and Jackson and Sutherland (1969) report that it was still in service after 20 years.

It has been pointed out that it is desirable to have equi-directional reinforcement in ferro-cement boats to accommodate shrinkage stresses during the curing period. Smaller boats having no transverse reinforcement other than the mesh do not appear to have developed any significant cracks during the curing period and the exponents of this argument are either unable or unwilling to substantiate their claims with any evidence.

It has been shown, Naaman and Shah (1970), that ordinary hexagonal (chicken) wire-type mesh produced premature spalling of the mortar matrix when panels of this material were subject to tensile loading. Some authorities consider that hexagonal wire mesh should be prohibited, but of the several hundred ferro-cement boats built in New Zealand, the mjaority use this form of mesh and there has never been any evidence of such spalling occurring in service, which indicates that service stresses are low enough to neglect this failing of hexagonal wire mesh. However, this spalling has been noted on a boat which was breaking up in surf after being stranded.

The Department usually includes the weight of this mesh in defining whether the criterion of 385 kg of steel/m^3 of mortar is obtained. No allowance is made for the use of higher-tensile steels.

Several attempts were made by designers to obtain scantlings for ferro-cement boats using the classic bending theory and it was apparent that an applied bending moment of $WL/20$, where W was the displacement (t) and L the length (ft) might be used to give scantlings typical of those in common use. It was considered in an early version of the Department's requirements that designers should be allowed to arrive at scantlings by means of calculations assuming the above longitudinal bending moment and transverse loading similar to that adopted by Saethre (1968). No attempts were made to determine scantlings working from first principles and it is now considered with experience that hulls with adequate strength are obtained using only the simple criterion of providing 385 kg of steel/m³ of mortar and requesting additional transverse wires when the registered length exceeds 13.71 m. It is probably true to say that the service stresses induced by normal loading in a seaway are very low for a boat of the size with which the Department is concerned (i.e. say less than 22 m). This is borne out by experience, for with more than 1000 vessels in survey built of different materials no instance of structural failure due to the natural loading of the vessel at sea has occurred. The loading criterion for small boats is undoubtedly local damage brought about by the working and misuse of the craft and this is considered later.

In framing the Department's requirements for a boat-building medium which is still in the development stage, it was necessary to allow for new methods of construction which might originate. Where a surveyed boat is to be constructed with other than the conventional wire stringer/mesh principle the Department would wish to evaluate the performance of the hull material demonstrated by tests on panels and any service performance.

Plastering: Undoubtedly the most critical aspect of building a ferro-cement boat is the plastering. Many defects or failures examined by the Department to date can be attributed to either deleterious materials in the mortar mix or poor application of the mortar.

The mortar mix used is commonly a 2 : 1 sand to cement ratio with the addition of pozzolan or other admixtures. In most cases the mix is prepared in an ordinary tilting-drum concrete mixer, but larger contractors claim advantages for the revolving paddle or revolving pan and paddle mixer. The Department has found no evidence that boat hulls built using the tilting-drum mixer were in any way inferior to those built using the less common type of mixer.

Application of the mortar has been made in several ways:

(1) Mortar has been compacted from both sides of the reinforcement at one time and smoothed off inside and outside. This practice is not approved by the Department as it leads to voids and laminations midway through the shell thickness in a non-compacted region. Fig. 1 shows a cross-section through the fore deck of a boat plastered in this manner.

(2) The method originally used by Nervi and at first favoured by the Department was for the mortar to be compacted from the inside, being forced right through the wire mesh and smoothed off with a wooden float outside. This system has its disadvantages, for to complete an average hull in one day, a number of plasterers must work inside the boat at one time and care is needed to see that the reinforcement and mesh are not displaced. Adequate staging is required and a facility must be provided for lifting all the mortar into the hull and prevent it from being dropped into the bottom of the boat. It is not uncommon to see a distorted hull caused by men walking on mesh covered with wet mortar.

Fig. 1   Cross-section showing voids

(3) Another method is to plaster the outside of the hull first followed by a curing period before finishing the inside. The mortar is forced through the mesh from the outside until it is almost through the mesh and it is usual to have an observer inside who watches for the possible occurrence of voids and is then able to push a wire through the soft plaster so that the plasterer outside can re-compact the mortar at that point. The outer mortar is then cured for a period of 10 to 14 days and coated with a grout of cement and water, the inside of the hull being plastered whilst the grout is still wet. Plastering the inside is done from the keel upwards. Fig. 2 shows a section through a test panel plastered by this method and used to establish that the bond between the two layers was satisfactory.

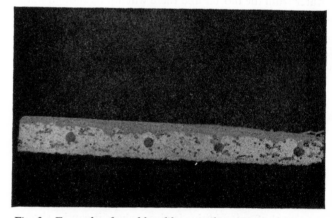

Fig. 2   Example of good bond between layers

It is normal practice to plaster the hull first and the deck subsequently, a clean interface with rich grout or bonding agent being employed. Some bonding agents are unstable in water and obviously should not be used. Similarly, on a large boat it is quite permissible to plaster the hull in sections.

At thicker sections, to obtain adequate compaction of mortar, it is as well to make use of vibrators. Fig. 3 shows the section at a coaming of a ferro-cement deckhouse which was replaced by a wood deckhouse to reduce topweight. This shows clearly a lack of compaction at the thicker section.

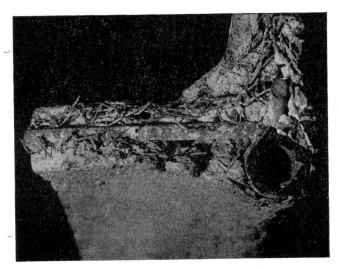

Fig. 3 *Thicker section showing lack of compaction*

The Department has surveyed a large number of amateur-built boats but has always insisted on the hull being plastered professionally.

Once the hull is plastered, the detection of any voids may not be easy but if the surveyor does suspect that these may be present as a result of poor plastering or visual surface defects, then holes are drilled to determine their extent. Cavities may be pumped full with grout later but it is preferred that a homogenous hull is obtained initially. The Department's surveyors and others would find it of advantage to have a tool with which to test the finished hull for incomplete penetration and tests are being conducted to test the suitability of ultrasonic echo equipment for this purpose.

Curing is usually accompanied by a water spray but professionally-built boats have been steam-cured.

Structural details

Bulkhead and deckhouses: An early sports fishing boat built under survey was subsequently wrecked after running on to rocks. It provided two lessons with regard to hull fixtures. This craft had wood bulkheads bolted to wood grounds which in turn were through-bolted to the hull. The wooden deckhouse was through-bolted to the ferro-cement coaming, the bolts bearing directly on to the plaster. On inspecting the wreck a surveyor found the collision bulkhead lying on the beach intact, the bent bolts still through the grounds where they had torn out of the hull; the aft bulkhead was also recovered in the same condition. The wood superstructure was washed ashore in a reasonable condition, the trunking still carrying the bolts which had pulled out of the ferro-cement coaming. The Department now requires that grounds for bulkheads or the bulkheads themselves are cast integral with the hull and that wood or another suitable bearing surface is provided for tie bolts to harden on to.

A number of fishing boat deckhouses have been built in ferro-cement but they are now usually plywood-framed, which is cheaper and more easily built, and reduces topweight.

Floors: Ferro-cement hulls are often constructed as shells with the bulkheads as the only internal stiffening members. Although the shell is sufficient to accommodate the normal stresses experienced in service, the provision of internal strengthening members to help maintain the hull form under exceptional conditions of loading has been desirable. Two surveyed vessels which were stranded, both had the bottom set up rather badly, the sports fishing boat referred to previously being set up 300 to 450 mm along the entire length. If these vessels had been fitted with floors it is suggested the bottom damage would not have been so severe.

Bulwarks: Bulwarks which are an extension of the main hull are not considered a very desirable feature on ferro-cement fishing boats, particularly if the pipe frames are extended to carry them. Ferro-cement is susceptible to impact damage and bulwarks standing 18 in (45 cm) or more high above the deck would appear (in our experience) to be very vulnerable. The better New Zealand ferro-cement fishing boats do not have this feature and Fig. 4 shows the damage that can occur with this type of bulwark.

Sterntube: A constructional detail which requires a little more thought than has hitherto been given to it is at the points where the propeller shaft and rudder stock breach the intact hull. Particularly critical is the sterntube arrangement where considerable vibration, torsional and other local forces could be present. The Department would prefer to see a proper steel sterntube

Fig. 4 *Bulwark damage*

fitted and provision made to see that this is secured within the reinforcement and the inboard gland bolted to a flange on the sterntube. Shaft logs have been made from reinforcement and mortar (see Fig. 5), a temporary plastic tube forming the sterntube being removed from the log before the mortar had set. The stern gland is then bolted to the shaft log, using stainless steel bolts set into the mortar. A 38-ft fishing boat with this sterntube arrangement developed a serious leakage through this assembly and was subsequently lost when under tow. It is suggested that the local forces could have loosened the gland and bearing fastenings set in the mortar. A better sterntube arrangement as fitted to a 36-ft fishing boat is shown in Fig. 6.

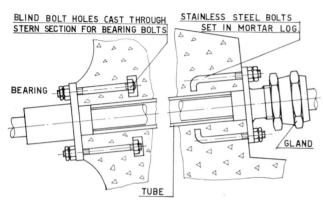

Fig. 5   *Stern gland and bearing similar to that on fishing boat lost through leaking stern tube.*

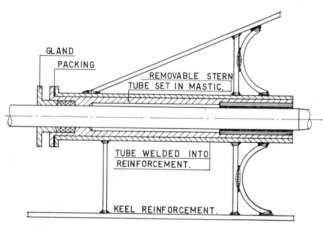

Fig. 6   *A preferred stern tube arrangement*

Fish hold insulation: The department's requirements ask for special attention to be paid to insulation in fish holds. This is to prevent a sharp temperature drop occurring through the mortar hull thickness which may produce icing within the pores at the surface of the mortar and subsequent disintegration. The outer surface barrier is important in this respect to prevent moisture penetration of the mortar and the effect is much worse if the inner surface is subjected to temperature reversals as would be the case in a fish hold.

In one case, a 13.4-m fishing boat ran aground after dragging anchor and subsequently broke up in way of the fish hold only. Some 3½ years later the hull was reported still perfectly sound except for the freezer

region and a number of experts who have examined this hull have questioned the insulation of the hold and suggested that a sharp temperature gradient may have accounted for this failure. The insulation consisted of polyurethane sprayed on to the hull to a depth of 100 mm and to underside of deck to 125 mm with a ferro-cement lining. The owner/builder reports that this was an early attempt at lining a hold with polyurethane and the material did in fact shrink leaving a gap of about 25 mm at each end of the hold. However, in service, no instances of external icing were noted. The probable reason for the early failure of the hull in way of the fish hold was that this was the least supported part of the hull, the rest having built-in fuel tanks, closely-spaced bulkheads, etc. The boat was built in 1964 and it is reported that beach sand was used as the aggregate. Figure 7 shows the stranded hull.

Fig. 7   *Wreck showing localized fishhold damage*

SERVICE EXPERIENCE

The Department has 28 fishing boats built or building under survey. Three of these having been lost, two being stranded (one breaking up on stranding) and the third sinking after flooding through the sterntube. Another vessel was condemned after 5 years' service, the hull being waterlogged or crumbling as the original mortar mix aggregate contained a porous element.

Service damage: Without doubt, the most serious failing of ferro-cement in fishing boats is the lack of resistance to impact damage. This is illustrated by considering a fairly typical repairs record for a 13.71-m registered length boat over a period of two years. The boat was built professionally in 1967, had 7-mm high-tensile steel wires longitudinally at 75 mm centres and 5-mm wires diagonally at 150 mm centres over pipe frames, two layers of 19 mm mesh; 0.91-mm wire and two layers of 0.71-mm wire netting were used inside and outside the reinforcement and the hull was plastered with compaction from inside only with a minimum finished thickness of 21 mm. The record for this boat for the period April 1969 to April 1971 is shown in Table 1.

The repairs needed to make good the shattered hull in way of the impact damage involved cleaning out the unsound mortar and restoring the wire reinforcing and mesh. The cleaned surfaces were then coated with an

TABLE 1. REPAIR RECORD FOR 13.71-M FISHING BOAT

April 1969	Hull port quarter above waterline and bulwarks starboard side forward repaired at annual survey. Damage due to chafing.
November 1969	Hull above waterline and bulwarks portside only repaired. Five areas affected, ranging in size from 50 mm × 75 mm to 450 mm. Damage due to chafing when fuelling from barge lying alongside.
May 1970	Hull damaged when vessel riding alongside wharf. Damage above waterline portside in three areas ranging in size from 300 mm square to 775 mm × 450 mm. Whilst removing fuel tanks to facilitate repairs these were dropped and three further holes about 125 mm ⌀ below the waterline had to be repaired.
May 1971	Vessel slipped to repair 300 mm ⌀ hole below waterline starboard side amidships. Hole resulted from vessel running aground.

epoxy-resin glue and hardener in proportion 1 : 1. A rapid-hardening cement and sand mix in 1 : 2 proportion with 10 per cent pozzolan was applied with the aid of vibrator, compaction being completely from one side. Repair of this nature in a bulwark may be noted in Fig. 4.

Fishing-boat owners who have worked ferro-cement vessels have expressed concern at the impact damage suffered by their vessels and on this account would be reluctant to build in this medium again. It is reported that two boats working with a fleet of steel vessels from Auckland are careful to stand off the dock until the rest of the fleet is tied up, and are then moored outside the other boats. Despite this precaution they have suffered shell damage whilst riding against another boat in a storm as shown in Fig. 8.

Fig. 8   Abrasion damage

The Department requires that special attention be given to providing sufficient and adequate fendering. Also, that large flat unsupported areas of hull should be avoided, particularly forward. Although no failure of a surveyed fishing boat has been reported to date, due to pounding in such regions, cracks have appeared in the unsupported shell areas of a yacht after driving into seas during an international race.

Surveys: At annual inspections the boat is slipped and it is useful to observe how the hull dries out. If wet patches remain, the hull skin could be waterlogged and breaking the outer surface would release this water. The Department permits a surveyor to drill holes in the hull if he suspects voids or laminations. These can easily be made good subsequently.

The hull can be inspected for cracks; it is not unusual to find that the paint surface has cracked and the mortar below is intact. Hair cracks are often observed on the surface which, if chipped out, are only found to penetrate 3 or 4 mm at the most into the mortar and can be disregarded.

CONCLUSIONS

Fishing boats up to 17 m in length with ferro-cement hulls have been built under survey in New Zealand and a number have remained in survey for five or six years. Satisfying the requirement at building that the steel reinforcement should not be less than 385 kg/m^3 o reinforcement and that additional reinforcement should be added transversely when the registered length exceeds 13.71 m, no structural failure has been encountered due to normal forces experienced by these craft in service.

The requirement applies to boats having wire stringer reinforcement with layers of mesh inside and outside.

The number of requests for the survey of ferro-cement fishing boats has diminished in the past 18 months and there is a reported lack of enthusiasm amongst fishermen, particularly those who have worked these craft, due almost solely to the incidence of impact damage experienced. The undoubted advantages of these hulls, lack of rot and corrosion, fireproof, ease of forming complicated curved shapes, etc., which has given the small fisherman the opportunity to build his own boat, have been outweighed in many fishermen's minds by the nuisance of repairing shell damage. Cost savings are not very significant in New Zealand, where the hull is only a small part of total cost.

The Department would like to see more attention given to the analysis of the actual loads experienced by the smaller boat at sea, although it suspects these are low and that any strength criterion will have to be based on local loads applied when working the boat. Also, more attention should be given to the impact properties of the material rather than tensile and other properties which appear well established. Until the fisherman in well developed countries such as New Zealand can be convinced he may as confidently strike a ferro-cement hull with a 3-kg hammer as he might a steel, or timber boat, then he will remain somewhat reluctant to accept the medium.

References

BENFORD, J R *Practical Ferro-cement Boatbuilding*. Washing-
1971   ton 98250, USA: Jay R. Benford Assoc. Inc.
BEZUKLADOV, V F, *et al. Ship Hulls Made of Reinforced*
1968   *Concrete*. Navships Translations No. 1148. Washington, DC, USA: Scientific Documentation Division (205), US Department of the Navy, 229 pp.
COLLEN, L D G Some experiments in design and construction
1960   with ferro-cement. *Civ. Eng. and Public Works Rev.* **55** (643).

HARTLEY, R T and REID, A J *Hartley's Ferro-cement Boat*
1971 *Building*. Auckland, New Zealand: Boughtwood
Printing House.
JACKSON, G W and SUTHERLAND, W M *Concrete Boat-*
1969 *building*. London, England: George Allen and
Unwin.
LLOYD'S REGISTER OF SHIPPING *Tentative Requirements for*
1967 *the Construction of Yachts and Small Craft in Ferro-*
cement. Technical Note FC/REQ/1, Jan.
MOAR, H M *Ferro-cement—the design of its properties for*
1972 *marine usage. FAO Seminar on the Design and Con-*
struction of Ferro-cement Fishing Vessels, Paper
No. I-9. Wellington, New Zealand.

NAAMAN, A E and SHAH, S P *Mechanical Properties of Ferro-*
1971 *cement*. University of Illinois, USA: Department of
Materials Engineering.
SAETHRE, J Some notes on stress analysis and construction of
1968 fishing vessel structures. *Proceedings Conference on*
Fishing Vessel Construction Materials. Montreal,
Canada: Fisheries Service, Department of Fisheries
and Forestry, Fisheries Report No. 12: 31.
SCRIVENER, J C and CARR, A J An analysis of ferro-cement
1971 boat hulls. *Pacific Symposium on Hydromechanically*
Loaded Shells, Part I. Honolulu, Hawaii, USA:
International Association for Shell Structures.

Experience of 300 Commercially Built Craft in More Than 20 Countries   T M Hagenbach

Ferro-cement is now universally recognized as a material for the construction of craft of many types, including commercial and fishing boats. The demand is growing and will continue to grow.

CUSTOMER REACTION

To assess customer reaction to the material a questionnaire was sent to over 50 customers in some 20 countries; 29 replies were received.

A breakdown of the users was: (1) charter fleet operators each with a number of craft; (2) fishing and commercial craft owners; (3) motor cruiser, yacht and houseboat owners.

The questions asked and customer reactions were:

1. When you purchased your hull, you clearly expected it to perform better than the available alternatives. In the light of your experience, is the performance vis-à-vis other materials:

	Charter fleet operators	Commercial and fishing boat owners	Private owners
Far better than you expected	10%	40%	36%
Better than you expected	30%	20%	36%
Exactly as you expected	40%	20%	14%
Slightly worse than expected	20%	20%	14%
Far worse than expected	0	0	0

2. Two areas of particular strength for ferro-cement are its low maintenance and its high resistance to collision and abrasion damage. Taking these specific areas, has your hull been:

	Charter fleet operators	Commercial and fishing boat owners	Private owners
(a) Maintenance:			
Far better than you expected	10%	40%	43%
Better than you expected	20%	60%	14%
Exactly as expected	40%	0	29%
Slightly worse than expected	10%	0	14%
Far worse than expected	20%	0	0
(b) Damage resistance:			
Far better than you expected	10%	40%	57%
Better than you expected	30%	20%	14%
Exactly as expected	30%	0	22%
Slightly worse than expected	20%	20%	7%
Far worse than expected	10%	20%	0

3. Would you choose ferro-cement again, given your experience up to date?

	Charter fleet operators	Commercial and fishing boat owners	Private owners
Would definitely choose ferro-cement again	10%	60%	86%
Might choose ferro-cement again	30%	20%	7%
Undecided	0	0	7%
Unlikely to choose ferro-cement again	60%	20%	0
Certainly would not choose ferro-cement again	0	0	0

4. Over the next ten years would you expect ferro-cement as a hull material to:

	Charter fleet operators	Commercial and fishing boat owners	Private owners
Increase rapidly in popularity	10%	40%	50%
Increase slowly in popularity	50%	40%	36%
Stay about static	20%	20%	14%
Decline in popularity	20%	0	0
Cease to be used	0	0	0

Detailed comment

All of this data, while generally favourable, is less favourable than is really merited. Where adverse comments appear there was usually some extraneous criticism not applicable to the hull, e.g. "paint flaked off" or "we have persistent gearbox trouble". We are all human—it is difficult to be enthusiastic about the ferro-cement hull when the engine has had to have three gearboxes fitted!

Some of the "general comments" that customers were invited to make follow:

Of charter fleet operators some had had their fleets in operation for 10 years and some for only 2 years. Average service was 6.3 years.

A company from Nottingham, England, which operates a large hire fleet on the British canal system, wrote: "We have hired out ferro-cement hulled narrow boats for seven years and whilst the hulls generally are good and received little damage the bows required continual repair due to impact on entering locks. In private ownership the hulls stand up well and do exactly as expected. All the owners expressed satisfaction."

On the other hand, a Norfolk company writes: "Our 12 hulls have needed as much if not more attention than our timber hulls."

Another Norfolk Broads charter operator says damage resistance was "exactly as expected" but "maintenance far worse than expected".

Yet another Norfolk Broads charter operator with 10 craft wrote: "I am surprised at the low maintenance cost, the durability of the hull and the simplicity and speed with which repairs can be carried out."

It is easy to understand the feeling of a shipwright who has served a five-year apprenticeship and loves timber boats, hating the sight of a ferro-cement boat and the job of repairing one. This could account for the varying reaction of the charter fleet operators.

The author feels that it may have been a mistake not to set up a school for training operatives in the very easy and simple technique of repairing a ferro-cement hull.

Reaction of commercial boat owners

The University of West Indies, who have a 55-ft (16.8-m) fishery research vessel which has been in service for almost two years, state that they would definitely choose the same material again.

The Ministry of Fisheries at Burnham, who have had a 20-ft (6.2-m) oyster boat in commission for about 5 years, said, in regard to damage resistance: "None sustained", and added that they might well choose ferro-cement again.

On the other hand, a company who had operated four ferro-cement-hulled personnel launches in the Arabian Gulf for 5 or 6 years, wrote: "In general terms the material has proved successful in operation though more susceptible to damage than conventional materials when subjected to repeated contact such as may be experienced when berthing alongside a jetty or other craft in a seaway. The extent of damage from very heavy contact which could cause penetration is comparable to steel. However, most forms of damage are more readily repairable than steel."

As can be gauged from the foregoing, the overwhelming number of comments from private owners were extremely favourable.

SURVEY OF MISHAPS AND ACCIDENTS

Mishaps and accidents which have occurred to the author's knowledge to ferro-cement craft are reported in an endeavour to draw comparisons with other boat-building materials.

There are some 3000 charter boats on the waterways known as the Norfolk Broads and they receive notoriously rough treatment in the hands of unskilled holiday-makers. Great Yarmouth Yacht Station is a particularly popular mooring and craft are frequently tied up three and four abreast. On the ebb, the tide can run at 4 knots.

One holidaymaker in a big heavy 40-ft (12.3-m) mahogany cruiser endeavoured to come in to moor with the tide. He sank two timber cruisers and in the turmoil a ferro-cement-hulled cruiser was lifted on to an iron stake and lifted off again. A neat hole about 1 in in diameter was punched through the bottom of the hull. Water—salt water—spouted through the hole to a height of about 10 in (0.25 m). The Yacht Station attendants got a pump going and prevented the cruiser sinking and 'phoned the author's company for a repair gang, which arrived 45 min later, stopped up the hole and obviated the leak in 20 min. This would not have been possible with any other material.

Also some 8 years ago the author received a telephone call from an English holidaymaker in France. He was in a ferro-cement-hulled charter cruiser on the River Marne and had run on to a submerged uncharted wall at the approach to a lock. The cruiser had bounced along the wall five times without doing damage but finally came to rest on a corner of the wall. This caused a deflexion in the hull about the size of an outstretched hand and water percolated through the fissures. Instructions were given to the holidaymaker on the phone and this leak was cured without taking the boat from the water. This was a tremendous benefit because the nearest slipway was 55 miles away.

Another accident involved a charter cruiser on the canals in Great Britain. The holidaymakers started off on a brand-new ferro-cement cruiser and within 2 h, by taking a wrong turning on the approach to a lock, found themselves heading for a weir with torrents of water pouring over it. To avoid going over they turned port side on and were carried straight on to the weir and an iron pile luckily prevented them being carried over. The task of recovering the cruiser, then half-filled with water, was formidable indeed. Finally, a stout steel hawser was passed through the engine room vents on the port and starboard sides of the hull and attached to a steam roller on the bank. With sheer brute force this was able to tow the cruiser, against the current, to the bank. An indication of the strain involved is that the steel hawser tore 6 in (0.15 m) through the skin of the hull both on the port and starboard sides, otherwise the hull sustained no damage whatsoever.

In Ireland the holidaymakers on board a charter craft decided to go off the marked channel to picnic on a romantic-looking little island, which turned out to be well protected by submerged rocks. They ran on to the rocks and abandoned the boat. There was an incredible spell of bad weather and the vessel was pounded on the rocks for 5 or 6 weeks, at times with waves breaking right over her.

When some initial repairs became possible frogmen patched up the holes in the hull under water which enabled the cruiser to be refloated and towed to a slipway, where the necessary repairs were carried out by two men in one week.

The author knows of no other material where even first-aid repairs could be carried out under water.

The report by an FAO civil engineer consultant concerning 46-ft (14.0-m) trawlers supplied to Yemen was as follows: "I had a look at these ferro-cement hulls in Aden and, except for one patch of damage on one hull where the gunwale had been ripped off, they appeared quite sound. Although they had been stripped and left in the scrapyard for some years they were in excellent condition and had nothing wrong with them. The damage could easily be repaired and is less than 1 m in extent."

The author's company has been building in series a 35-ft (10.8-m) ketch designed especially for ferro-cement by a young American naval architect.

One of the first ones completed, *Susie G*, was wrecked on her maiden voyage.

An article in the 19 May 1972 issue of *Yachts and Yachting* reads: "It was considered by eye-witnesses that the ferro-cement hull withstood the pounding as well as if not better than one built in other materials would have done but the fact that she had grounded on a patch of boulders meant that she could not survive for long in the pounding seas."

Finally, there was the collision between a partly completed 67-ft (20.4-m) ferro-cement-hulled motor yacht being delivered to the Thames and the 45-ft (13.7-m) solidly-built Scots motor fishing vessel towing her. The towing vessel ran aground and stopped, the motor yacht continued and hit the MFV on the port quarter and did the following damage to the MFV: The deck, hull and beam shelf were penetrated for a distance of about 4 ft (1.2 m), entering the deck about 15 in (0.38 m). The main force of the impact was taken by a 1½ in (38 mm)-diameter steel bar acting as a tow stop for the tow rope. This bar was bent through 100°. The tow itself was attached to the aft steel mast of the MFV and this was torn out of the deck and away from the back of the wheelhouse. The hole in the deck was approximately 6 × 4 ft (1.8 × 1.2 m). The bulwarks of the vessel were smashed over a distance of approximately 6 ft (1.8 m). The damage to the bow of the ferro-cement hull was only at the point where the steel bar hit the stem and penetrated sufficiently to deform the reinforcement about 1½ in (38 mm). The damage apparent on the outside of the hull covered an area of 36 in² (232 cm²) and on the inside of the hull approximately 72 in² (464 cm²). A temporary repair was carried out in approximately 40 min and the permanent repair in 1½ h, after which the hull was returned to its original state.

AREAS FOR FURTHER RESEARCH

Scantlings data: If a vessel is built in timber, glass fibre or steel scantlings data is available from Lloyd's Register of Shipping and equivalent authorities in other parts of the world.

Equivalent data are required for ferro-cement craft. Lloyd's Register, the American Bureau of Shipping, Norske Veritas, the New Zealand Marine Department and others have issued provisional rules and it is hoped that further investigation will result in such scantling data as is necessary for the construction of ferro-cement boats. A set of rules has been developed by the author's company for its licensees but these rules are only applicable to hull structures conforming in every way with their own rules relating to the reinforcement used, the mesh make-up and disposition, additional strengthening where required, mortar formulation, etc. All of these items contribute to the ultimate characteristics of the material.

Painting: The ideal paint for a ferro-cement hull is one that can be applied while the hull is still "green" so that curing is slowed as much as possible.

Originally craft built by the author's company were used exclusively on the Norfolk Broads in fresh water and swimming pool paint—chlorinated rubber—was used successfully. This could be applied while the hull was still "green", would act as a base for normal paints and the results seemed very satisfactory.

Craft similarly treated and used at sea were little short of disaster. The bond between the swimming pool paint and the ordinary paint seemed to disappear and the top coats came off in sheets. After following rigidly the instructions of one manufacturer the paintwork flaked.

Two British manufacturers now issue painting specification for ferro-cement craft. Manufacturer 1: "Allow at least one month and preferably two for the cement to cure". Manufacturer 2: "Allow ferro-cement to dry and cure for one month before priming".

This sort of delay, if not inconvenient, can be frequently impracticable.

Epoxy resin composition has been used successfully but it is expensive, most unpleasant to apply and of course cannot be applied to a green hull. Again, "if epoxide resin composition is subjected to continuous strong sunlight it will chalk slightly". Also repainting procedure is not easy.

Further research is necessary.

Electrolysis: The author's company has had a variety of experience in regard to electrolysis in ferro-cement craft.

Originally it was their practice to build with a steel-shoed keel to which the reinforcement was welded. In use, some of these craft suffered very badly from electrolysis, whilst others built in identical fashion were unaffected.

To combat the problem, zinc anodes were fitted in positions similar to those that would have been chosen in a steel vessel. In some cases these provided a suitable protection. In one case, however, the wastage of the anode was three times what it would have been in a steel boat. The owner finally refused to renew the anodes and no deterioration of the hull took place!

At one stage the company wondered, due to a variety of different experiences, if the framework held a static charge due to electric welding and always earthed the mesh. They no longer hold this view.

It has been suggested that the mild steel in the framework and the concrete itself is as potentially dangerous as a mild steel plated hull will be: the reason here being that with the multiplicity of small wires or rods in the hull, the actual surface area of steel is far greater than it would be in a steel boat. In these circumstances the greatest care should be taken to ensure that all components in the vessel are properly bonded. This naturally must include water pumps, sanitary facilities, radios, propulsion motors, rudders, any steel rigging, etc., and it is important to ensure that the starting motors and indeed all electrical fixtures, battery systems, including generators or the newer types of alternators be negative to ground.

Recently such trouble has been avoided without using anodes by eliminating all exposed steelwork (e.g. steel-shoed keels) and paying exceptional attention to the finish of the hull both inside and out. Further research is still considered to be necessary.

Reinforcement: From experience gained through carrying out considerable research and many tests on panels made up using various types and combinations of mesh and rods, including hexagonal galvanized chicken wire, they found that chicken wire did not produce a good product and for this reason have never used this type of mesh for reinforcement. Several different meshes are made exclusively for them and in their own manufacture they scramble the meshes and other reinforcement to give the result wanted.

The author feels that much research is necessary in the use of random orientated wire which might be put in the mix or perhaps gunned. Again, reinforcement with glass fibre merits attention, although in his view this cannot produce ferro-cement it might well result in an intriguing reinforced mortar. He believes that it would be helpful to consider the use of factory-made structures of interconnecting metal combining with mesh. Additional additives to consider were such as asmospheres—microscopic hollow glass balloons—which would greatly reduce the specific gravity of the ferro-cement.

A whole new area of research is opened by the advent of carbon fibres.

Man hours: One of the outstanding advantages of ferro-cement construction is that labour to be employed on hull construction can be trained in a comparatively short period of time. Sophisticated skills are unnecessary and the cost of the necessary plant to initiate manufacture is comparatively low.

In spite of this considerable research is necessary—due to rapid wage increases everywhere—to evolve ways and means of reducing the labour content in a ferro-cement hull.

One licensee of the author's company claims to have developed a highly successful spraying technique. The company itself has been less successful with it.

The author is sure that before long it will be possible to spray a hull with strands of wire in a similar fashion to a fibreglass hull and knows of a dinghy which has been manufactured experimentally in this manner.

Impregnating the mesh with a mortar pump does involve a saving in man-hours but the real time is consumed in making the mesh framework.

Experiments are being made on a new type of framework with parts interconnecting to make rapid assembly possible but final test results are not yet available. A lot of work needs to be done in this sphere. Finally, more consideration should be given to the "ferro-shotcrete" method evolved in Canada and published in *L'Ingenieur* in March 1970.

Further research would be rewarding in all these fields.

WHAT OF THE FUTURE?

It is the considered opinion of many people with whom the matter has been discussed that in 10 years time more commercial and fishing boats between 35 ft (10.7 m) and 80 ft (24 m) will be built in ferro-cement than any other material.

The advantages are:

1. Monolithic structure. The ability to build hull, decks, bulkheads, floors, engine bearers, fish tanks and bulkheads in one piece resulting in a monolithic structure of immense strength.
2. Ease of construction and ability to train labour quickly.
3. Raw materials being almost universally available.
4. Low maintenance costs.

In those spheres and for the reasons indicated the demand will increase rapidly.

For private owners and prospective purchasers of motor cruisers, yachts and houseboats 35 ft (10.7 m) and up, the reaction is overwhelmingly favourable. A particular field in which the demand is growing apace is the sale of hulls only for fitting out and completion by the purchaser. They maintain their shape even when transported without decks and bulkheads, do not deteriorate if left without cover and are easy to fit out.

Most amateurs now find it wise to buy a commercially-built hull and use their energies for fitting it out rather than undertake the hazard of building their own hull. The author's order book at the time of writing is a record for his company and consists of:

1 × 52-ft (16.0-m) twin screw motor yacht
1 × 50-ft (15.25-m) twin screw motor yacht
1 × 40-ft (12.2-m) Dutch botter
3 × 40-ft (12.2-m) auxiliary ketches
2 × 40-ft (12.2-m) auxiliary schooners
2 × 40-ft (12.2-m) houseboats
5 × 35-ft (10.7-m) auxiliary ketches
1 × 34-ft (10.36-m) houseboat

To guard their future, commercial manufacturers must concentrate on quality and must maintain a clear distinction between their product and the often ill-conceived and badly constructed results produced by the back-street boatyard and the amateur. Just as no one now attempts to build their own fibreglass hull and the junk builders are out of business—so it will be with this exciting and remarkable material ferro-cement.

Ferro-Cement Boats—Service Experience in New Zealand W M Sutherland

A final authoritative evaluation of ferro-cement as a material for use in boat construction can only be made when the following conditions have been satisfied:

The complete physical properties of the material have been established.
The design loading and usage requirements of particular types of boats have been determined.
Boats designed to comply with these requirements have been constructed to specification.
These boats have been in service under the designed condition for a sufficient period of time to satisfy the owner.

Many reports have been published during the last 10 years extolling the virtues and success of ferro-cement as well as a few reports which have been disparaging.

It is the author's opinion that at this stage in the entire history of ferro-cement there are certainly very few, if any, boats afloat which satisfy completely the requirements listed.

In order to comply with these requirements much research, development and usage are still required.

The shipbuilding industry already has many established materials at its disposal which permit the above conditions to be satisfied and as a result there is very little incentive to finance the necessary research and development.

In this report the author can only express his personal evaluation of performances either personally experienced or as reported and investigated.

The author has been personally responsible or directly involved in the construction of approximately 50 boats which have been in service for periods ranging up to 10 years. Of these, approximately 15 have, in fact, been designed as pleasure craft but later used as some form of work boat such as fishing or tug work. Approximately 12 have been designed and constructed as commercial fishing boats or tugs.

In addition to the above 50, the author has personal knowledge of or has inspected 30 other boats.

There is certainly evidence which clearly indicates that ferro-cement can be utilized very satisfactorily, but it is proposed in this report to describe in general, the problems, mistakes or abuses which have been experienced.

WEIGHT FACTORS

There are very few craft completed which have been constructed to meet the designer's weight intents. The reasons for this underestimating of weight have been:

Careless plastering with excessive cover to the steel.
Increased hull thickness due to excessive lapping of meshes, which results in extra plaster being required to provide a fair hull between high spots.
Bad steel assembly creating very irregular thickness such as flats between frames;
Inadequate allowances made for extra thickness at stern, keel, gunwhale, bulkhead, engine beds, etc.
The normal skin thickness for the average pleasure hull has been theoretically about 22 mm, which represents approximately 68 kg/m^2. In practice, due to the above problem, 100 kg/m^2 has been the actual figure in many cases.
The theoretical weight per m^3 of mortar has been underestimated due to high steel contents, which can vary considerably.

Comments

It requires considerable expertise or sophisticated methods to insure that true design weights are obtained.

Many boats have been constructed in ferro-cement using plans designed for timber or even steel and as a result this, combined with the above factors, creates a wrong impression and causes criticism of ferro-cement due to its excessive weight.

Many amateur cement boats have been very much overweight and, as a result, proved very sluggish sailers.

Surprisingly, there are several fishing boats around Auckland and New Zealand which, although excessively heavy, have resulted in satisfied owners. The main reasons for this appear to be that in fishing boats, the heavy slow motion hull is preferred by the operators and it has been found that the thicker hull has withstood the large impacts encountered in service.

There have also been many cases where the trim of the hull has been seriously affected as a result of the above conditions and in some instances it has been necessary to remove concrete bulkheads, decks and even cabin tops completely.

In pleasure yachts, the weight distribution is very critical in relation to performance and concrete decks are invariably too heavy. Some small areas of side deck have proved to be a valuable asset structurally.

As a result of experience, accurate weight assessment and correct design weights are now being achieved in the New Zealand commercial production yards, and it is understood that this is also the case in the United Kingdom and some other areas.

MORTAR APPLICATION AND PENETRATION

This operation is without doubt the greatest problem area in ferro-cement boat construction. Unfortunately, there are many boats afloat today which will undoubtedly fail due to faulty plastering. Some already have. In many of the early hulls, large areas of voids occurred, due to lack of mortar penetration. Many other problems have been found to be due to this fault.

Where large areas of overlapping mesh or concentrations of steel occur, it is almost impossible to ensure complete penetration. When such areas have been considerable and undetected, the weight of the hull has often been affected and this to some extent has caused incorrect assessment of weight factors by designers.

Standard practice on all hulls under control of the author has been to check the hull as thoroughly as possible for such voids and then to inject cement grout to fill any located. This process is extremely difficult to execute correctly and several cases have been found where faulty grouting procedure has led to, actual splitting of the skins over considerable areas.

There have been many instances in Auckland of amateur cement hulls having been launched only to find them leaking extremely badly. Slipping and thorough grouting has been necessary and satisfactory.

The lack of suitable vibrating equipment has been a major handicap in plastering, and different plastering techniques have attracted some discussion. There is still much room for improvement in the plastering application. At the end of 1970, it was found that the ordinary woodworking type of orbital sander can be utilized with great success to overcome many of the difficulties. The introduction of this tool in the author's opinion, has made it possible to advance considerably with multi-layer construction techniques.

STEEL CORROSION

This will occur as soon as water can flow into the voids and unfortunately may remain undetected until failure occurs.

Several hulls constructed by both commercial and amateur builders after a period of some 3–5 years, have shown signs of weakness at such points and repairs have

been necessary. In several cases, bumping or colliding with some object has resulted in holing the hull.

The author on his own yacht *Marire*, examined the hull carefully after 2 years of service and detected several void spaces below the waterline. These were approximately 20 × 15 cm and they were opened up to expose fully all the steel and mesh, which were in perfect or as new condition. There was no sign of water at all in the areas. This was due to the outer layer of plaster, approximately 6 cm, being completely dense and watertight, plus the protection of the anti-fouling paint. The holes were simply plastered up and repainted. This yacht was constructed in 1964 and launched in December. After extensive coastal sailing and motoring under all extremes of weather, it was sold in 1969. The new owner then took the boat for a cruise to Fiji, where unfortunately it was grounded on a coral reef (see Appendix 1).

There have been several occasions in which damage to hulls has revealed serious corrosion but in every instance there have been voids present. From the many damaged areas repaired in the author's yards, no corrosion of the steel has been found in dense mortar.

ELECTROLYSIS

The action of electrolysis is a most complex one and is a subject in itself. Many cases of electrolysis have been experienced in many different forms. The most usual is in the form of rust spots which occur below the waterline. Frequently, these occur when the boat is first placed in the water and after a period of chipping out the spots and filling with a suitable epoxy filler, they can be reduced. It would appear that in each case the rust spot is caused by electrolysis at a point where steel or mesh is very close to the surface. Paint and even high-quality epoxy coatings cannot prevent these occurring.

There have also been several identical boat hulls in service, where one specific hull shows excessive pitting. Attention to the earthing system in the hull and electrical installation have reduced the problem.

In several other cases, steel external fittings such as rudder gudgeons, pintles, etc., have been seriously corroded within a short time without any apparent effect on the hull.

The greatest number of failures have occurred where voids or interface surfaces have permitted sea water to come into contact with the steel. A serious fault has been the addition of a surface layer of mortar when used to "fair" the hull. It is extremely difficult to ensure either a perfect bond between such layers or the identical density between the two layers. In such cases, the presence of sea water at the interface completes the requirements for an electrolytic cell and corrosion of the steel occurs.

Examples of this have been more obvious where the filler has been completely dissimilar to the parent mortar.

SKIN FITTINGS

The placement of skin fittings can lead to serious electrolysis. In one instance, aluminium fittings were set into holes cut in the hull. The through-fastening bolts were also aluminium and although the fittings were set in an epoxy compound, at least two of the bolts in each fitting made contact with the reinforcing in the hull. The resulting electrolysis was sufficient to completely corrode away the bolts within 48 h and to cause serious erosion to the surface of the fitting in contact with the water. Due to the non-availability of replacements at short notice, it was necessary to remove the fittings completely, coat them in epoxy resin, and replace them using stainless steel bolts encased in a plastic sheath. Careful attention to isolating the fitting from the steel eliminated the problem and these particular fittings have shown no deterioration in the subsequent 12 months.

OIL

The effect of fuel oil or similar materials becomes obvious very quickly if allowed to come in contact with untreated ferro-cement. Unprotected areas can be quickly detected by the presence of oil on the paint outside the hull.

Questions have been raised regarding the effect of fuel oil, steel and salt water in concrete. It has been suggested that rapid corrosion of the steel will occur, but after eight years, no such effect has been noticed by the author.

The difficulty of paint adherence to such areas is a separate issue. Fuel oil penetrates mortar very rapidly, so care must be taken if fresh water tanks are incorporated in the hull.

The use of epoxy paints has proven very satisfactory in protecting against such oil penetration.

PAINT

The greatest nuisance to ferro-cement builders to date has been the inconsistent results with paint formula. It appears to be a simple problem but the author cannot at this stage offer any foolproof system.

Porosity or voids in the mortar have accounted for many of the paint failures. Areas of a hull have become covered in blisters up to 2 cm in diameter which subsequently disappeared and did not return. This has occurred on several occasions, even after 2 years in service.

The problem of moisture content of the mortar at the time of application is important, and where hulls have been allowed to "weather" for a minimum of three months, blistering has been extremely rare.

Possible causes for paint failures have been suggested, such as the use of sands containing salt water, the effect of galvanizing the mesh, and etch priming the surface. However, there has been no consistency to date and the simplest solution appears to be to ensure adequate cover to all steel or mesh and allow a minimum of three months weathering. There have been extremely good results in such cases with ordinary house type paints whereas expensive epoxy coatings have failed.

The use of epoxy paints with high impermeability properties applied to both sides of the hull can result in any moisture entrapped in the mortar creating bubbles or failure of one of the paint surfaces. Strangely enough, although this appears obvious, there have been numerous occasions where this has not happened and hulls fully coated on both surfaces have shown no detrimental effect.

STRUCTURAL STRENGTH CRACKING—

The overall structural strength of a ferro-cement hull appears to be more than adequate to cope with normal loading conditions and it is the secondary stresses which appear to be the governing criteria.

There are only two types of basic cracking which can occur in a ferro-cement hull.

Shrinkage

In this case, the extent of the cracking is directly proportional to the quality of the mortar used and the conditions of its application and curing. It is most important that strict quality control be maintained to reduce such shrinkage cracking to a minimum. However, shrinkage cracks will occur (unless special cements are utilized), but their presence is of no consequence as long as they are restricted to a minimum design width. The curing of mortar automatically necessitates shrinkage and the design requirements of ferro-cement take this into account.

Nearly all the early hulls constructed in New Zealand showed quite considerable shrinkage cracking and this was due mainly to the inexperience in mixing and placing of mortar with a low water : cement ratio. The use of proper mortar mixers was not introduced in the New Zealand ferro-cement industry until approximately 1966 and since this time the quality of plastering has improved considerably. In the author's opinion not using pozzolan in the early hulls assisted in the healing of such cracks. Even quite severe shrinkage cracking has sealed itself and in most cases no ill effect has been noticeable.

Working load cracks

Cracks which occur under working conditions are very critical and great care must be taken to keep them within design limits. It is impossible to load ferro-cement without cracking occurring but the control of it is imperative. Unfortunately, as there have been no specific design criteria available, the construction of ferro-cement hulls up to the present have been calculated guesswork. Naturally, mistakes have been made and it is from these mistakes that research and development has renewed its direction.

Flexural cracking

Perhaps the most critical cracking failures have been due to straight overloading of a section in bending. In such cases the cracks "work" and, if excessive, failure of the section can occur. There have been cases of such cracking due to the underestimation of applied loads. In one instance, the extreme overloads induced in the section were created by a "slamming effect" peculiar to the design of the hull. To overcome the problem, extra frames were added to this section of hull, thus limiting the stresses. No further cracking occurred and the repairs were completely satisfactory. There have also been several cases of hulls with flat sections developing longitudinal flexural cracking but only after several years of heavy use. In these cases the cracked areas were sanded down and a layer of fibreglass added. The results were satisfactory. Such flexural cracking does not usually extend through the hull and would appear only on the side under tension. In such cracking, leaking is unlikely, although failure to carry out a repair can lead to a break-down at the cracked section.

Direct tension

This type of cracking seldom occurs but will appear if the total applied load in direct tension exceeds the allowable working limit of the total steel acting in that specific direction. No reports of such cracking have been received.

Deck fittings

Frequently, cracking will appear in the paintwork in areas adjacent to deck fittings such as winches, etc. These cracks may occur after the first maximum loading of the fittings and subsequent loadings will not cause increased cracking. This type of cracking is noticeable due to the inelastic properties of some paints and simply indicates that the concrete surrounding the fittings has suffered initial cracking due to loading, but subsequent loads do not usually increase the cracks or cause them to fail. The nature of these cracks is very much dependent on the yield properties of the mesh in the area and the extent of loading. If after the initial cracking is noticed and subsequent paint applied, no further cracks occur, the situation is quite normal. Such cracking should not cause unnecessary alarm as cracking the mortar is necessary to permit maximum working loads to be achieved. However, crack widths are extremely critical and if any sign of rusting along these cracks occurs, it is a sign of excessive loading of the area and remedial action should be taken.

Frequently in both shrinkage and initial flexural cracking, a definite line may appear under the paintwork without actually penetrating it. After many inspections of such cases, particularly below the waterline, it has been shown that on exposure of the apparent crack line, healing of the crack has occurred. This is caused by the free lime in the cement and tests have shown that complete regain of mortar strengths are possible in some cases. There is usually in such cases a slight build-up of deposit along the crack line and this gives the appearance of cracking.

In early hulls, where the diameter of the internal steel rods was increased in larger boats, cracking occasionally occurred along the line of rods. These were the direct result of excessive shrinkage combined with insufficient mesh in the mortar cover to the steel rods.

This type of failure directed attention to the need to research carefully the composition and placement of reinforcing in ferro-cement sections. The original empirical rules of approximately 800 kg of steel/m^3 of mortar can lead to dangerous mistakes.

Joints

In several early hulls, construction joints showed signs of movement and rusting. Examinations indicated that faulty workmanship at the joint was responsible. When forming such joints, it is imperative that clean dense edges be left, against which the new mortar can be applied. Epoxy jointing materials can be used successfully although a well-formed and grouted joint should give no trouble.

Hard points or bulkheads

The action of a ferro-cement hull is invariably taken as a membrane of some shell type structure and when correctly analysed as such, stresses are relatively small and major cracking should not occur. On some larger-type hulls with rather flat sections cracking has appeared directly at bulkhead or similar hard spots. Naturally, designers can allow for such cases if the analysis of the shell is possible. To date, very little knowledge of this subject has been available. Scrivener and Carr (1972) have progressed considerably in this direction but caution is needed to design for the necessary stress increases and reversals which occur at such points.

In small hulls, the effects of temperature have not been signicant, although in some larger hulls the movement of decks and topsides subjected to hot sun has caused stresses to increase and reverse to the extent where cracking has occurred.

PUNCHING

This has been the greatest area of concern and many cases of such failures have been experienced. Design specifications now establish suitable criteria for limiting such stresses; it is, however, unlikely that any major breakthrough will be achieved to dramatically improve this situation.

Bolt heads in fender piles, heavy anchor flukes, or the sharp corner of heavy steel objects may easily cause a very localized punching effect. Fortunately, this type of failure will be unlikely to lead to serious damage as the inflow of water is invariably relatively small and repairs can be made very rapidly and without difficulty. Many such holes have occurred but there is no instance on record where serious problems have arisen.

In pleasure hulls the owners are usually careful and attention to fendering and awareness of this problem prevent such accidents occurring, whereas in work boats with less careful masters, damage occurs to ferro-cement or in fact, to any other material.

It has been interesting to observe that in Bangkok, a large 100-ft (30-m) barge constructed in ferro-cement suffered several minor accidents of this nature on its initial trip, but with the operators' livelihood dependant on the continual use of the barge, adequate fendering and attention to handling eliminated further damage on the second and subsequent trips.

In fishing boats there are certain minimum loading conditions which even a careful owner operator must accept and it is the correct evaluation of these which will enable designers to produce a material capable of withstanding such loads.

In New Zealand, minimum skin thicknesses have been established which appear adequate for local conditions.

Condensation

As with any material, condensation will occur under the appropriate conditions but ventilation or insulation can be used equally well with ferro-cement.

FIRE RESISTANCE

The author has no knowledge of a boat experiencing a complete fire but a simulated fire test in a 27-ft (8.25-m) launch hull with a 1.2-cm thick hull showed spalling of the cover to the reinforcing in the area of maximum flame intensity only.

In this instance some 3 gall (13 l) of petrol were placed in the engine-bed area, ignited and allowed to burn it out. The damage was surprisingly small.

From laboratory tests conducted at Auckland University College, spalling of the surface mortar was found in sample panels under normal atmospheric humidity conditions. When similar samples were thoroughly dried and free from moisture content, no spalling occurred.

In a normal boat (apart from the fuel), the volume of combustible material incorporated would be unlikely to create sufficient heat to cause any significant damage.

PERMEABILITY

Questions have been raised repeatedly regarding the watertightness of ferro-cement hulls. The author can only comment that in every well-constructed hull, dust and sawdust from the original building operation frequently remain in the bilges after many years. Only in cases of faulty plastering has permeability been encountered.

CONCLUSIONS

It is very easy to be wise *a posteriori* and in the absence of such criteria as laid down in the opening of this report, it is most heartening to observe the many successful ferro-cement yachts and launches operating from the New Zealand coast. In the last ocean race from New Zealand to New Caledonia, approximately 8 per cent of the fleet were ferro-cement yachts and in one week alone, in May 1972, four ferro-cement yachts set out on world cruises.

It would be interesting to learn the number of ferro-cement yachts which have left New Zealand for overseas cruises and the author feels confident that in 1972 the majority of departing yachts would be ferro-cement.

The great flexibility of the material to cope with extreme design, construction and loading conditions must make it attractive to all areas where sophisticated and skilled expertise is in short supply. However, the need for basic expertise and a high standard of supervision must not be overlooked.

References

SCRIVENER, J C and CARR, A J *An Analysis of Ferro-cement*
1971   *Boat Hulls.* IASS Pacific Symposium on Hydro-mechanically Loaded Shells, Part I. Honolulu, Hawaii, USA, October 10–15, Paper No. 3–7.
UNIDO   *Boats from Ferro-cement.* United Nations, New
1972   York, USA. Utilization of Shipbuilding and Repair Facilities Series No. 1, 123 pp.

Discussion on Aspects of Service Experience

Mowbray (Rapporteur) considered that the three papers which had been presented for discussion, along with others in previous sessions had made an extremely valuable contribution to the mixture of art and science which forms ferro-cement construction. The paper by Eyres reported the view of a certifying authority and outlined the problems facing the Naval Architect and Surveyor of Ships when dealing with a material so unlike timber and metal, and so dependent on faithful workmanship and the need for care at each and every step in the fabrication process. The official requirements for boats built in New Zealand under survey was an excellent basic document for a code of practice without rigid rules. Until such time as a more rational system of design was evolved, these regulations together with the requirement of the production of drawings and calculations seemed reasonable and not likely to frustrate development unduly.

The contribution from Hagenbach was mainly devoted to a preliminary survey of customer reaction. It showed that while ferro-cement was not a universal choice it had a considerable degree of popularity amongst private owners and charterers of pleasure craft. Perhaps this contribution might have been more useful if the results of the survey for commercial boats had been separated and expanded. The author's record of

damage and repairs was worthwhile, as it indicated the essential robustness of ferro-cement, in contradiction to the belief popularly held by the layman that this material was extremely tender and brittle.

The submission from Sutherland was based on personal experience as a designer and constructor; it contained references to many of those tricky points which had to be considered so carefully. As a tailpiece in that account a question was asked, namely "How strong is strong enough?" This was indeed the essence of the purpose of this review.

ACCIDENT DAMAGE AND ITS REPAIR

Donovan (New Zealand) said that as one concerned with the repair of vessels he had observed that service damage was greater than any caused by sea action. Service damage occurred in handling, slipping, improper positioning of vessels in cradles, weights landing heavily on decks or swung against sides, vessels striking against one another at the quayside, etc. None of this damage was caused by forces encountered at sea but by people handling and operating the vessels. When designing and building ferro-cement vessels the possibility of such damage should be taken into consideration.

Wheeler (New Zealand) had repaired about a dozen different types and sizes of ferro-cement boats which had been involved in various kinds of accidents and sustained various degrees of damage. He had generally found the repair a simple task. One example was a 48-ft trawler which had collided with another fisheries vessel. It had damage forward that at first inspection appeared to be about 30 × 30 cm (12 × 12 in) in area, but when cleaned out was found to be about 76 cm (2 ft 6 in) in length and nearly 60 cm (2 ft) in width. Damaged mesh had been replaced and some extra rod reinforcement put in to ensure a good lap between new and old reinforcement. This had taken about three to four hours. He had used an epoxy wet-to-dry glue around the edge of the mortar and plastered back, making sure that the mortar was well compacted. A membrane curing agent had then been painted over both sides of the repair, and the owners operated the boat next day, the whole job taking about six hours, Another case was damage to a ferro-cement fishing vessel at wharfside. The boat had been crushed by a 70-ft steel vessel and had damage extending about 2.1 to 2.4 m (7 to 8 ft) along the gunwhale area, tapering to minor cracking at the end. Two men cleaned out the damaged mortar resulting in an area to be replastered 4.9 m (16 ft) long and 0.6 m (2 ft) wide; man hours for the repair were 25 to 30. The job had not been difficult and had not required any special skill. If it had been a timber vessel it might not have been damaged to the same extent, but even so, in his opinion, repair would have taken longer.

Walker (Australia) had repaired three boats, one was a 11.5 m (37 ft 6 in) fishing boat which had been in a head-on collision with a steel barge. The hull was stoved in over a 1.5 × 1.2 m (5 × 4 ft) area but had been simple to repair. He had placed a piece of heavy steel on the outside and pulverized the damaged mortar with a hammer from the inside, cut away the damaged reinforcement, replaced it and then replastered. The whole job was done by three men in a total of 22 hours and the boat was only out of commission for a day and a half. The repair had been perfectly satisfactory but during curing in seawater, salt had penetrated the fresh mortar and there had since been some blistering of paintwork and rust stains in the area of the repair. Another 8.8 m (29 ft) boat with a damaged area 76 × 76 cm (2 ft 6 in × 2 ft 6 in) in the topsides had been repaired in a similar manner, but in this case the patch had been water-cured as for a hull and no difficulty had been experienced. For smaller moulded boats where a minor repair was required he had broken out the damaged mortar and refilled with epoxy concrete. Due to the rapid curing of the epoxy concrete the boat was ready for use the next day.

Hall (New Zealand) considered that from a strength point of view there was no reason why a boat should not go into the water within a few hours of the plastering being finished. However, fresh mortar is very absorbent, so there could be difficulties with salt water penetrating the mortar and attacking the steel reinforcement, as reported by Walker.

Wood (New Zealand) said his company manufactured epoxy mortars which were very suitable for repairs of ferro-cement boats. These mortars could also be cured under water. For example, a ferro-cement barge had been repaired afloat by two underwater swimmers using epoxy mortar carried in a plastic bag to the damaged area and then applied under water. The quality of such a repair was, of course, of a lesser strength than that carried out above water but would be perfectly satisfactory in the case of an emergency.

Hunt (New Zealand) felt that an underwater curing epoxy mortar was an essential material to carry in a ferro-cement boat. He pointed out that such mortars are not cheap, costing about 4-5 NZ cents a cubic inch, but have an unlimited storage

life. Under reasonably warm conditions above 15°C (59°F) they will cure in less than 24 hours and should give more than the original strength of the concrete.

Mowbray (New Zealand) referred to the construction industry's experience with buildings in earthquake-prone countries where, to prevent excessive damage, one way of solving the problem had been to make the concrete plastic instead of using a lot of expensive steel; in other words, using a concrete reinforced with steel with a fairly long elongation plateau once it yielded. This reinforcement is confined basically to mild steel and a really good mild steel will have a long stretchable plateau rather like soft toffee. Higher strength bars have a tendency to break and shatter. Based on this experience he suggested that mild steel reinforcing might be an advantage in ferro-cement boats if impact damage was likely to be a serious problem. Instead of shattering, the mild steel would tend to move out of position but still retain the cracked mortar, preventing rapid ingress of water and possible permitting a damged vessel to reach port.

Donovan (New Zealand) said that he and a number of other New Zealand builders had discontinued the use of high tensile rods. He preferred hard drawn rods because they were more ductile and easier to repair.

Rossiter (Australia) asked about the effect of shock waves travelling through the hull after impact, and wanted to know whether any particular area of the boat should be specially reinforced against such effects, particularly in areas where the material changes direction rapidly such as at a transom/hull joint.

Hagenbach (UK) said that his company had had a boat explode due to a gas or petrol explosion. The hull had been most damaged in areas such as those suggested by Mr Rossiter where the transom joined the hull. A fire had followed the explosion and the superstructure was destroyed, but even so the hull could have been quite easily repaired. This and other experiences showed the advisability of putting a radius on all sharp corners.

Pama (Thailand) said that a joint in a boat was basically a connexion between two shell structures and there would always be very high bending moments or stresses at these points which should be dispersed as much as possible.

Eyres (New Zealand) agreed with both the previous speakers and pointed out that not only do sharp corners present stress concentration points but are also areas which could get easily bumped or chafed causing local damage, which would frequently require repair.

Bowen (New Zealand) added that any damage seemed to be localized. No distortion of the hull occurred, doors would still close, other items would still fit and all that was necessary was to repair the damaged region.

CORROSION IN FERRO-CEMENT BOATS

Waters (New Zealand) raised the question of possible corrosion of steel tubes used in the pipe frame construction method. If serious hull damage occurred after impact, fractured tubes could result in sea water entering through the fractures causing serious corrosion. To prevent this possibility he suggested either a bituminous solution or a paint wash to coat the interior of the tubes.

Eyres (New Zealand) said that there had been a number of cases of water inside such pipes leading to corrosion. To avoid this the pipes were often filled with grout.

Fyson (FAO) had in 1969 inspected the 12.5-m (41-ft) ketch Nennelle built by Nervi in 1948. The hull had been built on a framing of 25 mm (1 in) black iron pipe at 1 m (3 ft 3 in) centres. The armature consisted of 6 mm ($\frac{1}{4}$ in) longitudinal iron rods at 50 mm (2 in) centres with seven layers of non-galavanized woven mesh. The hull thickness was 22 mm ($\frac{3}{4}$ in). At that time the hull had been stripped and was lying on a mooring being used as a store. There was no sign of leakage in the hull and the bilges were dry. The black iron pipe framing had not been filled and had rusted in certain areas due to moisture penetration through the mortar which caused spalling of mortar in the interior of the hull. It would appear to be difficult to prevent small voids occurring along the pipe frames. This is probably due to lack of a perfect bond between pipe and mortar. In the interior of the hull where mesh and mortar cover over the pipes was not great, moisture penetration could more easily occur causing corrosion with resulting spalling of the mortar.

Despite various other minor imperfections the hull was still watertight, although possibly not at that stage capable of going to sea without repair. The hull had since been scuttled as the owner had no further use for it.

Moar (New Zealand) referring to the subject of electrolysis raised in Hagenbach's paper, said that it was not possible to avoid having a mixture of various metals in hulls fittings, and therefore it was most important to try to separate them from the hull armature and each other. Where this was not possible dissimilar metals should be earthed.

Hall (New Zealand) mentioned a theory that considered the degree of corrosion between fresh water and zinc-coated mesh to be determined by the chrome content of the cement. The amounts would be very small indeed but the presence of potassium dichromate in the cement appeared to be a major advantage in preventing corrosion. This presumably was linked to the prevention of the hydrogen bubble effect by the use of chromium trioxide which had already been mentioned.

DIESEL OIL IN CONTACT WITH FERRO-CEMENT

Donovan (New Zealand) in answer to a question about leak-proofing fuel tanks said that he had used coal tar epoxy to line the inside of fuel tanks on a boat which had now been operating for three years without problems.

Hagenbach (UK) had had problems with fuel tanks, mainly caused by leaks around flanges, but his company now used a proprietary lining product available in the UK which appeared to be quite satisfactory.

Wells (New Guinea) reporting on a vessel which he had repaired said that when the boat was on the slip it was possible to see diesel oil oozing through the side of the boat. Inspection revealed that the fuel tanks had been tar epoxyed but in his opinion it only needed a workman to drop a spanner or a screw driver into such a tank to chip the paint. The diesel oil then had direct access to the hull.

Hunt (New Zealand) said that tar epoxy was a very hard tough material but it was only 0.26–0.36 mm (10-15 thousandths of an inch) thick and he agreed with Wells that if something sharp and heavy was dropped the impact point could puncture the coating and cause deterioration as described by Moar.

Boden (Australia) said that an independent set of steel tanks was an added cost that must be taken into account. It was a very important factor because as vessels become larger it was uneconomic to use separate fuel tanks.

Donovan (New Zealand) did not agreed and considered that on economic grounds ferro-cement tanks would be unacceptable. Steel tanks would be very much quicker and cheaper to fabricate.

Moar (New Zealand) suggested that water tanks in ferro-cement should be lined because water is polluted by the alkaline content of the cement if it is left unused in a tank for some time.

Bowen (New Zealand) in answer to a question about the widespread use of concrete water tanks said that a student at the University of Auckland had been studying the physiological effects of water exposed to cement and considered this a function of the ratio of container area to volume. There was evidence to suggest that in containers with a large surface area and a small volume of water there was quite an increase in the calcium carbonate content of the water.

Moar (New Zealand) considered that the bilge area of a ferro-cement boat should always be covered with a protective coating against fuel leakage because fairly rapid deterioration could occur. This might lead to some blistering of paint work on the outside of the hull due to both surfaces being protected against water vapour.

Ellen (Australia) answering a question about the possibility of using rubber as a lining for ferro-cement fuel tanks said that there was extensive work being done on the use of styrene-butyl rubber for protective coating. He had laid some 2800 m² (30,000 ft²) of flooring in fish marketing areas. The finish had a white exposed surface which was coated with a very low solvent polyurethane to avoid undue slipperiness. The use of styrene-butaldine rubber, cement and acrylics provided a satisfactory answer; the cement actually dehydrating these water-based rubbers and producing a new compound altogether. Some work was being done on these materials for linings of diesel tanks and wine vats made of ferro-cement.

COMBINATION OF MATERIALS TO IMPROVE CERTAIN CHARACTERISTICS OF FERRO-CEMENT

Boden (Australia) said that service experience had shown the need for an improvement in certain characteristics of ferro-cement. The addition of various types of additives to the mortar mixture to improve abrasion resistance, bonding, etc., had already been discussed. There was also the possibility of combining materials to take advantage of the improved characteristics that such a mixture could give. If, for example, the use of fibreglass outer covering on a ferro-cement hull could produce some distinct advantages in strength or lack of absorption of salt water, etc., methods should be evolved to achieve a suitable combination and so a better product.

Hunt (New Zealand) mentioned the well-known ferro-cement yacht Awahnee which had been fibreglassed using epoxy resin and a very light-weight glass cloth. He had had doubts about the efficacity of this because of the uncertain water content of the hull, but the result had definitely been successful with increased abrasion resistance. A number of other boats had been fibreglassed successfully. He had found that with wooden hulls it was necessary to have an equilibrium water content of the timber which in his area would be about 14 or 15 per cent. It would also be desirable to establish a suitable equilibrium water content for ferro-cement hulls before fibreglassing. With regard to fibreglass reinforced plastics (FRP) there were two resins commonly used—polyester and epoxy. FRP moulded boats were normally made from polyester resin which was remarkable for its physical strength and for its rigidity, but it was also subject to alkaline attack. In addition, the adhesion of polyester resin to most other substances was poor. Epoxy resin, however, had good adhesion to concrete. In the case of the yacht Awahnee a single layer of a very fine woven glass cloth about 85 gm/m² (2½ oz/yd²) was used with epoxy resin. This seemed to have contributed greatly to the impact resistance of the hull. Other possible uses of epoxy resin materials were for engine mounts, under skin fittings, etc. The epoxy composition was laid and the fitting tightened down lightly on to it. The next morning it would be possible to take up tight on the bolts and so get maximum compression strength in less than 24 hours.

O'Kell (Australia) had used an epoxy resin with glass fibre mat to cover a boat after a considerable amount of weather curing. When the boat was slipped there were great areas of blistered mat which could be pulled off like loose wall paper. Behind this was water with a high alkaline content. He assumed that not enough time had been allowed for weather curing.

Hunt (New Zealand) said that from O'Kells's remarks it appeared that he had used glass fibre mat and the epoxy coating may, therefore, have been a very thick one. There was a big difference in the thermal coefficient of expansion of ferro-cement and epoxy resin with or without glass cloth, and he considered it important to use the thinnest possible coating. He did not subscribe to the use of glass mat and a thick application of resin to the outside of a ferro-cement hull because adhesion of any coating to concrete or ferro-cement was no better than the peel resistance of individual grains of material.

Reid (New Zealand) said that quite a lot of work had been done on various combinations of fibreglass and ferro-cement. Quite extensive tests had been made on the strength of ferro-cement with a fibreglass skin and it appeared that the addition of fibreglass did increase the punching and bending strengths to a surprising extent. The combination seemed to offer interesting possibilities.

FIRE RISK AND INSURANCE OF FERRO-CEMENT BOATS

Behnke (USA) said one problem related to service experience which had not been mentioned was that of insurance for ferro-cement fishing boats. Insurance companies tend to be conservative, analytical and objective in assessing alternative boat construction materials and methods. He asked if anyone had data on differences in insurance rates for ferro-cement, wood, steel or FRP hulls. Rate differences, if any, should provide a measure of the relative effectiveness of ferro-cement as a boatbuilding material.

Donovan (New Zealand) said that the present high standard of New Zealand amateur-built hulls could be attributed to an inspection system set up by two associations in New Zealand.

The willingness of owners to have their boats inspected was brought about by the cooperation of the insurance companies. Insurance was much easier to arrange if a hull had been inspected by one of these associations.

Hermanson (Norway) had not had any problems in acquiring insurance for ferro-cement boats in Norway. In fact the rates were some 15-20 per cent cheaper than for wooden vessels, probably because of the reduced fire hazard.

Gulbrandsen (FAO) considered the question of fire resistance very important especially for small fishing craft in developing countries, where cooking on board was often done over an open fire.

Reid (New Zealand) reported on results of tests carried out by his company on an open hull. Several gallons of petrol had been poured into the bilges and ignited. The resultant fire was quite intense but only minor spalling of mortar had occurred in the region of the engine bed which would indicate the good fire-resistant properties of ferro-cement hulls.

STANDARDS FOR REPORTING SERVICE EXPERIENCE

Gulbrandsen (FAO) asked representatives of the classification societies whether it would be possible to have an exchange of information regarding damage.

Tait (Australia) and Betteridge (New Zealand) said that any information provided by their societies would be conditional on permission being obtained from owners but provided this was done they saw no objection to furnishing such information.

Bowen (New Zealand) noted that various ferro-cement marine associations existed in different parts of the world, such as those in Australia and New Zealand. Several of them had publications and could report on information which had been sent to them on construction details, damage reports and other problems.

Gurtner (FAO) commented on the service experience questionaire provided in Hagenbach's paper and also that published in Bigg, GW, An Introduction to Design for Ferro-Cement Vessels, 1972. The Fishing Vessel and Engineering Branch of FAO had also prepared a basic questionaire designed to obtain service experience on the operation of ferro-cement vessels in different parts of the world. He considered that a standardized format for obtaining information on constructional details and operational experience of ferro-cement vessels would prove of considerable value to companies and organizations interested in promoting the development of the material. To this end he suggested the draft layout here included.

SERVICE REPORT ON FERRO-CEMENT FISHING VESSEL...
(Note: Where applicable, indicate ✓ for yes, × for no. Add any additional information in spaces.........provided).

1. General Information

1.1 Owner (name/address) ....

....

1.2 Designer (name/address) ....

....

1.3 Builder (name/address/no. of ferro-cement boats built)

....

....

1.4 Date of completion of vessel...

1.5 Dimensions

        LOA ....   Displacement ....

        LWL.........   Main engine............hp............at rpm......

        Beam ....   Fuel/FW capacity ....

        Draft ....   Fishold capacity (fish/ice) ....

1.6 Fishing methods ....

2. Design

2.1 Hull thickness (designed............/actual..............)

2.2 Keel reinforcement (no. of rods........./size and type........./spacing........./steel shoe)

2.3 Skeletal steel (longitudinal/transverse/diagonal/size & type............/spacing..............)

2.4 Mesh reinforcement (size & type.............../no. of layers............)

2.5 Framing (none/pipe/web/other..........................)

2.6 Longitudinal stiffening (none/ferro-cement/steel/wood)

2.7 Bulkheads (ferro-cement/wood/steel/no. and position..........................)

2.8 Deck material (ferro-cement/wood/other..........................)

                    (thickness........./steel........./mesh reinforcement.........)

2.9 Engine beds (ferro-cement/steel angle/wood/dimensions..........................)

2.10 Fishold (insulation type and thickness........./lining........./refrigeration.........)

2.11 Deckhouse (ferro-cement/wood/steel/other..........................)

2.12 Tanks (integral ferro-cement/steel/other..........................)

2.13 Bulwarks (ferro-cement/wood/other..........................)

2.14 Deck gear (mast....../winches....../gallows....../other.........)

3. Construction

3.1 Building method (upright/upside-down/open mould/solid mould/other..........................)

3.2 Mortar mix proportion (cement....../sand....../water....../addditives.........)

3.3 How mixed (hand/drum mixer/paddle mixer)

3.4 Plastering method (hand, one-shot/two-shot/mortar pump/other..........................)

3.5 Use of vibrators (pencil vibrator/orbital plate vibrator/none)

3.6 Penetration (complete/mesh exposed/voids/mortar cover over mesh..........................)

3.7 Curing (water/steam/other..........................)

3.8 Fendering (wood/steel/number and dimensions..........................)

3.9 Special provisions against (abrasion...............impact............)

3.10 Painting—type (topsides....../underwater....../deck....../interior....../tanks and bilges......)

4. Condition Report

4.1 Condition of paintwork:

Topsides (good/flaking/blistering/rust marks/other...........................)

Below water-line (good/flaking/blistering/rust marks/other..........................)

Deck (good/flaking/blistering/rust marks/other...........................)

Interior (good/flaking/blistering/rust marks/other...........................)

4.2 External hull damage (abrasion/impact/cracking/spalling of mortar/corrosion/exposed reinforcement/signs of repair/leaking/none)

4.3 Damage to bulwarks (abrasion/impact/cracking/spalling/none)

4.4 Electrolytic corrosion of steelwork incorporated in hull (stem band/keel shoe/skin fittings/rudder/skeg/through-bolts/

other..........................)

4.5 Internal structural fittings:
Floors and framing (mesh exposed/stress cracks/mortar spalling/corrosion of reinforcement/no problem)
Bulkheads) mesh exposed/stress cracks/mortar spalling/corrosion of reinforcement/no problem)
Longitudinal stiffeners (rusting/mesh exposed/stress cracks/mortar spalling/corrosion of reinforcement/no problem)
Engine beds (stress cracking/vibration/misalignment/loose holding-down bolts/no problem)
Stern bearing, tube, stuffing box (leaks/corrosion of reinforcement/bolt corroded or loose/no problem)
Shaft and intermediate bearings (vibration/excessive wear/no problem)
Tanks in ferro-cement (protected against diesel oil penetration/leaking/no problem)
Tanks in steel (rusting/loose tank supports/stress cracks around supports/no problem)
Fishold insulation (resistant to heat transfer/deterioration)
Fishold, ferro-cement lining (corrosion of reinforcement/impact damage/signs of repair/no problem)

Fishold, other lining...

Fishold refrigeration ....

4.6 Superstructure general condition:
Coamings (bolted to deck/ferro-cement upstand/leaks/no problem)
Hatches (Coamings in wood/ferro-cement/steel/damage/leaks/no problem)

4.7 Deck gear general condition:

Winches (how fastened.............../stress cracks around seating/leaks through bolt holes)

Other fishing gear ....

5. Owner's Comments

Structural strength (strong/not strong)
Stability (poor/adequate/good)
Sea kindliness (roll too great/roll too quick/pitches/wet/good)
Resistance to service damage (poor/adequate/good)

Maintenance problems ....

General opinion ....

....

6. Surveyor's Comments

....

....

....

THE POTENTIAL OF FERRO-CEMENT IN DEVELOPING COUNTRIES

Romualdi (USA) outlined some of the recommendations in a report entitled Ferro-Cement: Applications in Developing Countries, prepared by a special panel of the Board of Science and Technology for International Development of the National Academy of Sciences. The panel considered that the potential application of ferro-cement would be as a universal engineering material as well as a boatbuilding material. It had great potentials in agriculture and industry.

Wylde (New Zealand) thought that the use of ferro-cement was being considered in relation to developing countries because the material was readily available and the skills could be easily taught, yet some of the problems such as that caused by diesel fuel leakage could be serious and quick acting. The cures suggested appeared to be fairly sophisticated and perhaps outside the resources of a developing country.

Romualdi (USA) said that looking at the applications of ferro-cement in advanced vessels design tended to obscure the simplicity of the material in indigenous craft. For example, 10.7 m (35-ft) sampans being built in China were made from unsophisticated materials and they carried highly corrosive cargoes. Sophisticated considerations did not necessarily apply in such cases.

Wells (New Guinea) considered that initial distrust in such a new material could be overcome by demonstration, and described his experience in New Guinea where fishermen, who originally did not believe in the material, watched the boats being built, saw the amount of steel going into them and were given an opportunity of participating in trials. Mistrust had changed to acceptance and the boats were now popular.

Richardson (New Zealand) said that one set of rules applied very well indeed to highly developed countries with technical knowledge and skills available but a very different set of guidelines must be considered for countries which were seeking to train unskilled native labour for this type of work.

One should take into consideration the fact that, if the required knowledge and ability were *too* technical, the operation risked failure.

For an operation based in the more remote areas where few supplies were available, prior information was necessary on the following points:

1. A thorough knowledge of the site and possibilities of deep water launching.
2. Resources, such as equipment, cranes, bulldozers, etc.
3. Educated tradesmen, labour force, if any
4. Local buying and supplies of materials
5. Saw mills for timber
6. Availability of water, electricity, sand and cement
7. Land and adequate housing for the building operation
8. Training of labour force; if unskilled items 7 and 8 take time to accomplish and develop and *must* be allowed for.

If these factors were known then adequate precautions and adjustments could be made so that there were no hold-ups in production once work was commenced.

If the construction of fishing vessels was envisaged under such conditions he suggested that a type of "kitset" of all materials not available in the area be shipped to the site, thus ensuring a smooth running operation.

Ali (Bangladesh) said that in his country they had not yet been able to introduce ferro-cement technology and had found that the fishermen did not like the type of boat proposed. This was perhaps because the design was changed to such an extent that it was completely unfamiliar. He personally felt that in the introduction of ferro-cement, local boat designs should be used as a guideline. If the people felt that it was the same boat only the material had been changed, they would be more willing to accept the innovation. He considered that FAO was in a good position to introduce and popularize ferro-cement in developing countries.

Mowbray (Rapporteur) summing up, said that the discussion had ranged widely, relating in the main to details in ferro-cement boats with little comment being made on the gross problem of the suitability of the material as a shipbuilding medium.

The principal facts discussed were the correctness of using chicken wire as reinforcing mesh, the grouting and repair of voids when these were indicated by blisters in the paintwork, the penetration of ferro-cement by diesel oil and appropriate methods of lining fuel and water tanks, the insulation and protection of fish tanks and the problems of fastening fittings to ferro-cement hulls.

One notable fact was the ease with which both temporary and permanent repairs could be performed at the site of an accident and at a shipyard, even if the damaged section had to be treated under water.

Many participants felt that the time was near when ferro-cement would be designed by calculation, using the usual design processes of load analysis, determination of induced stresses and design of suitable resistance from known material properties.

It could be safely said that ferro-cement, having proved a safe and durable marine material for use in amateur pleasure craft, had now been developed to a stage where it must be considered seriously as an economic alternative to the traditional media, namely timber and steel and the more recently developed glass-reinforced plastic. The time had come to rationalize the design processes, using knowledge already available to structural engineers and marine architects. There was no doubt that ferro-cement would remain a material appropriate to communities with relatively low wage rates because it was a labour-intensive process. However, even in countries with high labour costs as exist for example in New Zealand, developments of new fabrication techniques could easily make this material economically competitive.

Some information had been presented on which to judge the serviceability of ferro-cement craft, not in great detail but sufficient to justify continuing faith in both the material and the techniques of construction when these were properly applied.

One aspect was clear, namely that there seemed to be no evidence of gross failure under normal service conditions nor unexplained losses at sea. Such comment as had come forward related more to detail rather than to the constructional system as a whole.